D1094018

SELECTED READINGS IN PHYSICS

GENERAL EDITOR: D. TER HAAR

MEN OF PHYSICS

J. WILLARD GIBBS

American Mathematical
Physicist *par excellence*

J. Willard Gibbs (photograph about 1895).

MEN OF PHYSICS

J. WILLARD GIBBS

American Mathematical Physicist *par excellence*

RAYMOND J. SEEGER
George Washington University

PERGAMON PRESS
Oxford · New York · Toronto · Sydney

Pergamon Press Ltd., Headington Hill Hall, Oxford
Pergamon Press Inc., Maxwell House, Fairview Park, Elmsford, New York 10523
Pergamon of Canada Ltd., 207 Queen's Quay West, Toronto 1
Pergamon Press (Aust.) Pty. Ltd., 19a Boundary Street,
Rushcutters Bay, N.S.W. 2011, Australia

First edition 1974

Library of Congress Cataloging in Publication Data

Seeger, Raymond John, 1906–
Men of Physics.

(Selected readings in physics)
1 Gibbs, Josiah Willard, 1839–1903. I. Title. QC16. G5S43 1974   530'.092'4 [B]
74–8412
ISBN 0–08–018013–2

Printed in Northern Ireland at The Universities Press, Belfast.

To Vivian May Millen Seeger
For faith, hope, and love.

Contents

Illustrations

Preface

WE ARE concerned nowadays with the role of science in human affairs and, therefore, with the role of mathematics in science, particularly in science as an evolving social phenomenon. We are becoming more and more sensitive to the cultural and humanistic values inherent in science, its philosophical and aesthetic, ethical and spiritual implications. At the same time we find ourselves puzzled by the complexity of the social aspects of science, its impact upon society and the impact of society upon it. We are, on the one hand, impressed by the achievements of cooperative enterprises like the initial development of the atomic bomb; on the other hand, we are depressed by the abundance of information now available through mechanization. We wander bewildered in a maze of apparently aimless social activity aggravated by increasingly specialized professional methodologies and by increasingly generalized problem interrelationships. The individual himself seems to be lost in a crowd of people milling in a hazy atmosphere of mass media. Does the individual *per se* have any particular role in society, or is he merely a Brownian social movement? We need to examine critically this history of science in terms of the lives of scientists, to ascertain if any individuals have personally influenced its growth without being predominantly activists (to be sure, "no man is an island, entire of itself"). Such a person, I believe, was J. Willard Gibbs.

Gibbs was an American researcher when both America and research were quite unknown in graduate education. He was a physicist who determined the direction of interdisciplinary physical chemistry in the early stages of its development; he was a physicist who used "simple" mathematics as a primary means—not as an end in itself. When both mathematics and physics were at the exciting period of their nineteenth-century developments, and their interactions mutually influential, he was a mathematical physicist *par excellence*.

Westmoreland Hills   RAYMOND J. SEEGER

Acknowledgements

I AM indebted to the Physics Department of Yale University for all photographs; the libraries of the National Science Foundation, the U.S. Naval Observatory, and Yale University for materials used as Selected Readings; the library of Yale University for permission to reproduce a portion of J. Willard Gibbs' "Elements of Vector Analysis."

PART I
His life

CHAPTER 1

Engineering Student

JOSIAH WILLARD GIBBS was born on February 11, 1839, in New Haven, Connecticut, then an overgrown village of elm trees and wooden houses with some 20,000 inhabitants (founded in 1638 as theocratic Quinnipiac by Puritans under the Coventry clergyman John Davenport (1597–1670), joint capital with Hartford (1701–1875)). He was the scion of a colonial, educated, distinguished family of divines, professors, and librarians.

His father had descended from Robert Gibbs (1634–74) (son of Sir Henry Gibbs (1593–1667) of Honington, Warwickshire), who had come to Boston about 1658, and from Jacob Schaefe (1616–58), who had immigrated to Boston in 1643. On his father's side also there was Major Simon Willard (1604–76), an Indian fighter, who arrived in Boston in 1634; his son, the Rev. Samuel Willard (1639–1707), a graduate (1639) of the Puritan Harvard College (1636), pastor of Old South Church in Boston, became acting President of Harvard College; in turn, his son, Josiah Willard (1661–1756), also a Harvard College graduate (1698), was a sea captain and a "good Secretary" of the Province of Massachusetts Bay. John Prescott (1604–83), an ancestor of his father's mother Mercy Prescott (*ca.* 1755–1809), came to Boston in 1640. Gibbs' father, Josiah Willard Gibbs (1790–1861), was born in Salem and graduated from Yale College in 1809; in 1824 he became Yale librarian (until 1843) and Professor of Sacred Literature in the recently (1822) organized Yale Department of Theology (he was a licensed preacher). He involved himself on behalf of the Armistad Africans. For his philological studies, he received an honorary M.A. from Harvard College in 1818 and an honorary LL.D. in 1853 from the Presbyterian College of New Jersey (1746 Elizabethtown, 1747 Newark, 1752 Princeton, New Jersey; 1896 Princeton University).

Johannes Van Cleve (b. 1646), an ancestor of his mother, emigrated from Amsterdam; he became president of the provincial council and later chief justice of the colony of New York. Another, Colonel William Henry Smith (d. 1705), Governor of Morocco (1675), came to America in 1686. His mother's mother descended from the Rev. Jonathan Dickinson (1688–1747), a graduate (1706) of the Connecticut Collegiate School (Yale University 1887), was a physician and the first President of the College of New Jersey. Another ancestor, William Churchill Houston (1746–88), a graduate (1768) and Professor of Mathematics and Natural Philosophy of the College of New Jersey, was Treasurer of the College and a delegate to the Constitutional Convention. Gibbs' mother, Mary Anna Van Cleve (1805–55), was the daughter of Dr. John Van Cleve (1788–1826), a graduate (1797) and trustee of the College of New Jersey, a physician and Professor of Chemistry.

His parents had four other children: Anna Louisa (1831–98), Eliza Phillips (1834–49), Julia (1836–1916), Emily (1841–64). The family lived in the vicinity of Yale College, first on Crown Street (J. Willard Gibbs was born there) and then from 1846 in a house on High Street with a garden of irises (Plate 1): they had a carriage and two servants. J. Willard Gibbs never married; after the death of his parents he and his sisters lived together in the jointly inherited home. In 1867 his sister Julia married Gibbs' classmate (valedictorian) Addison Van Name (1835–1922), Yale Librarian (successor to D. C. Gilman), a licensed preacher and student of Oriental philology, who came to live with the family in a close-knit relationship; they had three children. The entire household ate together.

After a year at a small private primary school, in 1849 Gibbs entered the Hopkins Grammar School, located then at High and Wall Streets (later the site of the Yale Law School) diagonally across from his home. Founded in 1660, it was the third oldest classical secondary school in the United States. In 1854 he entered Yale College, which had been moved in 1716 to New Haven after its founding in 1701 by ten Congregational clergy in old Saybrook (occupied by the Dutch in 1623, fort of Massachusetts Bay Colony 1635). The Boston-born Elihu Yale (1649–1721), English East India Co. official, Governor of Madras, had made two donations to the Collegiate School of Connecticut (1701) which was then named in his honor in 1718; his father David Yale had lived in New Haven; he himself is buried in Wrexham, Wales.

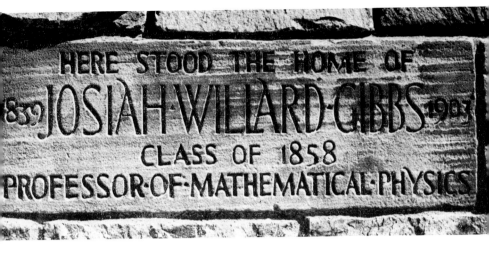

PLATE 1. High Street House Marker, New Haven.

PLATE 2. (Old) Sloane Physical Laboratory, Yale College.

PLATE 3. Gibbs' Governor.

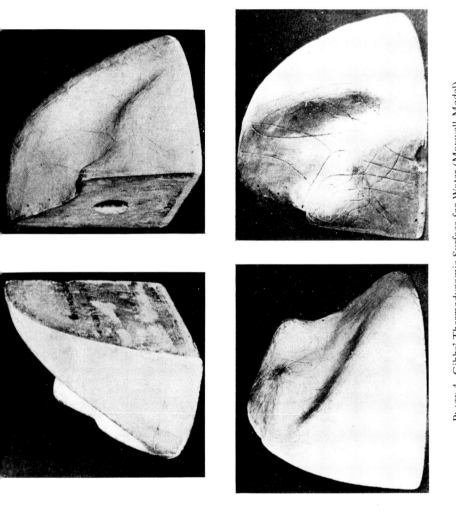

PLATE 4. Gibbs' Thermodynamic Surface for Water (Maxwell Model).

PLATE 5. J. Willard Gibbs Research Laboratory, Yale University.

Gibbs won prizes in Latin and in mathematics; he was elected to the honor society Phi Beta Kappa (1776, Yale Chapter 1780) and gave the salutatory address (in Latin) upon his graduation with highest honors in 1858. The President was the classicist Theodore Dwight Woolsey (1801–89); among his teachers were the natural philosopher and astronomer Denison Olmsted (1791–1859), the geologist James Dwight Dana (1813–95), the chemist Benjamin Silliman, Jr. (1816–85, Yale 1837), and the mathematician Hubert Anson Newton (1830–96). It was probably the last who influenced him the most and whose obituary he wrote. He then entered as an engineering student in the new Department of Philosophy and the Arts, which had been established in 1847 for non-traditional (Yale had previously trained students primarily for the church and politics, for law and commerce) academic work, including laboratory chemistry and graduate studies (the first in the United States, formally organized in 1892). This Department led in 1854 to the establishment of a separate undergraduate Yale Scientific School (combination of School of Applied Chemistry and of School of Engineering, 1852), named the Sheffield Scientific School in 1861 (independently incorporated 1871) in recognition of a building and an endowment received from Joseph Earl Sheffield (1793–1882), a New Haven merchant (it became a Land Grant institution in 1863 until 1893). Its first graduate student in engineering, Gibbs was awarded in 1863 the first Ph.D. (initiated by Yale in 1860) in engineering (second in science) in the United States. His thesis, "On the Form of the Teeth of Wheels in Spur Gearing",[19] was essentially an exercise in applied geometry (not comparable in purpose with current dissertations). Some of his teachers were the mathematical astronomer Elias Loomis (1811–99), the engineering astronomer William Augustus Norton (1810–83), and the Rev. Chester Smith Lyman (1814–90; Yale 1837), who became Sheffield Professor of Astronomy and Physics in 1872.

It is not surprising that this scientifically gifted student should be attracted by the popular American emphasis upon applications. Not only had eighteenth-century navigation problems required mathematics and astronomy, but the year 1858 had seen the laying of the transatlantic cable under the sponsorship of the American businessman Cyrus West Field (1819–92). New Haven, indeed, could boast of its own inventors: Charles Goodyear (1800–60), the vulcanization of rubber (1844);

Samuel Finley Breese Morse (1791–1872, Yale 1810), the electric tele-
graph (1832); Eli Whitney (1765–1825, Yale 1792), the cotton gin
(1793); Ithiel Town (1784–1844), the truss bridge (1820). In 1865 Gibbs
himself applied for a patent and a year later received it, namely, "An
improved Railway Car Brake" for a train moving forward or backward.
His last technological concern along this line was his 1872 generalized
(three torques instead of two) improvement (Plate 3) of the conical
pendulum governor of the Scottish engineer James Watt (1736–1819),
who had invented the steam engine (1765).

In 1863 Gibbs was appointed a tutor in Yale College with an office
in old South Middle (Connecticut Hall 1752). During the first two years
he was requested to teach Latin; in the third year he chose natural
philosophy. In this postdoctoral period he subscribed to various
scientific journals, including the *Proceedings of the Royal Society of
London.* Meanwhile, in the fall of 1858 he had been elected to the
Connecticut Academy of Arts and Sciences (1799). He presented his
first paper (unpublished)[18] there in the spring of 1866; it was entitled
"The Proper Magnitude of the Units of Length and of other Quantities
used in Mechanics", illustrative of his lifelong interest in this field. He
was primarily concerned with the constant of proportionality occurring
in the basic relations involving length, time, mass, and force. He sur-
veyed the various attempts in engineering to give it a value that would
be simple and convenient. He himself proposed a modification of the
unit of length—an original idea. H. A. Newton, who was promoting
American adoption of the metric system in line with the classic report
(1821) on weights and measures to the U.S. Senate by the then Secretary
of State John Quincy Adams (1769–1848), had solicited Gibbs' aid in
this regard.

In 1861 Josiah Willard Gibbs, Snr. died and left a legacy of about
$23,500 for the family and a responsibility of three sisters for his 22-
year-old son; the loss to the latter was irreparable in view of their
closeness. Three years later his younger sister Emily also died. By
renting their house, Gibbs and his two sisters, the quiet (weak) Anna
and the lively Julia, were enabled to go to Europe in August 1866; the
following year (August) Julia married A. Van Name in Berlin and
went back home. Gibbs and his sister Anna did not return until June
1869.

The American historian Henry Brooks Adams (1838–1918) remarked in his *Autobiography* (1906) at the close of his Harvard schooling (Chapter IV) that the "education of Henry Adams had not begun". So, too, the scientific education of Gibbs had not yet really begun when he left Yale. The American practical emphasis was to be succeeded by the European theoretical regard of science for the sake of science. A new world of intellectual interest was to be discovered in the old world. In the fall of 1866 the group lived on the Paris left bank where Gibbs spent about 16 hours each week attending lectures in the Sorbonne, University of Paris (*ca.* twelfth century), and at the Collège de France (1518). He listened to the mathematicians Michel Chasles (1793–1880), Jean Gaston Darboux (1842–1917), Jean Marie Constant Duhamel (1797–1872), Joseph Liouville (1809–82), Joseph Alfred Serret (1819–85), and to the physicist Charles Eugène Delaunay (1816–72). He devoted much of his time to reading French mathematical and scientific classics; he did, however, attend lectures also in other fields. Gibbs' health suffered during this period so that the family sojourned to Cannes in the south of France. They went to Berlin in the summer of 1867. Here Gibbs attended University (1810) lectures on mathematics by Wilhelm Foerster (1832–1924), Leopold Kronecker (1823–91), Ernst Eduard Kummer (1810–93), Karl Theodor Weierstrass (1815–97), and on physics by August Kundt (1839–94), Heinrich Gustav Magnus (1802–70), Georg Hermann Quincke (1834–1924).

The academic year 1868–69 was spent at the University of Heidelberg (1386). It is not known whose lectures he attended there. At that time, however, the following possible professorial contacts were available: mathematicians Moritz Benedikt Cantor (1829–1920), Paul du Bois-Reymond (1818–96), Ludwig Otto Hesse (1811–74); the chemist Robert Wilhelm Bunsen (1852–89), the physicist Gustav Robert Kirchhoff (1824–87), the physicist and physiologist Hermann Ludwig Ferdinand von Helmholtz (1821–94). His readings emphasized mechanics, electrical theory, electrodynamics, and optics.

His studies in Europe undoubtedly gave him a new perspective of science, mathematics, and their relations. After a short spring vacation on the Riviera, he and Anna returned to New Haven in June 1869. He had left it an engineering graduate; he came back a mathematical physicist.

CHAPTER 2

Mathematical Physicist

THE newly elected President of Yale, the philosophical clergyman Noah Porter (1811–92), secured on July 13, 1871 the appointment of Gibbs as Professor of Mathematical Physics in the Yale College Department of Philosophy and the Arts (1847) in line with the faculty recommendation of four new chairs (one in physics) in its pamphlet on *The Needs of the University* (July 11, 1871). (About the same time (1869) the historian Henry Adams and (1872) the philosophical psychologist William James (1842–1912) began teaching at Harvard.) The general academic regard for Gibbs, who was only 32, is locally attested to by the fact that he had published nothing as of this date. Unfortunately, the Corporation stipulated "without salary". It is, therefore, not surprising that in 1873 Bowdoin College (1794) sought his services in mathematics or physics with an annual remuneration of $2000. Fortunately for Yale, Gibbs was content to live modestly with his inherited income in his New Haven home. By 1880, however, Gibbs had apparently become more seriously concerned about his academic status.

Henry Augustus Rowland (1848–1901), first Chairman of the Physics Department at the research-oriented graduate Johns Hopkins University (1876), arranged for Gibbs to give early in 1880 a course of lectures on theoretical mechanics; it was based on the principle of virtual velocities and utilized vectors. Gibbs considered favorably the subsequent invitation of Daniel Coit Gilman (1831–1908, Yale 1852), who had been Librarian (until 1865), Professor of Geography in the Sheffield Scientific School (1861–72), and in 1875 had become the first president of Johns Hopkins, to join the faculty there at a salary of $3000. The Yale authorities were influenced by some of the faculty (e.g. the classicist Thomas Anthony Thacher (1815–86)) to offer Gibbs some salary ($2000), which he accepted as an indication of their sincere desire to keep him (he did not receive a full salary ($3250) until 1896). He remained as Professor of Mathematical Physics at Yale until his death; his office (second floor front, right of tower) was in the old (Henry T. and William D.) Sloane Physical Laboratory (1883, Plate 2). It is interesting that this first appointment of a full-time physicist on the Yale faculty coincided with the appointment of the Scottish physicist James Clerk Maxwell (1831–79) as first Professor of Experimental Physics and Director of the new Cavendish Laboratory at the University of Cambridge, where laboratory instruction in physics would be possible for the first time in England. In view of Gibbs' individual method of investigation and the social adjustments of his family to New Haven, it is questionable whether the research atmosphere of Johns Hopkins would have afforded any significant contribution to his work.

Gibbs' initial studies were in physical optics, probably owing to the interest aroused by his earlier contacts with the French; he encountered, however, formidable difficulties with the elastic–solid explanation of double refraction. His interest in such problems was renewed after the publication of J. C. Maxwell's *A Treatise on Electricity and Magnetism* (1873) with its exposition of the electromagnetic theory of light. In keeping with his general avoidance of special hypotheses, he assumed that matter was only sufficiently fine-grained (not infinitely so) with respect to the wavelength of light and that it did not disturb the electrical changes in the luminiferous ether. His results were published in three articles in the *American Journal of Science* (1882, 1883). The physicist Henry Andrews Bumstead (1870–1920), Gibbs' student and later colleague, remarked in his excellent biographical sketch that Gibbs' rigorous considerations "would have sufficed to firmly establish this theory [electromagnetic theory of light] even if the experimental discoveries [1886] of [Heinrich] Hertz [German physicist (1857–94)] had not supplied a more direct proof of its validity".[2] Gibbs' final publication on optics reviewed critically a proposal of the Scotch-Irish physicist Sir William Thomson (Lord Kelvin, 1824–1907) for an infinitely compressible ether. Recognizing the satisfactoriness of this *ad hoc* theory, nevertheless, Gibbs wisely concluded: "It is difficult to account for the coincidences between the electrical and optical properties of media, unless we regard the motions of light as electrical."[2]

Meanwhile, having a predilection toward mechanical explanations of physical phenomena, Gibbs had turned his attention to more comprehensive thermodynamics with its inherent concern for the relation of heat to mechanical work. He considered graphical, i.e. geometrical, representations of the basic equations with particular attention to the utility of the concept of entropy, a function of the physical state, introduced in 1865 by the German mathematical physicist Rudolf Julius Emanuel Clausius (1822–88), whom Gibbs had never met but whom he is said to have regarded as one of his two "masters". He published two papers[2] on this subject in 1873 in the little-known *Transactions of the Connecticut Academy of Arts and Sciences*, which had about 170 (140 foreign) exchanges with other societies. Despite the importance of the papers, which can be regarded as creating graphical thermodynamics, either because of their unavailability or because of the supposed difficulty of their presentation, they attracted practically no notice. The one exception was that of J. C. Maxwell himself who sent Gibbs a plaster cast of a model he had constructed for the Gibbs thermodynamic surface for water (Plate 4, at present in the Gibbs Research Laboratory at Yale).

His third paper, "On the Equilibrium of Heterogeneous Substances",[2] was published in two parts in the *Transactions of the Connecticut Academy of Arts and Sciences* (1875–8), which generously collected funds (primarily through the efforts of his colleague E. Loomis) to defray the expenses of this 321-page "monumental memoir", so described in 1910 by the Irish mathematician Sir Joseph Larmor (1857–1942). The first part of the paper was cited in 1876 by J. C. Maxwell at a meeting of the Chemical Society in London; later at a meeting of the Cambridge Philosophical Society he stated that Gibbs' method threw new light on thermodynamics. It stands out as a classic in the history of science, a beautiful monument to the human spirit, a noble claim of its intelligence to paraphrase what the French mathematical astronomer Marquis Pierre Simon de Laplace (1749–1827) claimed about astronomy. In a theoretical sense it contained no new principle; it was strictly rigorous, analytical deductions from the two experimental laws of thermodynamics (expressed sometimes in terms of new thermodynamic functions), an exhaustive study, the result of systematic industry. It should be kept in mind that thermodynamic concepts themselves were still not completely accepted as a part of modern culture. For example, as late as 1865 the Scottish engineer William John Macquorn Rankine (1820–72) still regarded heat as a material, and the popular German philosophical biologist Ernst Heinrich Haeckel (1834–1919) denied entropy increase as a universal law (*cf.* his *Riddle of the Universe* (1899)). Nevertheless, Gibbs can be said to have created "chemical energetics", or preferably, chemical thermodynamics. For the first time a mixture of chemical substances was considered continuous or continuous phases of matter acted upon by forces with so-called chemical potentials—regarded by some as Gibbs' greatest discovery. It determined the direction of the newly developing physical chemistry (particularly in Holland) with its many contributions to emerging industrial chemistry. Of particular significance was his qualitative phase rule, which relates the degrees of freedom of a chemical system to its constituents and their phases without any reference to the chemical constitution of the components themselves or to their reaction rates. The Polish theoretical physicist Paul Sophus Epstein (1883–1966) considered this feat "a phenomenon almost unparalleled in the history of science. A young investigator, having discovered an entirely new branch of science, gave in a single contribution an exhaustive treatment of it which foreshadows the development of theoretical chemistry for a quarter of a century".[2]

History has revealed two remarkable consequences of this synthesis: (1) algebraic statements of Gibbs in advance of their laboratory verification and (2) continual rediscovery of Gibbs' results (cf. F. G. Donnan, F. Haber, H. L. F. von Helmholtz, J. J. Thomson, J. H. van't Hoff). One is amazed how far his precision of thought advanced beyond the precision of instruments, which is frequently responsible for scientific discoveries nowadays. It was apparently Gibbs' intention to revise and extend his work on thermodynamics before his untimely death. Called the "father of physical chemistry", he is said to have been disappointed that Yale never permitted him to teach physical chemistry.

His last work, *Elementary Principles in Statistical Mechanics*[1] (1902), was a Yale University Bicentennial Publication. (In 1884 he had published an abstract which contained his fundamental equation of statistical mechanics, indicative of his comprehension of this subject almost twenty years prior to his comprehensive book on it.) In 1894–95 statistical mechanics had been added to the Yale curriculum as a separate course supplementary to thermodynamics. It represented the kinetic approach to thermal phenomena, which is based upon molecular assumptions about matter—as contrasted with thermodynamics *per se*, which strictly avoids all references to atomistic concepts. Gibbs himself had already indicated in 1876, in connection with his famous paradox, the need for supplementation of thermodynamics with atomistic ideas; in his discussion of the non-increase in entropy due to the mixture of portions of the same gas by diffusion, he had concluded, "The impossibility of an uncompensated decrease of entropy seems to be reduced to improbability"—a quotation placed at the top of the Foreword to *Lectures on Gas Theory*,[5] Part II (1898), by the Austrian theoretical physicist Ludwig Boltzmann (1844–1906), who regarded Gibbs as "the greatest synthetic philosopher since Newton". The ending of the long title of the book (usually omitted) is particularly instructive in indicating the primary purpose of this work, viz. "Developed with especial reference to the Rational Foundation of Thermodynamics"—akin to the popular eighteenth-century rational mechanics. This objective is achieved in the next to last chapter on "Discussion of Thermodynamic Analogies", namely, those that are sufficient, but not necessary interpretations of thermodynamic experience.

The essential feature is the statistical consideration of an ensemble of dynamical systems (described by the so-called Hamiltonian canonical equations of motions) which differ only in phase (generalized coordinates and momenta). Gibbs selected a particularly simple group of systems, designated a canonical ensemble, which he compared with microcanonical ensembles, defined in terms of limiting distributions. The so-called modulus of the canonical ensemble has the thermodynamic property of temperature; the mean of a function η (defined as the logarithm of the ratio of the density-in-phase to the whole number of systems in the ensemble) has the property of entropy. In the last chapter of the book the canonical ensemble is generalized to the concept of a grand ensemble in which the systems vary not only in phase, but also in the numbers of particles of different substances—analogous to the thermodynamics of the equilibrium of heterogeneous substances. Thus Gibbs was able to demonstrate a rational mechanical explanation of heat. By not framing hypotheses concerning the constitution of matter, of course, he had to forego the satisfaction of "attempting to explain the mysteries of nature". Yet he was able by this very restriction to establish a broad enough foundation of statistical mechanics that would support the future developments of quantum mechanics as well as of the extensions of contemporary kinetic theory, quantum statistics as well as classical statistics. As the Czechoslovakian theoretical physicist Arthur Haas (1884–1941) commented: "Probably nothing reveals in a grander way the surpassing genius of J. Willard Gibbs than the fact that the one man who became the real founder of an exact molecular-statistical theory of heat also perfected at the same time the purely thermodynamic method in a manner scarcely dreamt of earlier."[2]

Gibbs' success was due in part to his physical intuition and his acute perception, in part to his exhaustive comprehensiveness, but above all, to his rigorous methodology, his accurate thinking. At a time when the exciting interrelatedness of physics and mathematics was being widely scrutinized, the use of mathematics by this outstanding physicist is particularly noteworthy. Formal mathematics was never for him a primary end in itself; rather he sought the elegance and conciseness of mathematics as a means. It was the union of reflective analytical thought and the phenomenological synthetic world that he regarded as physically more important than mathematical rigor *per se*. He preferred imagination tempered with reasoning to speculative generalization; he avoided mere guesswork and wishful thinking. He liked the point of view expressed in *The Grammar of Science* (1892) by the English mathematician Karl Pearson (1857–1936). He saw mathematics as a servant of science, not its queen. He opened his vice-presidential address "On Multiple Algebra" at the American Association for the Advancement of Science with a quotation from a book review in *Nation* (1881): "The human mind has never invented a labor-saving machine equal to algebra."[2] He himself had excellent analytical and geometrical skills. It is truly wonderful how physical insight and creative imagination combined with deductive logic can enable man to understand in part this mysterious universe; it is even more amazing to find the investigations by any particular man remaining unchanged in the dawn of a new day. Such a person was Gibbs.

Gibbs developed a pragmatic vector analysis in preference to the mathematical elegance and logical completeness of the quaternions used by J. C. Maxwell and others. He found it more intuitive for dealing with physical quantities, many of which have a directional property. In this connection he prepared in 1881 and 1884 a privately printed pamphlet for his students. One of these, his later colleague, the mathematician Edwin Bidwell Wilson (1879–1964), published a textbook on Gibbs' *Vector Analysis*[20] in connection with the Yale University Bicentennial. Gibbs' distinctive contribution to pure mathematics was his theory of the linear vector function and dyadics (1884), which fulfils the definition of a linear associative algebra given by the American mathematician Benjamin Peirce (1809–1880). (*N.B.* Vector analysis does not fulfil this requirement inasmuch as the scalar product of two vectors is not itself a vector.) It involves the so-called indeterminate or open product (i.e. no equations exist between the factors—modern theory of matrices). Dyadics are particularly useful in discussing solid rotations and strains, as well as the propagation of light in crystals. Gibbs was greatly indebted to the German mathematician Hermann Gunther Grassmann (1809–77) for his general work on multiple algebra; Gibbs is said to have regarded him as a second "master". Vector analysis, however, was Gibbs' own doing. It exemplifies the belief he expressed in his acceptance of the Rumford Medal in 1881: "The office of theoretical investigation is to give the form in which the results of experiment may be expressed."[18] He is said to have remarked informally, "A mathematician may say anything he pleases, but a physicist must be at least partially sane".

CHAPTER 3

Gentleman and Scholar

GIBBS was a gentleman—in the original sense of that word. His tastes were simple, his appearance neat; he did not smoke, but he was not a total abstainer. His way of life was sincere and abstemious; he performed his daily chores (he was the household repair man); he never avoided college duties, however trivial. He was happy in his intellectual pursuits; he could not be diverted from his chosen vocation of truth seeking. He could be found industriously at work each afternoon in his study at home or in his office (first in the Brick Row and then in the old Sloane Physical Laboratory (1883), where he customarily paced in thought about a large table near a blackboard); he could concentrate intensely. He confessed about his own work, "Anyone having these desires will make these researches"—not so much a mark of his modesty as an appreciation of the industry requisite.

He was a solitary walker; he enjoyed swimming and skating, mountain climbing and horseback riding. He was wont to spend his vacation in the Adirondacks (Keene Valley, New York) and later (1896) in the White Mountains (Intervale, New Hampshire). On the whole, after tubercular tendencies while young, his health was good except for his eyesight (he early detected his own astigmatism, designed and prescribed a lens, but used it only for reading). He was apparently a successful man of affairs; when called upon, he responded to extracurricular responsibilities: he was trustee (1881) and then secretary and treasurer (1886) of the Hopkins Grammar School; for ten years he was executive officer of the Yale faculty-student Mathematical Club, which he himself had founded (1877). In 1886 he was Vice President (Section A, Mathematics) of the American Association for the Advancement of Science. In 1884 Chester Alan Arthur (1830–80), President of the United States, appointed him a Commissioner to the National Conference of Electricians at Philadelphia (he presided at one session). Upon his death his estate was valued at $100,000, owing to wise investments.

Gibbs was not self-seeking, he sought no rewards; he was not a faculty activist, he was not a science propagandist. He avoided controversial discussions, e.g. politics (he was a Republican) and religion; his silences were judicious. His exemplary character is revealed in his writings just as his work was largely his life. He was modest, but not pretentious; meek, but not diffident; he had a reserved dignity—in a formal society. He was grave, contemplative, and serene; nevertheless, he was approachable and courteous, cheerful and cordial. He was sympathetic with students and helpful to children; he was kindly, tolerant and generous. He never knowingly killed a living creature; in principle, he was opposed to war. He had, however, only one close friend, his teacher and colleague, his neighbor, the mathematician H. A. Newton (later the mathematician Andrew Wheeler Phillips (1844–1915, Sheffield 1873), Dean of the Graduate School (1895)). He had a sense of humor, a spontaneous but subdued laugh, a pleasant smile that would occasionally light up his countenance. In the conservative Calvinistic atmosphere of Yale, he regularly attended the chapel of the Church of Christ in Yale College (1757), being a short walk from his home; he had become a member of it in his first year in the College. His particular religious views are not known, but were undoubtedly in the context of Congregationalism with its intellectual breadth and local autonomy (including credal matters). His very life testifies that he was a Christian gentleman.

It is always difficult to evaluate a teacher, whose primary function is to communicate thoughts to others. The ideas, however, are actually his own conceptions: the communication really himself. In keeping with his character, Gibbs was always graciously responsive to the individual requirements of his graduate students, regardless of their ability; he was quick to diagnose student difficulties, to respond to questions—if asked; but he did not adjust his material to the preparedness of his students (he certainly did not practise spoon feeding). He was, however, quite indifferent to the broader social need for the popularization of science, in general, and of physics, in particular—for the educational growth of the average intellectual person; for example, he gave no introductory courses for the benefit of undergraduates. Despite the exciting curriculum developments, the elective system initiated (1869) at Harvard by its chemist President Charles William Eliot (1834–1926) and the program envisaged by the Yale faculty in its pronouncement on "The Needs of the University" (1871), he seemed to have been attracted more to the European graduate approach with the breadth of its academic viewpoints and with its research freedom and productivity. He was wont to stress general principles rather than problem-solving skills; in answering questions, however, he would exemplify the general with the particular. At the graduate level, where he had less than 100 students (about fifteen doctoral theses) in his teaching span of more than 30 years, he was certainly a good teacher, i.e. for the good student. The physicist Lynde Phelps Wheeler (1874–1959), whose experimental dissertation had been under Gibbs' "direction", regarded him "as the greatest teacher as well as the greatest mind with which I ever came in contact".[18] The economist Arthur Twining Hadley (1856–1930; Yale 1876), first lay President of Yale (1899–1921), described Gibbs as "emphatically a teacher of teachers". He seemed to be in the tradition of the European concern for an exclusive group (survival of the fittest) rather than in that of the American goal of an all-inclusive group (greatest number of survivors). He even began his professional career with formal lectures for his class of two graduate students, but quickly allowed informal discussion. He gave about six one-hour lectures a week; they were carefully prepared. He required a large blackboard, but no notes. His style was terse and dry; his reasoning general, rigorous, and unerring—but undoubtedly difficult even for the average graduate student. Assigned problems were returned—corrected; his courses were concluded with comprehensive examinations. Unfortunately, students never had an opportunity of seeing a great mind at work except for conceptual digressions during lectures; in the development of a subject he never differentiated between his own contributions and those of others so that one got the false notion of a completed building (all scaffolding removed) rather than of a growing field (the same criticism can be made of many others, including one of his graduate successors at Yale, the mathematical physicist Leigh Page (1884–1952, Sheffield 1904)). This method is usually justified in its supposedly objective search for the essence of things rather than with the subjective influence of personalities; but these aspects cannot be wholly separated. (Some researchers prefer to work out exciting conclusions for themselves rather than to follow the tedious reasoning of others. Undoubtedly this characteristic was true of Gibbs—a good trait for one's own investigations, but not necessarily so for communicating them.) Less formal contacts were available in the Mathematical Club and the Physics Club, which he helped to establish in 1899; he arranged a meeting of the two groups together. At the former he himself gave a talk in 1893 on "The Paces of a Horse", at another time on "Values". Although a regular attendant at faculty meetings, he is reported as speaking infrequently. A discussion was once going on as to whether there should be more or less languages, more or less mathematics. In the spirit of his father this silent participant arose and succinctly remarked, "Mathematics is a language". At the last faculty meeting he attended, the question being debated was whether or not modern languages should be permitted as a substitute elective for the classics; he was among the progressive minority.

If a teacher is to be judged in terms of his students, the following distinguished persons would answer to Gibbs' roll call: the so-called American "father of radio", the inventor Lee De Forest (1873–1961); physicists H. A. Bumstead, Arthur Woolsey Ewell (1873–   ); L. P. Wheeler; optical physicist Charles Sheldon Hastings (1848–1932, Yale 1870), who was Sheffield Professor in Physics from 1884 to 1915; mathematicians Eliakins Hastings Moore (1862–1932), Percey Franklyn Smith (1867–1956), E. B. Wilson, political economist Irving Fisher (1867–1947) and others. In a sense the Yugoslavian physicist-inventor Michael Pupin (1858–1935) could be said to be a foster student inasmuch as his dissertation topic had been suggested by Gibbs' work; with the approval of his Berlin thesis advisor he boldly stated: "This whole theory of physical chemistry was made in the state of Connecticut and not in Germany" (*The New Reformation* (1927)).

Gibbs was not a joiner. He did not become a member of the American Mathematical Society until shortly before his death; he was never a member of the American Physical Society, nor of the Yale Chapter (Sheffield, 1895) of the honor scientific Society of the Sigma Xi (1886), which was established initially as a student group. He did, however, devote himself arduously to reviewing current scientific literature;

indeed, he was generally well read. He maintained a large list of names for sending reprints, which has been carefully analyzed by L. P. Wheeler;[18] it contained 507 names (160 U.S. and Canada, 119 Great Britain, 104 Germany, 57 France, 11 Italy, 10 Holland and so on). He carried on a scientific correspondence with many scholars; even the following selection from them reads like *Who Was Who* in nineteenth-century physical science: American geologist George Ferdinand Becker (1847–1919); chemists Wilder Dwight Bancroft (1867–1963), Joseph Parsons Cooke (1827–94), Oliver Wolcott Gibbs (1822–1903); physicists Albert Abraham Michelson (1852–1931), H. A. Rowland, John Trowbridge (1843–1923); the philosophical physicist Charles Sanders Peirce (1839–1914); astronomers Benjamin Apthorp Gould (1824–96), Asaph Hall (1829–1907), Samuel Pierpont Langley (1834–1906), Simon Newcomb (1835–1909), Charles Augustus Young (1834–1908); meteorologist Cleveland Abbe (1838–1916); Scottish physical chemist Sir James Dewar (1842–1923); English chemist Sir William Ramsay (1852–1916); mathematicians James Joseph Sylvester (1814–97), Isaac Todhunter (1820–84); meteorologist John Aitken (1839–1919); physicists Sir Richard Tetley Glazebrook (1854–1935), Sir Oliver Lodge (1851–1940), J. J. Thomson; mathematical physicists Oliver Heaviside (1850–1925), John William Strutt (Lord Rayleigh 1842–1919); Scotch-Irish physicist W. Thomson (Kelvin); the Irish mathematical astronomer Sir Robert Stawell Ball (1840–1913); Dutch physicists Heike Kamerlingh Onnes (1853–1926), Hendrik Antoon Lorentz (1853–1928), Johannes Diderik van der Waals (1837–1923); physical chemist Hendrik William Bakhuis Roozeboom (1854–1907); French mathematical physicists Pierre Maurice Marie Duhem (1861–1916), Jules Henri Poincaré (1854–1912); chemist Henry Louis Le Chatelier (1850–1936); German mathematicians H. G. Grassman, Felix Klein (1849–1925), L. Kronecker; theoretical physicist Max Karl Ernst Ludwig Planck (1858–1947); physicist H. R. Hertz; physical chemist Wilhelm Ostwald (1853–1932); the Austrian physicist L. Boltzmann.

Gibbs became gradually recognized (particularly in Holland, Germany, France)—abroad more than at home. In 1879, however, he was elected to the National Academy of Sciences (he presented three papers and occasionally presided at its sessions), in 1880 to the American

Academy of Arts and Sciences, in 1895 to the American Philosophical Society. He was made a corresponding member of many (mostly European) organizations: British Association for the Advancement of Science (1885), Dutch Society of Sciences (Haarlem, 1886), Royal Society of Sciences (Göttingen, 1889), Cambridge Philosophical Society (England, 1891), Royal Institution (1892), London Mathematical Society (1892), Manchester Literary and Philosophical Society (1892), Royal Academy of Amsterdam (1892), Royal Society of London (1897), Royal Prussian Academy of Sciences (1900, Berlin), French Institute (1900), Washington Academy of Sciences (Washington, D.C., 1900), Royal Bavarian Academy of Sciences (1902). The geologist Arthur Louis Day (1869–1960), first Director of the Geophysical Laboratory of the Carnegie Institution of Washington reported that about 1900 Gibbs was elected President of the Berlin Physical Society, but informally declined it through Day. He received the following scientific awards: the Rumford Medal of the American Academy of Arts and Sciences (1881), and the Copley Medal of the Royal Society of London (1901); the citation for the latter stated: "He was the first to apply the second law of thermodynamics to the exhaustive discussion of the relation between chemical, electrical, and thermal energy and the capacity for external work." He did not receive a Nobel Prize, which was first awarded in 1901 for physics to the German physicist Wilhelm Conrad Röntgen (1845–1923) and for chemistry to the Dutch chemist J. H. van't Hoff; in 1902 the physics prize was given to the Dutch physicists H. A. Lorentz and Pieter Zeeman (1865–1943). He was not elected to the American Hall of Fame at New York University until 1950. He received four honorary degrees: Ph.D. (1893) University of Erlangen (Germany, 1742); LL.D. (1893) Williams College (1793); LL.D. (1896) Princeton University sesquicentennial; D.Math. (1902), University of Christiana (1811; Oslo, 1924).

The Chicago Section of the American Chemical Society awards annually a Willard Gibbs medal (1910) (given generally to a chemist); the American Mathematical Society has had an annual Josiah Willard Gibbs Lecture since 1923 (to date, 44 lectures distributed as follows: pure mathematics 15, physics 10, applied mathematics 8, chemistry 4, astronomy 3, biology 3, engineering 1).

Only his alma mater, Yale University, was slow in honoring this outstanding American scientist of the nineteenth century; in 1927 it established a Gibbs memorial Professorship (held 1931–1938 by the mathematician Ernest William Brown (1866–1938), 1945–1972 by the Norwegian theoretical chemist Lars Onsager (1903—Chemist Nobel Prize winner 1968), 1972 by the physicist Willis Eugene Lamb, Jr. (1913—Physics Nobel Prizeman 1955)), and the J. Willard Gibbs Research Laboratory in 1955 (Plate 5), which contains some memorials of him, including a bronze bas-relief (initially in the new Sloane Laboratory 1912) by the American sculptor Lee Lawrie (1877–1963) (initiated with the gift of the $500 Silliman lecture fee by the Göttingen physical chemist Walther Hermann Nernst (1864–1941) when he visited Yale in 1906); the corresponding portrait by the artist Leslie Emmet is in the Yale Graduate Club, which Gibbs never joined. On the outside of the garden wall of the Master of Berkeley College is a plaque (Plate 1) marking the location of his home. The last resting place of this truly American Scientist and American Scholar is simply marked in the nearby Grove Street Cemetery in New Haven (W. H. Nernst placed a wreath on Gibbs' grave at the time of his visit):

Josiah Willard Gibbs

Born February 11, 1839   Died April 28, 1903

On the reverse side it reads:

Professor of Mathematical Physics
in Yale University, 1871–1900

Gibbs died of a sudden intestinal attack. The simple funeral services consisted of a read hymn, Scripture readings, and prayer. A special memorial meeting of the Physics Club and certain other Yale Clubs was held May 19, 1903, in the old Sloane Physical Laboratory. Among the attendees was J. J. Thomson, Nobel Laureate, who had had as students the later Director of the Laboratory (1906–19) A. H. Bumstead, who succeeded C. S. Hastings in 1915, and the later Chairman (1920–40) of the Department, John Zeleny (1874–1951). In his *Recollections and Reflections* (1937) he commented, "Scientific Yale had in Willard Gibbs one of the very greatest mathematical physicists in his generation"—in contrast to C. W. Eliot's more literary Harvard.

Gibbs wrote only two obituaries;[2] in each he revealed part of himself. In the obituary for H. A. Newton (1897) he remarked: "These papers show more than the type of mind of the author; they give no uncertain testimony concerning the character of the man. In all these papers we see a love of honest work, an aversion to shams, a distrust of rash generalizations and speculations based on uncertain premises. He was never anxious to add one more guess on doubtful matters in the hope of hitting the truth, or what might pass as such for a time, but was always willing to take infinite pains in the most careful test of every theory. To these qualities was joined a modesty which forbade the pushing of his own claims, and desired no reputation except the unsought tribute of competent judges."

The words with which Gibbs concluded his remarkable obituary (1889) of P. J. E. Clausius are also appropriate here: "His true monument lies not on the shelves of libraries, but in the thoughts of men and in the history of more than one science." He embodied the spirit of his alma mater, *Lux et Veritas*!

Biographical Sketch

1839	Born February 11 in New Haven, Connecticut (father a professor in Yale College Theological Seminary)
1848	Attended small private school
1849	Entered Hopkins Grammar School
1854	Entered Yale College
1855	Death of mother
1858	B.A., Yale College Enrolled as engineering student in Yale College, Department of Philosophy and Arts
1861	Elected to Connecticut Academy of Arts and Sciences Death of father
1863	Ph.D. (engineering), Yale College
1866	Trip with two sisters to Paris, Riviera, Berlin, Heidelberg Patent for "An Improved Railway Car Brake"
1869	Returned to New Haven
1871	Appointed Professor of Mathematical Physics, Department of Philosophy and the Arts, Yale College
1873	Articles on graphical thermodynamics
1875–8	Article on heterogeneous equilibria
1879	Elected to National Academy of Sciences
1880	Elected to American Academy of Arts and Sciences
1881	Rumford Medal
1885	Vice President (Mathematics), American Association for the Advancement of Science
1892	German translation of heterogeneous equilibria
1893	LL.D., University of Erlangen and William College
1895	Elected to American Philosophical Society

1896	LL.D., Princeton University
1897	Elected to Royal Society of London (foreign associate)
1899	French translation of heterogeneous equilibria
1901	Copley Medal
1902	*Elementary Principles in Statistical Mechanics* *Gibbs' Vector Analysis* (edited by E. B. Wilson) D.Math., University of Christiana (Oslo)
1903	Died, April 28
1912	Bronze tablet, new (1912) Sloane Physics Laboratory, Yale University
1927	Gibbs Memorial Professorship, Yale University
1955	J. Willard Gibbs Research Laboratory, Yale University
1974	"Centennial of Gibbs' Thermodynamics", symposium of Washington Academy of Sciences February 21

Bibliography

1. GIBBS, J. WILLARD. "Elements of Vector Analysis, Arranged for the Use of Students in Physics". New Haven (1881, 1884; unpublished). *Elementary Principles in Statistical Mechanics*, New York, Charles Scribner's Sons (1902).
2. *The Collected Works of J. Willard Gibbs.* I. *Thermodynamics.* II. *Statistical Mechanics, Dynamics, Vector Analysis, Light, etc.* New York, Longmans, Green (1928).
3. *A Commentary on the Scientific Writings of J. Willard Gibbs.* I. *Thermodynamics* (ed. F. G. DONNAN and A. HAAS). II. *Theoretical Physics* (ed. A. HAAS). New Haven, Yale University (1936).
4. President's Committee on University Development. *A Professor's Theory and Its Practical Uses—The Work of J. Willard Gibbs.* Yale University (1939).
5. BOLTZMANN, LUDWIG. *Vorlesungen über Gastheorie I.* (1896), *II.* (1898) (trans. S. BRUSH, *Lectures on Gas Theory*, Berkeley, University of California (1960)). Leipzig, Barth.
6. BRUSH, STEPHEN GEORGE. *Kinetic Theory.* I. *The Nature of Gases and of Heat* (1965). II. *Irreversible Processes* (1966). Oxford, Pergamon.
7. CHITTENDEN, RUSSELL HENRY. *History of the Sheffield Scientific School of Yale University*, I, II. New Haven, Yale University (1928).
8. DONNAN, FREDERICK GEORGE. *The Influence of J. Willard Gibbs on the Science of Physical Chemistry.* Philadelphia, Franklin Institute (1924).
9. HASTINGS, CHARLES SHELDON. "Josiah Willard Gibbs" in *Biographical Memoirs.* Washington, National Academy of Sciences, VI, pp. 375–93 (1909).
10. GUGGENHEIM, EDWARD ARMAND. *Modern Thermodynamics by the Methods of Willard Gibbs.* London, Methuen (1933).
11. KLEIN, MARTIN JESSE. *Paul Ehrenfest. I. The Making of a Theoretical Physicist.* Amsterdam, North Holland (1970).
12. McKEEHAN, LOUIS WILLIAMS. *Yale Science—The First Hundred Years 1701–1801.* New York, Henry Schuman (1947).
13. MAXWELL, JAMES CLERK. *Theory of Heat* (4th ed.). London, Longmans, Green (1875).
14. PIERSON, GEORGE WILSON. *Yale College, I–IV.* New Haven, Yale University (1952, 1955).
15. RUKEYSER, MURIEL. *Willard Gibbs.* Garden City (N.Y.), Doubleday Doran (1942).
16. TER HAAR, DIRK. *Elements of Thermostatistics* (2nd ed.). New York; Holt, Rinehart & Winston (1966).

17. TOLMAN, RICHARD CHACE. *The Principles of Statistical Mechanics*. Oxford University (1938).
18. WHEELER, LYNDE PHELPS. *Josiah Willard Gibbs* (rev. ed.). New Haven, Yale University (1952).
19. WHEELER, LYNDE PHELPS, EVERETT OYER WATERS, and SAMUEL WILLIAM DUDLEY. *The Early Work of Willard Gibbs in Applied Mechanics*. New York, Henry Schuman (1947).
20. WHEELER, LYNDE PHELPS (ed.). "Personal Recollections and Impressions of J. Willard Gibbs" by His Niece, Nephews, and Certain of His Pupils. Sterling Memorial Library, Yale University 1947 (unpublished).
21. WILSON, EDWIN BIDWELL. *Vector Analysis Founded Upon the Lectures of J. Willard Gibbs*. New Haven, Yale University (1901).
22. *Centennial of Gibbs' Thermodynamics, J. Wash. Acad. Sci.* (to be published 1974)

PART II
His Scientific Writings

CHAPTER 4

Thermodynamics

(a) HISTORICAL PERSPECTIVE

Thermodynamics, the relation between heat and mechanics (preferably the more general term, thermophysics), is rooted in the measurement of temperature, the nature of heat, and the association of heat with mechanical work.

It is strange that no measurement of thermal phenomena was attempted until the development (1592–1603) of the thermoscope by the Italian physicist Galileo Galilei (1564–1642). In this case a glass tube with a bulb of confined air is inverted in water; when heated, the air expands and depresses the water in the tube (subject, of course, to variations in the barometric pressure). Later (1632) the French physician Jean Rey (1583–1645) utilized water in an upright tube. Quantitative scales were introduced in 1717 by the German physicist Gabriel Daniel Fahrenheit (1686–1736), in 1731 by the French naturalist René Antoine Ferchault de Réaumur (1683–1757), and in 1742 by the Swedish astronomer Anders Celsius (1701–44). In 1702 the French physicist Guillaume Amontons (1663–1705) introduced air as the thermometric material. In general, the fixing of a common reference point on all scales made a comparison of their readings possible: two fixed points minimized the variability of the thermometric substance itself. The French chemist Joseph Louis Gay-Lussac (1778–1850) investigated in 1802 volumetric changes of gases with temperature change (unpublished work had already been done by the French physicist Jacques Alexandre César Charles (1746–1823)).

The nature of heat has been a matter of speculative curiosity from antiquity. Quantitative concepts, viz. specific heat and latent heat, were first formulated about 1757 by the Scottish chemist and physician Joseph Black (1728–99). The French chemist Antoine Laurent Lavoisier (1743–94) treated heat as a chemical element in his *Traité élementaire de chimie* (1789) and named it caloric.

Thermodynamics *per se* can be said to have been initiated in 1824 with the *Réflexions sur la puissance motrice du feu* by the French physicist Nicolas Léonard Sadi Carnot (1796–1832), who was regarded as late as 1896 by W. Thomson (Kelvin) as the "profoundest thinker in thermodynamic philosophy". He considered the practicable cyclic operation of an engine performing mechanical work while taking in and giving out heat during the process—a process independent of the working substance and the particular operations. This Carnot cycle is conveniently represented on the so-called indicator diagram introduced by J. Watt; it indicates volume and pressure values of a gas, in this case during an isothermal expansion followed by an adiabatic expansion, and then during an isothermal contraction followed by an adiabatic contraction, back to the initial stage of the gas. Defining the efficiency of the operation by the ratio of the net heat loss by the gas to the total heat taken in by it, Carnot showed that the efficiency of an engine cannot be greater than that utilizing only reversible processes in a cycle operating between a high temperature and a low one. The work done was regarded as analogous to that available in falling water. The French mining engineer Benoit Pierre Émile Clapeyron (1799–1864) put Carnot's principle in mathematical form in 1834; he showed that the efficiency of a reversible engine is a function only of the temperatures of the reservoirs used for the transference of heat. W. Thomson (Kelvin) devised in 1848 an absolute thermodynamical scale of temperature by considering a sequence of reversible engines operating in Carnot cycles, in each of which the work done is equal to the net heat absorbed and the heat transfer is proportional to the temperature. Its zero is absolute in that it is the lowest temperature attainable.

The direct relation of the work performed by an engine to the heat involved in the process was investigated independently in inconclusive experiments by the English–American physicist Sir Benjamin Thompson (Count Rumford, 1753–1814) and by the English chemist Sir Humphry Davy (1778–1829). The subsequent development of the idea of the physical equivalence of work and of heat was complicated by the cultural environment in the first half of the eighteenth century. The climate of opinion was influenced by the popular European *Natur-philosophie*, which involved many metaphysical speculations. At the same time, scientific publications were restricted by the imposition of academic accreditation, as well as by genuine doubts of some senior scientists, owing particularly to the implications of the popular caloric theory. Accordingly, major investigations were pursued primarily by uninhibited young persons (ages 22–26), not by professional physical scientists. Fortunately, the experiential soil was favorable; for example, the everyday experience with machines from antiquity, particularly their mechanical advantage. The physical properties of gases were being quantitatively determined (e.g. adiabatic expansion by J. L. Gay-Lussac). Finally, the concept of work, which had not been necessary in eclestial mechanics, was being utilized in evaluating the practical performance of engines. In addition, there were two conditions favorable to the development of the relation of work to heat: (1) the general acceptability of mechanical explanations (cf. the dynamic theory of gases initiated by J. P. Joule in 1848), and (2) the popular interest in the conversion of energy into different forms.

The three outstanding contributions to the formulation of what came to be termed the first law of thermodynamics can be classified as theory, experiment, and generalization. In 1842 the German physician Julius Robert von Mayer (1814–78) calculated the so-called mechanical equivalent of heat by determining the heat produced in the adiabatic compression of gas. The English physicist James Prescott Joule (1818–89) measured first in 1843 and subsequently thereafter (until 1878) the heat produced in a liquid churned by a paddle wheel rotated by a falling weight. These results were generalized in 1847 by H. L. F. von Helmholtz to all forms of energy in the modern principle of the conservation of energy. Nevertheless, its particular expression as the first law of thermodynamics, namely, that any change in the internal energy of a substance is independent of the thermal and/or mechanical method of achieving it, was not accepted until 1851 by scientific leaders such as W. Thomson (Kelvin), and even then not generally until about 1860. The basic conflict was between the new idea of the conversion of work into heat and the old one of the conservation of heat assumed by N. L. S. Carnot; reconciliation was finally made possible by regarding heat as a degraded form of energy. Consideration of the transformation of energy in 1851 led W. Thomson (Kelvin) to a statement of the so-called second law of thermodynamics. In 1850, however, R. J. E. Clausius had already enunciated this law on the basis of heat-transfer phenomena. In 1865 he expressed it in terms of a new concept entropy, which simplifies the expression of Carnot's principle; entropy is a function of the state of a substance and can only increase in natural processes. Unfortunately, the concept lacks sensory perceptibility and hence intuitive comprehensibility; Gibbs used this new idea in his first paper on thermodynamics.

Although Gibbs had no personal acquaintance with Clausius, he was familiar with Clausius' memoir of 1850 and regarded it as establishing the science of thermodynamics (he himself recognized the merits of entropy as a concept). Indeed, he placed Clausius' succinct (but operationally questionable) statements (1865) of the two laws of thermodynamics at the beginning of his own classic paper, "On the Equilibrium of Heterogeneous Substances" (1876), viz.

> Die Energie der Welt ist constant.
> Die Entropie der Welt strebt einem maximum zu.

It was, therefore, not surprising that he accepted an invitation to write Clausius' orbituary. In it he reviewed the whole history of thermodynamics in order to make evident Clausius' own significant contributions to its development.

Rudolf Julius Emanuel Clausius

(From *Proceedings of the American Academy of Arts and Sciences*, XVI, pp. 458–65 (1889) (Obituary).)

RUDOLF JULIUS EMANUEL CLAUSIUS was born at Cöslin in Pomerania, January 2, 1822. His studies, after 1840, were pursued at Berlin, where he became Privat-docent in the University, and Instructor in Physics in the School of Artillery. He was Professor of Physics at Zürich in the Polytechnicum (1855–67) and in the University (1857–67), at Würzburg (1867–69), and finally at Bonn (1869–88), where he died on the 24th of August, 1888.

His literary activity commenced in 1847, with the publication of a memoir in Crelle's Journal, "Ueber die Lichtzerstreuung in der Atmosphäre, und über die Intensität des durch die Atmosphäre reflectirten Sonnenlichts."* This was immediately followed by other writings relating to the same subject, two of which were subsequently translated from Poggendorff's Annalen† for Taylor's Scientific Memoirs. A treatise entitled "Die Lichterscheinungen der Atmosphäre" formed part of Grunert's "Beiträge zur meteorologischen Optik."

An entirely different subject, the elasticity of solids, was discussed in his paper, (1849), "Ueber die Veränderungen, welche in den bisher gebräuchlichen Formeln für das Gleichgewicht und die Bewegung fester Körper durch neuere Beobachtungen nothwendig geworden sind."‡

But it was with questions of quite another order of magnitude that his name was destined to be associated. The fundamental questions concerning the relation of heat to mechanical effect, which had been raised by Rumford, Carnot, and others, to meet with little response, were now everywhere pressing to the front.

"For more than twelve years," said Regnault in 1853, "I have been engaged in collecting the materials for the solution of this question:—Given a certain quantity of heat, what is, theoretically, the amount of mechanical effect which can be obtained by applying the heat to evaporation, or the expansion of elastic fluids, in the various circumstances which can be realized in practice?"§ The twenty-first volume of the Memoirs of the Academy of Paris, describing the first part of the magnificent series of researches which the liberality of the French government enabled him to carry out for the solution of this question, was published in 1847. In the same year appeared Helmholtz's celebrated memoir, "Ueber die Erhaltung der Kraft." For some years Joule had been making those experiments which were to associate his name with one of the fundamental laws of thermodynamics and one of the principal constants of nature. In 1849 he made that determination of the mechanical equivalent of heat by the stirring of water which for nearly thirty years remained the unquestioned standard. In 1848 and 1849 Sir William Thomson was engaged in developing the consequences of Carnot's theory of the motive power of heat, while Professor James Thomson in demonstrating the effect of pressure on the freezing point of water by a Carnot's cycle, showed the flexibility and the fruitfulness of a mode of demonstration which was to become canonical in thermodynamics. Meantime Rankine was attacking the problem in his own way, with one of those marvellous creations of the imagination of which it is so difficult to estimate the precise value.

---

* Vol. xxxiv. p. 122, and vol. xxxvi. p. 185.
† Vol. lxxvi. pp. 161 and 188.
‡ *Pogg. Ann.*, vol. lxxvi. p. 46 (1849).
§ *Comptes Rendus*, vol. xxxvi. p. 676.

Such was the state of the question when Clausius published his first memoir on thermodynamics: "Ueber die bewegende Kraft der Wärme, und die Gesetze, welche sich daraus für die Wärmelehre selbst ableiten lassen."[*] This memoir marks an epoch in the history of physics. If we say, in the words used by Maxwell some years ago, that thermodynamics is "a science with secure foundations, clear definitions, and distinct boundaries,"[†] and ask when those foundations were laid, those definitions fixed, and those boundaries traced, there can be but one answer. Certainly not before the publication of that memoir. The materials indeed existed for such a science, as Clausius showed by constructing it from such materials, substantially, as had for years been the common property of physicists. But truth and error were in a confusing state of mixture. Neither in France, nor in Germany, nor in Great Britain, can we find the answer to the question quoted from Regnault. The case was worse than this, for wrong answers were confidently urged by the highest authorities. That question was completely answered, on its theoretical side, in the memoir of Clausius, and the science of thermodynamics came into existence. And as Maxwell said in 1878, so it might have been said at any time since the publication of that memoir, that the foundations of the science were secure, its definitions clear, and its boundaries distinct.

The constructive power thus exhibited, this ability to bring order out of confusion, this breadth of view which could apprehend one truth without losing sight of another, this nice discrimination to separate truth from error,—these are qualities which place the possessor in the first rank of scientific men.

In the development of the various consequences of the fundamental propositions of thermodynamics, as applied to all kinds of physical phenomena, Clausius was rivalled, perhaps surpassed, in activity and versatility by Sir William Thomson. His attention, indeed, seems to have been less directed toward the development of the subject in extension, than toward the nature of the molecular phenomena of which the laws of thermodynamics are the sensible expression. He seems to have very early felt the conviction, that behind the second law of thermodynamics, which relates to the heat absorbed or given out by a body, and therefore capable of direct measurement, there was another law of similar form, but relating to the quantities of heat (i.e. molecular *vis viva*) absorbed in the performance of work, external or internal.

This may be made more definite, if we express the second law in a mathematical form, as may be done by saying that in any reversible cyclic process which a body may undergo

$$\int \frac{dQ}{t} = 0,$$

where dQ is an elementary portion of the heat imparted to the body, and t the absolute temperature of the body, or the portion of it which receives the heat. Or, without limitation to cyclic processes, we may say that for any reversible infinitesimal change,

$$dQ = t\, dS,$$

where S denotes a certain function of the state of the body, called by Clausius the *entropy*. The element of heat may evidently be divided into two parts, of which one represents the increase of molecular *vis viva* in the body, and the other the work done against forces, either external or internal. If we call these parts dH and dQ_w, we have

$$dQ = dH + dQ_w.$$

Now the proposition of which Clausius felt so strong a conviction was that for reversible cyclic processes

$$\int \frac{dQ_w}{dt} = 0,$$

and that for any reversible infinitesimal change

$$dQ_w = t\, dZ,$$

where Z is another function of the state of the body, which he called the *disgregation*, and regarded as determined by the positions of the elementary parts of the body without reference to their velocities. In this respect it differed from the entropy. An immediate consequence of these relations is that for any reversible cyclic process

$$\int \frac{dH}{t} = 0,$$

and therefore that H, the molecular *vis viva* of the body, must be a function of the temperature alone. This important result was expressed by Clausius in the following words: "Die Menge der in einem Körper wirklich vorhandenen Wärme ist nur von seiner Temperatur und nicht von der Anordnung seiner Bestandtheile abhängig."

To return to the equation

$$dQ_w = t\, dZ.$$

This expresses that heat tends to increase the disgregation, and that the intensity of this tendency is proportional to the absolute temperature. In the words of Clausius: "Die mechanische Arbeit, welche die Wärme bei irgend einer Anordnungsänderung eines Körpers thun kann, ist proportional der absoluten Temperatur, bei welcher die Aenderung geschieht."

Such in brief and in part were the views advanced by Clausius in 1862, in his memoir, "Ueber die Anwendung des Satzes von der Aequivalenz der Verwandlungen auf die innere Arbeit."* Although they were advanced rather as a hypothesis than as anything for which he could give a formal proof, he seems to have little doubt of their correctness, and his confidence seems to have increased with the course of time.

The substantial correctness of these views cannot now be called in question. The researches especially of Maxwell and Boltzmann have shown that the molecular *vis viva* is proportional to the absolute temperature, and Boltzmann has even been able to determine the precise nature of the functions which Clausius called entropy and disgregation.† But the anticipation, to a certain extent, at so early a period in the history of the subject, of the ultimate form which the theory was to take, shows a remarkable insight, which is by no means to be lightly esteemed on account of the acknowledged want of a rigorous demonstration. The propositions, indeed, as relating to quantities which escape direct measurement, belong to molecular science, and seem to require for their complete and satisfactory demonstration a considerable development of that science. This development naturally commenced with the simplest case involving the characteristic problems of the subject,—the case, namely, of gases.

The origin of the kinetic theory of gases is lost in remote antiquity, and its completion the most sanguine cannot hope to see. But a single generation has seen it advance from the stage of vague surmises to an extensive and well established body of doctrine. This is mainly the work of three men, Clausius, Maxwell, and Boltzmann, of which Clausius was the earliest in the field, and has been called by Maxwell the principal founder of the science.‡ We may regard his paper, (1857,) "Ueber die Art der Bewegung, welche wir Wärme nennen,"§ as marking his definite entrance into this field, although many points were incidentally discussed in earlier papers.

This was soon followed by his papers, "Ueber die mittlere Länge der Wege, welche bei der Molecularbewegung gasförmiger Körper von den einzelnen Molecülen zurückgelegt werden,"‖ and "Ueber die Wärmeleitung gasförmiger Körper."¶

A very valuable contribution to molecular science is the conception of the *virial*, defined in his paper, (1870,) "Ueber einen auf die Wärme anwendbaren Satz,"** where he shows that in any case of stationary motion the mean *vis viva* of the system is equal to its virial.

---

*   *Pogg. Ann.*, vol. cxvi. p. 73. See also vol. cxxvii. p. 477 (1866).
†   *Sitzungsberichte Wien. Akad.*, vol. lxiii. p. 728 (1871).
‡   *Nature*, vol. xvii. p. 278.
§   *Ibid.*, vol. c. p. 353 (1857).
‖   *Ibid.*, vol. cv. p. 239 (1858). See also *Wied. Ann.*, vol. x. p. 92.
¶   *Ibid.*, vol. cxv. p. 1 (1862).
** *Ibid.*, vol. clxi. p. 124. See also Jubelband, p. 411.

In the mean time, Maxwell and Boltzmann had entered the field. Maxwell's first paper, "On the Motions and Collisions of perfectly elastic Spheres,"[*] was characterized by a new manner of proposing the problems of molecular science. Clausius was concerned with the mean values of various quantities which vary enormously in the smallest time or space which we can appreciate. Maxwell occupied himself with the relative frequency of the various values which these quantities have. In this he was followed by Boltzmann. In reading Clausius, we seem to be reading mechanics; in reading Maxwell, and in much of Boltzmann's most valuable work, we seem rather to be reading in the theory of probabilities. There is no doubt that the larger manner in which Maxwell and Boltzmann proposed the problems of molecular science enabled them in some cases to get a more satisfactory and complete answer, even for those questions which do not at first sight seem to require so broad a treatment.

Boltzmann's first work, however, (1866,) "Ueber die mechanische Bedeutung des zweiten Hauptsatzes der Wärmetheorie,"[†] was in a line which no one had preceded him, although he was followed by some of the most distinguished names among his contemporaries. Somewhat later (1870) Clausius, whose attention had not been called to Boltzmann's work, wrote his paper, "Ueber die Zurückführung des zweiten Hauptsatzes der mechanischen Wärmetheorie auf allgemeine mechanische Principien."[‡]

The point of departure of these investigations, and others to which they gave rise, is the consideration of the mean values of the force-function and of the *vis viva* of a system in which the motions are periodic, and of the variations of these mean values when the external influences are changed. The theorems developed belong to the same general category as the principle of least action, and the principle or principles known as Hamilton's, which have to do, explicitly or implicitly, with the variations of these mean values.

Among other papers of Clausius on this subject, we may mention the two following: "Ueber einen neuen mechanischen Satz in Bezug auf stationäre Bewegung,"[§] (1873,) and "Ueber den satz vom mittleren Ergal und seine Anwendung auf die Molecularbewegungen der Gase"[‖] (1874).

The first problem of molecular science is to derive from the observed properties of bodies as accurate a notion as possible of their molecular constitution. The knowledge we may gain of their molecular constitution may then be utilized in the search for formulas to represent their observable properties. A most notable achievement in this direction is that of van der Waals, in his celebrated memoir "On the Continuity of the Gaseous and Liquid States." To this part of the subject belong the following papers of Clausius: "Ueber das Verhalten der Kohlensäure in Bezug auf Druck, Volumen und

---

[*] *Phil. Mag.*, vol. xix. p. 19 (1860).
[†] *Sitzungsberichte Wien. Akad.*, vol. liii. p. 195.
[‡] *Pogg. Ann.*, vol. cxlii. p. 433.
[§] *Ibid.*, vol. cl. p. 106.
[‖] *Ibid.*, Ergänzungsband vii. p. 215.

Temperatur,"* and "Ueber die theoretische Bestimmung des Dampfdruckes und der Volumina des Dampfes und der Flüssigkeit" (two papers).†

Another matter in which Clausius showed his originality and power was the vexed subject of electrodynamics, as treated in his memoir, "Ueber die Ableitung eines neuen electrodynamischen Grundgesetzes."‡ Various points in the theory of electricity in which the principles of thermodynamics or of molecular science were involved, had previously been treated in different papers, of which the earliest appeared in 1852,§ while the doctrine of the potential (electrical and gravitational) was treated in a separate book, which appeared in 1859, with the title, "Die Potentialfunction und das Potential, ein Beitrag zur mathematischen Physik." This subsequently went through several editions, in which it was revised and enlarged. All these subjects, with others, were brought together in a single volume, "Die mechanische Behandlung der Electricität," which appeared in 1879, forming the second volume of his "Mechanische Wärmetheorie."‖ Later papers on electricity related to the principles of electrodynamics, ¶ electrical and magnetic units,** and dynamo-electric machines.††

The Royal Society's catalogue of scientific papers, and the excellent indices to the Annalen der Physik und Chemie, in which Clausius's work usually appeared, render it unnecessary to enumerate in detail his scientific papers. The list, indeed, would be a long one. The Royal Society's catalogue gives seventy-seven titles for the years 1847–1873. Subsequently twenty-five papers have appeared in the Annalen alone, and about half as many others elsewhere.

But such work as that of Clausius is not measured by counting titles or pages. His true monument lies not on the shelves of libraries, but in the thoughts of men, and in the history of more than one science.

* *Wied. Ann.*, vol. ix. p. 337 (1880).
† *Ibid.*, vol. xiv. p. 279 and p. 692 (1881).
‡ *Crelle's Journal*, vol. lxxxii. p. 85 (1877).
§ "Ueber das mechanische Aequivalent einer electrischen Entladung und die dabei stattfindende Erwärmung des Leitungsdrahtes." *Pogg. Ann.*, vol. lxxxvi. p. 337. "Ueber die bei einem stationären electrischen Strome in dem Leiter gethane Arbeit und erzeugte Wärme." *Pogg. Ann.*, vol. lxxxvii. p. 415 (1852). "Ueber die Anwendung der mechanischen Wärmetheorie auf die thermoelectrischen Erscheinungen." *Pogg. Ann.*, vol. xc. p. 513 (1853). "Ueber die Electricitätsleitung in Electrolyten." *Pogg. Ann.*, vol. ci. p. 338 (1857).
‖ The first volume of this work appeared in 1876, and contained the general theory with the more immediate consequences of the two fundamental laws. The third volume has not yet appeared, but it is expected very soon, edited by Professor Planck and Dr. Pulfrich. In a certain sense this work may be regarded as a second edition of an earlier one (1864 and 1867), which consisted of a reprint of papers and had the title "Abhandlungen über die mechanische Wärmetheorie."
¶ *Wied. Ann.*, vol. x. p. 608; vol. xi. p. 604.
** *Ibid.*, vol. xvi. p. 529; vol. xvii. p. 713.
†† *Ibid.*, vol. xx. p. 353; vol. xxi. p. 385.

(b) GRAPHICAL METHODS

In line with his engineering training and in keeping with his physical insights, Gibbs was inclined to use rigorous geometrical representations in preference to approximate mechanical models. His first paper as Professor of Mathematical Physics summarized the uses of two-dimensional graphs in the thermodynamics of fluids.

In the case of a "simple" substance like a homogeneous fluid there is a characteristic equation which describes its physical state in terms of its physical properties such as pressure p, volume v, and temperature t. In addition, of course, changes of the internal energy ϵ are given by the first law of thermodynamics, and those of the entropy η by the second. Thus there are three equations for five variables so that any two variables may be regarded as independent. (Symbols throughout this book are generally those employed by Gibbs. Some modern writers, however, prefer T for absolute temperature, E or U for internal energy, and S for entropy.) J. Watt had introduced a (v, p) plot of pressure against volume to indicate the state of the steam in the cylinder of an engine. Gibbs proceeded to investigate the possible use of Clausius' entropy function as an independent variable. For example, the entropy-temperature (η, t) diagram for the Carnot cycle is a rectangle, the area of which is proportional to the net gain of heat received by the substance (equal to the work done by it); these coordinates were later used by engineers on account of their practical convenience. The volume-entropy (v, η) diagram, on the other hand, has the theoretical advantage of having both variables proportional to the quantity of substance itself. Gibbs preferred the latter representation and gave most of his attention to it; he discussed particularly its advantages for coexistent states, e.g. the triple state.

The whole paper is reproduced here because it exemplifies clearly Gibbs' logical approach, as well as his geometrical skill. The last portion contains an initial indication of his later interest in thermal equilibria.

In 1871 the Scotch-Irish engineer James Thomson (1822–92), brother of W. Thomson (Kelvin), gave a three-dimensional (volume v, pressure p, temperature t) surface representation of the thermodynamic properties of a fluid, which provides a bird's-eye view of physiochemical changes (like a solid model or a relief map). In his second paper (1873,

Ref. (1)I, pp. 33–44) Gibbs considered a thermodynamic surface having as coordinates volume v, entropy η, and internal energy ϵ for a homogeneous substance. This so-called "primitive surface" represents the various solid, liquid, and vapor states of a homogeneous substance. It has the distinct advantage that the pressure and the temperature can be obtained by differentiation, whereas the converse is not true. Clausius' fundamental equation for a reversible process is:

$$d\epsilon = t\, d\eta - p\, dv, \qquad \epsilon(v, \eta),$$

where

$$t = -\left(\frac{\partial\epsilon}{\partial\eta}\right)_v,$$

and

$$p = \left(\frac{\partial\epsilon}{\partial v}\right)_\eta.$$

The temperature and the pressure are determined by the inclination of the tangent plane at a point on the surface to the planes $v = 0$ and $\eta = 0$, respectively. A "derived surface" can be formed of three developable surfaces representing the physical states (solid, liquid, vapor) of the substance; a "triangular plane" represents a mixture of all three. These two surfaces determine the thermodynamic properties of the substance in all possible states. For example, for stable equilibrium the thermodynamic surface must be convex to the tangent plane and above it. In general, for constant temperature and pressure, the points of contact of the tangent planes to the surfaces (primitive and derived) will be states of equilibrium, and the stability will depend upon the relation of the surface to the tangent plane at each point.

Gibbs discussed the geometrical conditions for equilibrium, the criteria for stability, the conditions for coexistent states and for the critical state, which had been experimentally discovered in 1863 by the Irish chemist Thomas Andrews (1813–85). (The distinction between liquid and gas disappears at the critical point of a one-component fluid.) J. C. Maxwell, to whom Gibbs sent reprints, was so impressed with the beauty and power of this method for solving directly and simply thermodynamic problems that he devoted 13 pages to a discussion of it in the fourth edition of his book on the *Theory of Heat*."[13] What is more, he personally constructed a model of such a surface (coordinates v, η, ϵ) for water and sent Gibbs a plaster cast (Plate 4) of it (now in the J. Willard Gibbs Research Laboratory). A mixture of different physical states of a substance can be represented by a single point determined by the points f or each state (like the center of mass of a triangle); it is generally within the solid bounded by the surface at an energy distance from it equal to the available energy of the surface.

Gibbs made special use also of the ζ, t, p surface, where $\zeta = \epsilon - t\eta + pv$. At the end of the paper he noted the possibility of applying the same method to a heterogeneous mixture of different chemical substances.

Gibbs geometrical viewpoint has been recently found to be invaluable in understanding the complex and experimentally difficult anomalous critical phenomena; it has led to the recognition of universal features that are independent of the nature of a particular fluid. (This development was accelerated by the 1966 Conference on "Critical Phenomena" sponsored by the U.S. National Bureau of Standards.)

Graphical Methods in the Thermodynamics of Fluids

(From *Transactions of the Connecticut Academy of Arts and Sciences*, II. pp. 309–42 (1873–4).)

ALTHOUGH geometrical representations of propositions in the thermodynamics of fluids are in general use, and have done good service in disseminating clear notions in this science, yet they have by no means received the extension in respect to variety and generality of which they are capable. So far as regards a general graphical method, which can exhibit at once all the thermodynamic properties of a fluid concerned in reversible processes, and serve alike for the demonstration of general theorems and the numerical solution of particular problems, it is the general if not the universal practice to use diagrams in which the rectilinear co-ordinates represent volume and pressure. The object of this article is to call attention to certain diagrams of different construction, which afford graphical methods coextensive in their applications with that in ordinary use, and preferable to it in many cases in respect of distinctness or of convenience.

QUANTITIES AND RELATIONS WHICH ARE TO BE REPRESENTED BY THE DIAGRAM.

We have to consider the following quantities:—

v, the volume,

p, the pressure,

t, the (absolute) temperature, $\Big\}$ of a given body in any state,

ε, the energy,

η, the entropy,

also W, the work done, $\Big\}$ by the body in passing from one state
and H, the heat received,*$\Big\}$ to another.

These are subject to the relations expressed by the following differential equations:—

$$dW = \alpha p\, dv, \tag{a}$$

$$d\varepsilon = \beta\, dH - dW, \tag{b}$$

$$d\eta = \frac{dH\dagger}{t}, \tag{c}$$

where α and β are constants, depending upon the units by which v, p, W and H are measured. We may suppose our units so chosen that $\alpha = 1$ and $\beta = 1$,‡

* Work spent upon the body is as usual to be considered as a negative quantity of work done by the body, and heat given out by the body as a negative quantity of heat received by it.

It is taken for granted that the body has a uniform temperature throughout, and that the pressure (or expansive force) has a uniform value both for all points in the body and for all directions. This, it will be observed, will exclude irreversible processes, but will not entirely exclude solids, although the condition of equal pressure in all directions renders the case very limited, in which they come within the scope of the discussion.

† Equation (a) may be derived from simple mechanical considerations. Equations (b) and (c) may be considered as defining the energy and entropy of any state of the body, or more strictly as defining the differentials $d\varepsilon$ and $d\eta$. That functions of the state of the body exist, the differentials of which satisfy these equations, may easily be deduced from the first and second laws of thermodynamics. The term *entropy*, it will be observed, is here used in accordance with the original suggestion of Clausius, and not in the sense in which it has been employed by Professor Tait and others after his suggestion. The same quantity has been called by Professor Rankine the *Thermodynamic function*. See Clausius, *Mechanische Wärmetheorie*, Abhnd. ix, § 14; or *Pogg. Ann.*, Bd. cxxv (1865), p. 390; and Rankine, *Phil. Trans.*, vol. 144, p. 126.

‡ For example, we may choose as the unit of volume, the cube of the unit of length, —as the unit of pressure the unit of force acting upon the square of the unit of length,—as the unit of work the unit of force acting through the unit of length,—and as the unit of heat the thermal equivalent of the unit of work. The units of length and of force would still be arbitrary as well as the unit of temperature.

and write our equations in the simpler form,

$$d\varepsilon = dH - dW, \tag{1}$$

$$dW = p\,dv, \tag{2}$$

$$dH = t\,d\eta. \tag{3}$$

Eliminating dW and dH, we have

$$d\varepsilon = t\,d\eta - p\,dv. \tag{4}$$

The quantities v, p, t, ε and η are determined when the state of the body is given, and it may be permitted to call them *functions of the state of the body*. The state of a body, in the sense in which the term is used in the thermodynamics of fluids, is capable of two independent variations, so that between the five quantities v, p, t, ε and η there exist relations expressible by three finite equations, different in general for different substances, but always such as to be in harmony with the differential equation (4). This equation evidently signifies that if ε be expressed as function of v and η, the partial differential coefficients of this function taken with respect to v and to η will be equal to $-p$ and to t respectively.*

On the other hand W and H are not functions of the state of the body (or functions of any of the quantities v, p, t, ε and η), but are determined by the whole series of states through which the body is supposed to pass.

FUNDAMENTAL IDEA AND GENERAL PROPERTIES OF THE DIAGRAM.

Now if we associate a particular point in a plane with every separate state, of which the body is capable, in any continuous manner, so that states differing infinitely little are associated with points which are infinitely near to each other,† the points associated with states of equal volume will form lines which may be called *lines of equal volume*, the different lines being distinguished by the numerical value of the volume, (as lines of volume 10, 20, 30, etc.). In the same way we may conceive of *lines of equal pressure*, *of equal temperature*, *of equal energy*, *and of equal entropy*. These lines we may also call

---

* An equation giving ε in terms of η and v, or more generally any finite equation between ε, η and v for a definite quantity of any fluid, may be considered as the fundamental thermodynamic equation of that fluid, as from it by aid of equations (2), (3) and (4) may be derived all the thermodynamic properties of the fluid (so far as reversible processes are concerned,) viz.: the fundamental equation with equation (4) gives the three relations existing between v, p, t, ε and η, and these relations being known, equations (2) and (3) give the work W and heat H for any change of state of the fluid.

† The method usually employed in treatises on thermodynamics, in which the rectangular co-ordinates of the point are made proportional to the volume and pressure of the body, is a single example of such an association.

isometric, isopiestic, isothermal, isodynamic, isentropic,[*] and if necessary use these words as substantives.

Suppose the body to change its state, the points associated with the states through which the body passes will form a line, which we may call the *path* of the body. The conception of a path must include the idea of direction, to express the order in which the body passes through the series of states. With every such change of state there is connected in general a certain amount of work done, W, and of heat received, H, which we may call the *work* of the *heat of the path*.[†] The value of these quantities may be calculated from equations (2) and (3),

$$dW = p \, dv$$
$$dH = t \, d\eta,$$

i.e.,
$$W = \int p \, dv \tag{5}$$

$$H = \int t \, d\eta, \tag{6}$$

the integration being carried on from the beginning to the end of the path. If the direction of the path is reversed, W and H change their signs, remaining the same in absolute value.

If the changes of state of the body form a cycle, i.e., if the final state is the same as the initial, the path becomes a *circuit*, and the work done and heat received are equal, as may be seen from equation (1), which when integrated for this case becomes $0 = H - W$.

The circuit will enclose a certain area, which we may consider as positive or negative according to the direction of the circuit which circumscribes it. The direction in which areas must be circumscribed in order that their value may be positive, is of course arbitrary. In other words, if x and y are the rectangular co-ordinates, we may define an area either as $\int y \, dx$, or as $\int x \, dy$.

If an area be divided into any number of parts, the work done in the circuit bounding the whole area is equal to the sum of the work done in all the circuits

---

[*] These lines are usually known by the name given them by Rankine, *adiabatic*. If, however, we follow the suggestion of Clausius and call that quantity *entropy*, which Rankine called the *thermodynamic function*, it seems natural to go one step farther, and call the lines in which this quantity has a constant value *isentropic*.

[†] For the sake of brevity, it will be convenient to use language which attributes to the diagram properties which belong to the associated states of the body. Thus it can give rise to no ambiguity, if we speak of the volume or the temperature of a point in the diagram, or of the work or heat of a line, instead of the volume or temperature of the body in the state associated with the point, or the work done or the heat received by the body in passing through the states associated with the points of the line. In like manner also we may speak of the body moving along a line in the diagram, instead of passing through the series of states represented by the line.

bounding the partial areas. This is evident from the consideration, that the work done in each of the lines which separate the partial areas appears twice and with contrary signs in the sum of the work done in the circuits bounding the partial areas. Also the heat received in the circuit bounding the whole area is equal to the sum of the heat received in all the circuits bounding the partial areas.*

If all the dimensions of a circuit are infinitely small, the ratio of the included area to the work or heat of the circuit is independent of the shape of the circuit and the direction in which it is described, and varies only with its position in the diagram. That this ratio is independent of the direction in which the circuit is described, is evident from the consideration that a reversal of this direction simply changes the sign of both terms of the ratio. To prove that the ratio is independent of the shape of the circuit, let us suppose the area ABCDE (fig. 1)

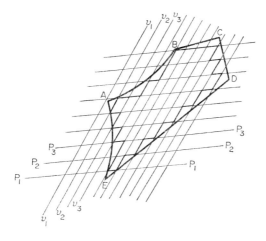

FIG. 1.

divided up by an infinite number of isometrics v_1v_1, v_2v_2, etc., with equal differences of volume dv, and an infinite number of isopiestics p_1p_1, p_2p_2, etc., with equal differences of pressure dp. Now from the principle of continuity, as the whole figure is infinitely small, the ratio of the area of one of the small quadrilaterals into which the figure is divided to the work done in passing around it is

---

* The conception of areas as positive or negative renders it unnecessary in propositions of this kind to state explicitly the direction in which the circuits are to be described. For the directions of the circuits are determined by the signs of the areas, and the signs of the partial areas must be the same as that of the area out of which they were formed.

approximately the same for all the different quadrilaterals. Therefore the area of the figure composed of all the complete quadrilaterals which fall within the given circuit has to the work done in circumscribing this figure the same ratio, which we will call γ. But the area of this figure is approximately the same as that of the given circuit, and the work done in describing this figure is approximately the same as that done in describing the given circuit, (eq. 5). Therefore the area of the given circuit has to the work done or heat received in that circuit this ratio γ, which is independent of the shape of the circuit.

Now if we imagine the systems of equidifferent isometrics and isopiestics, which have just been spoken of, extended over the whole diagram, the work done in circumscribing one of the small quadrilaterals, so that the increase of pressure directly precedes the increase of volume, will have in every part of the diagram a constant value, viz., the product of the differences of volume and pressure ($dv \times dp$), as may easily be proved by applying equation (2) successively to its four sides. But the area of one of these quadrilaterals, which we could consider as constant within the limits of the infinitely small circuit, may vary for different parts of the diagram, and will indicate proportionally the value of γ, which is equal to the area divided by $dv \times dp$.

In like manner, if we imagine systems of isentropics and isothermals drawn throughout the diagram for equal differences $d\eta$ and dt, the heat received in passing around one of the small quadrilaterals, so that the increase of t shall directly precede that of η, will be the constant product $d\eta \times dt$, as may be proved by equation (3), and the value of γ, which is equal to the area divided by the heat, will be indicated proportionally by the areas.*

---

* The indication of the value of γ by systems of equidifferent isometrics and isopiestics, or isentropics and isothermals, is explained above, because it seems in accordance with the spirit of the graphical method, and because it avoids the extraneous consideration of the co-ordinates. If, however, it is desired to have analytical expressions for the value of γ based upon the relations between the co-ordinates of the point and the state of the body, it is easy to deduce such expressions as the following, in which x and y are the rectangular co-ordinates, and it is supposed that the sign of an area is determined in accordance with the equation $A = \int y \, dx$:—

$$\frac{1}{\gamma} = \frac{dv}{dx} \cdot \frac{dp}{dy} - \frac{dp}{dx} \cdot \frac{dv}{dy} = \frac{d\eta}{dx} \cdot \frac{dt}{dy} - \frac{dt}{dx} \cdot \frac{d\eta}{dy},$$

where x and y are regarded as the independent variables;—or

$$\gamma = \frac{dx}{dv} \cdot \frac{dy}{dp} - \frac{dy}{dv} \cdot \frac{dx}{dp},$$

where v and p are the independent variables;—or

$$\gamma = \frac{dx}{d\eta} \cdot \frac{dy}{dt} - \frac{dy}{d\eta} \cdot \frac{dx}{dt}.$$

This quantity γ, which is the ratio of the area of an infinitely small circuit to the work done or heat received in that circuit, and which we may call the scale on which work and heat are represented by areas, or more briefly, the *scale of work and heat*, may have a constant value throughout the diagram or it may have a varying value. The diagram in ordinary use affords an example of the first case, as the area of a circuit is everywhere proportional to the work or heat. There are other diagrams which have the same property, and we may call all such *diagrams of constant scale*.

In any case we may consider the scale of work and heat as known for every point of the diagram, so fas as we are able to draw the isometrics and iso-piestics or the isentropics and isothermals. If we write δW and δH for the work and heat of an infinitesimal circuit, and δA for the area included, the relations of these quantities are thus expressed:—*

$$\delta W = \delta H = \frac{1}{\gamma} \delta A. \tag{7}$$

We may find the value of W and H for a circuit of finite dimensions by supposing the included area A divided into areas δA infinitely small in all directions, for which therefore the above equation will hold, and taking the sum of the values of δH or δW for the various areas δA. Writing W^C and H^C for the work and heat of the circuit C, and Σ^C for a summation or integration

---

where η and t are the independent variables;—or

$$\frac{1}{\gamma} = \frac{-\dfrac{d^2\varepsilon}{dv\,d\eta}}{\dfrac{dx}{dv} \cdot \dfrac{dy}{d\eta} - \dfrac{dy}{dv} \cdot \dfrac{dx}{d\eta}},$$

where v and η are the independent variables.

These and similar expressions for $\dfrac{1}{\gamma}$ may be found by dividing the value of the work or heat for an infinitely small circuit by the area included. This operation can be most conveniently performed upon a circuit consisting of four lines, in each of which one of the independent variables is constant. E.g., the last formula can be most easily found from an infinitely small circuit formed of two isometrics and two isentropics.

* To avoid confusion, as dW and dH are generally used and are used elsewhere in this article to denote the work and heat of an infinite short path, a slightly different notation, δW and δH, is here used to denote the work and heat of an infinitely small circuit. So δA is used to denote an element of area which is infinitely small in all directions, as the letter d would only imply the element was infinitely small in one direction. So also below, the integration or summation which extends to all the elements written with δ is denoted by the character Σ, as the character f naturally refers to elements written with d.

performed within the limits of this circuit, we have

$$W^C = H^C = \sum{}^C \frac{1}{\gamma} \delta A. \tag{8}$$

We have thus an expression for the value of the work and heat of a circuit involving an integration extending over an area instead of one extending over a line, as in equations (5) and (6).

Similar expressions may be found for the work and the heat of a path which is not a circuit. For this case may be reduced to the preceding by the consideration that $W = 0$ for a path on an isometric or on the line of no pressure (eq. 2), and $H = 0$ for a path on an isentropic or on the line of absolute cold. Hence the work of any path S is equal to that of the circuit formed of S, the isometric of the final state, the line of no pressure and the isometric of the initial state, which circuit may be represented by the notation $[S, v'', p^0, v']$. And the heat of the same path is the same as that of the circuit $[S, \eta'', t^0, \eta']$. Therefore using W^S and H^S to denote the work and heat of any path S, we have

$$W^S = \sum{}^{[S, v'', p^0, v']} \frac{1}{\gamma} \delta A, \tag{9}$$

$$H^S = \sum{}^{[S, \eta'', t^0, \eta']} \frac{1}{\gamma} \delta A, \tag{10}$$

where as before the limits of the integration are denoted by the expression occupying the place of an index to the sign Σ.* These equations evidently include equation (8) as a particular case.

* A word should be said in regard to the sense in which the above propositions should be understood. If beyond the limits within which the relations of v, p, t, ε and η are known and which we may call the limits of the known field, we continue the isometrics, isopiestics, &c., in any way we please, only subject to the condition that the relations of v, p, t, ε and η shall be consistent with the equation $d\varepsilon = t\,d\eta - p\,dv$, then in calculating the values of quantities W and H determined by the equations $dW = p\,dv$ and $dH = t\,d\eta$ for paths or circuits in any part of the diagram thus extended, we may use any of the propositions or processes given above, as these three equations have formed the only basis of the reasoning. We will thus obtain values of W and H, which will be identical with those which would be obtained by the immediate application of the equations $dW = p\,dv$ and $dH = t\,d\eta$ to the path in question, and which in the case of any path which is entirely contained in the known field will be the true values of the work and heat for the change of state of the body which the path represents. We may thus use lines outside of the known field without attributing to them any physical signification whatever, without considering the points in the lines as representing any states of the body. If however, to fix our ideas, we choose to conceive of this part of the diagram as having the same physical interpretation as the known field, and to enunciate our propositions in language based upon such a conception, the unreality or even the impossibility of the states represented by the lines outside of the known field cannot lead to any incorrect results in regard to paths in the known field.

It is easy to form a material conception of these relations. If we imagine, for example, mass inherent in the plane of the diagram with a varying (superficial) density represented by $\frac{1}{\gamma}$, then $\sum \frac{1}{\gamma} \, \delta A$ will evidently denote the mass of the part of the plane included within the limits of integration, this mass being taken positively or negatively according to the direction of the circuit.

Thus far we have made no supposition in regard to the nature of the law, by which we associate the points of a plane with the states of the body, except a certain condition of continuity. Whatever law we may adopt, we obtain a method of representation of the thermodynamic properties of the body, in which the relations existing between the functions of the state of the body are indicated by a net-work of lines, while the work done and the heat received by the body when it changes its state are represented by integrals extending over the elements of a line, and also by an integral extending over the elements of certain areas in the diagram, or, if we choose to introduce such a consideration, by the mass belonging to these areas.

The different diagrams which we obtain by different laws of association are all such as may be obtained from one another by a process of *deformation*, and this consideration is sufficient to demonstrate their properties from the well-known properties of the diagram in which the volume and pressure are represented by rectangular coordinates. For the relations indicated by the net-work of isometrics, isopiestics etc., are evidently not altered by deformation of the surface upon which they are drawn, and if we conceive of mass as belonging to the surface, the mass included within given lines will also not be affected by the process of deformation. If, then, the surface upon which the ordinary diagram is drawn has the uniform superficial density 1, so that the work and heat of a circuit, which are represented in this diagram by the included area, shall also be represented by the mass included, this latter relation will hold for any diagram formed from this by deformation of the surface on which it is drawn.

The choice of the method of representation is of course to be determined by considerations of simplicity and convenience, especially in regard to the drawing of the lines of equal volume, pressure, temperature, energy and entropy, and the estimation of work and heat. There is an obvious advantage in the use of diagrams of constant scale, in which the work and heat are represented simply by areas. Such diagrams may of course be produced by an infinity of different methods, as there is no limit to the ways of deforming a plane figure without altering the magnitude of its elements. Among these methods, two are especially important,—the ordinary method in which the volume and pressure are represented by rectilinear co-ordinates, and that in which the entropy and temperature are so represented. A diagram formed by the former method may be called, for the sake of distinction, a *volume-pressure* diagram,— one formed by the latter, an *entropy-temperature* diagram. That the latter as well as the former satisfies the condition that $\gamma = 1$ throughout the whole diagram, may be seen by reference to page 45.

THE ENTROPY-TEMPERATURE DIAGRAM COMPARED WITH THAT IN ORDINARY USE.

Considerations Independent of the Nature of the Body in Question.

As the general equations (1), (2), (3) are not altered by interchanging v, $-p$ and $-W$ with η, t and H respectively, it is evident that, so far as these equations are concerned, there is nothing to choose between a volume-pressure and an entropy-temperature diagram. In the former, the work is represented by an area bounded by the path which represents the change of state of the body, two ordinates and the axis of abscissas. The same is true of the heat received in the latter diagram. Again, in the former diagram the heat received is represented by an area bounded by the path and certain lines, the character of which depends upon the nature of the body under consideration. Except in the case of an ideal body, the properties of which are determined by assumption, these lines are more or less unknown in a part of their course, and in any case the area will generally extend to an infinite distance. Very much the same inconveniences attach themselves to the areas representing work in the entropy-temperature diagram.* There is, however, a

---

* In neither diagram do these circumstances create any serious difficulty in the estimation of areas representing work or heat. It is always possible to divide these areas into two parts, of which one is of finite dimensions, and the other can be calculated in the simplest manner. Thus, in the entropy-temperature diagram, the work done in a path AB (fig. 2) is represented by the area included by the path AB, the isometric BC,

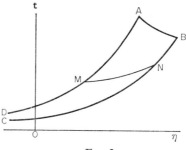

FIG. 2.

the line of no pressure and the isometric DA. The line of no pressure and the adjacent parts of the isometrics in the case of an actual gas or vapor are more or less undetermined in the present state of our knowledge, and are likely to remain so; for an

consideration of a general character, which shows an important advantage on the side of the entropy-temperature diagram. In thermodynamic problems, heat received at one temperature is by no means the equivalent of the same amount of heat received at another temperature. For example, a supply of a million calories at 150° is a very different thing from a supply of a million calories at 50°. But no such distinction exists in regard to work. This is a result of the general law, that heat can only pass from a hotter to a colder body, while work can be transferred by mechanical means from one fluid to any other, whatever may be the pressures. Hence, in thermodynamic problems, it is generally necessary to distinguish between the quantities of heat received or given out by the body at different temperatures, while as far as work is concerned, it is generally sufficient to ascertain the total amount performed. If, then, several heat-areas and one work-area enter into the problem, it is evidently more important that the former should be simple in form, than that the latter should be so. Moreover, in the very common case of a circuit, the work-area is bounded entirely by the path, and the form of the isometrics and the line of no pressure are of no especial consequence.

It is worthy of notice that the simplest form of a perfect thermodynamic engine, so often described in treatises on thermodynamics, is represented in the entropy-temperature diagram by a figure of extreme simplicity, viz: a rectangle of which the sides are parallel to the co-ordinate axes. Thus in figure 3, the circuit ABCD may represent the series of states through which the fluid is made to pass in such an engine, the included area representing the work done, while the area ABFE represents the heat received from the heater at the highest temperature AE, and the area CDEF represents the heat transmitted to the cooler at the lowest temperature DE.

There is another form of the perfect thermodynamic engine, viz: one with a perfect regenerator as defined by Rankine (*Phil. Trans.* vol. 144, p. 140), the

---

ideal gas the line of no pressure coincides with the axis of abscissas, and is an asymptote to the isometrics. But, be this as it may, it is not necessary to examine the form of the remoter parts of the diagram. If we draw an isopiestic MN, cutting AD and BC, the area MNCD, which represents the work done in MN, will be equal to $p(v'' - v')$, where p denotes the pressure in MN, and v'' and v' denote the volumes at B and A respectively (eq. 5). Hence the work done in AB will be represented by ABNM + $p(v'' - v')$. In the volume-pressure diagram, the areas representing heat may be divided by an isothermal, and treated in a manner entirely analogous.

Or, we may make use of the principle, that, for a path which begins and ends on the same isodynamic, the work and heat are equal, as appears by integration of equation (1). Hence, in the entropy-temperature diagram, to find the work of any path, we may extend it by an isometric (which will not alter its work), so that it shall begin and end on the same isodynamic, and then take the heat (instead of the work) of the path thus extended. This method was suggested by that employed by Cazin (*Théorie élémentaire des Machines à Air Chaud*, p. 11) and Zeuner (*Mechanische Wärmetheorie*, p. 80) in the reverse case, viz: to find the heat of a path in the volume-pressure diagram.

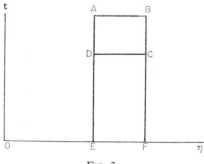

FIG. 3.

representation of which becomes peculiarly simple in the entropy-temperature diagram. The circuit consists of two equal straight lines AB and CD (fig. 4) parallel to the axis of abscissas, and two precisely similar curves of any form BC and AD. The included area ABCD represents the work done, and the areas ABba and CDdc represent respectively the heat received from the heater and that transmitted to the cooler. The heat imparted by the fluid to the regenerator in passing from B to C, and afterward restored to the fluid in its passage from D to A, is represented by the areas BCcb and DAad.

It is often a matter of the first importance in the study of any thermodynamic engine, to compare it with a perfect engine. Such a comparison will obviously be much facilitated by the use of a method in which the perfect engine is represented by such simple forms.

The method in which the co-ordinates represent volume and pressure has a certain advantage in the simple and elementary character of the notions upon

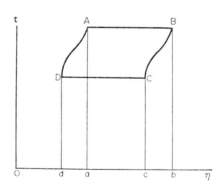

FIG. 4.

which it is based, and its analogy with Watt's indicator has doubtless contributed to render it popular. On the other hand, a method involving the notion of *entropy*, the very existence of which depends upon the second law of thermodynamics, will doubtless seem to many far-fetched, and may repel beginners as obscure and difficult of comprehension. This inconvenience is perhaps more than counter-balanced by the advantages of a method which makes the second law of thermodynamics so prominent, and gives it so clear and elementary an expression. The fact, that the different states of a fluid can be represented by the positions of a point in a plane, so that the ordinates shall represent the temperatures, and the heat received or given out by the fluid shall be represented by the area bounded by the line representing the states through which the body passes, the ordinates drawn through the extreme points of this line, and the axis of abscissas,—this fact, clumsy as its expression in words may be, is one which presents a clear image to the eye, and which the mind can readily grasp and retain. It is, however, nothing more nor less than a geometrical expression of the second law of thermodynamics in its application to fluids, in a form exceedingly convenient for use, and from which the analytical expression of the same law can, if desired, be at once obtained. If, then, it is more important for purposes of instruction and the like to familiarize the learner with the second law, than to defer its statement as long as possible, the use of the entropy-temperature diagram may serve a useful purpose in the popularizing of this science.

The foregoing considerations are in the main of a general character, and independent of the nature of the substance to which the graphical method is applied. On this, however, depend the forms of the isometrics, isopiestics and isodynamics in the entropy-temperature diagram, and of the isentropics, isothermals and isodynamics in the volume-pressure diagram. As the convenience of a method depends largely upon the ease with which these lines can be drawn, and upon the peculiarities of the fluid which has its properties represented in the diagram, it is desirable to compare the methods under consideration in some of their most important applications. We will commence with the case of a perfect gas.

Case of a Perfect Gas.

A perfect or ideal gas may be defined as such a gas, that for any constant quantity of it the product of the volume and the pressure varies as the temperature, and the energy varies as the temperature, i.e.,

$$pv = at, \qquad \text{(A)}^*$$

$$\varepsilon = ct. \qquad \text{(B)}$$

* In this article, all equations which are designated by arabic numerals subsist for any body whatever (subject to the condition of uniform pressure and temperature), and those which are designated by small capitals subsist for any quantity of a perfect gas as defined above (subject of course to the same conditions).

The significance of the constant a is sufficiently indicated by equation (A). The significance of c may be rendered more evident by differentiating equation (B) and comparing the result

$$d\varepsilon = c\,dt$$

with the general equations (1) and (2), viz:

$$d\varepsilon = dH - dW, \qquad dW = p\,dv.$$

If $dv = 0$, $dW = 0$, and $dH = c\,dt$, i.e.,

$$\left(\frac{dH}{dt}\right)_v = c,^* \tag{C}$$

i.e., c is the quantity of heat necessary to raise the temperature of the body one degree under the condition of constant volume. It will be observed, that when different quantities of the same gas are considered, a and c both vary as the quantity, and $c \div a$ is constant; also, that the value of $c \div a$ for different gases varies as their specific heat determined for equal volumes and for constant volume.

With the aid of equations (A) and (B) we may eliminate p and t from the general equation (4), viz:

$$d\varepsilon = t\,d\eta - p\,dv,$$

which is then reduced to

$$\frac{d\varepsilon}{\varepsilon} = \frac{1}{c}\,d\eta - \frac{a}{c}\frac{dv}{v},$$

and by integration to

$$\log \varepsilon = \frac{\eta}{c} - \frac{a}{c}\log v.\dagger \tag{D}$$

The constant of integration becomes 0, if we call the entropy 0 for the state of which the volume and energy are both unity.

Any other equations which subsist between v, p, t, ε and η may be derived from the three independent equations (A), (B) and (D). If we eliminate ε from (B) and (D), we have

$$\eta = a \log v + c \log t + c \log c. \tag{E}$$

---

* A subscript letter after a differential coefficient is used in this article to indicate the quantity which is made constant in the differentiation.

† If we use the letter e to denote the base of the Naperian system of logarithms, equation (D) may also be written in the form

$$\varepsilon = e^{\eta/c}v^{-(a/c)}$$

This may be regarded as the fundamental thermodynamic equation of an ideal gas. See the first note on page 43. It will be observed, that there would be no real loss of generality if we should choose, as the body to which the letters refer, such a quantity of the gas that one of the constants a and c should be equal to unity.

Eliminating v from (A) and (E), we have

$$\eta = (a + c) \log t - a \log p + c \log c + a \log a. \tag{F}$$

Eliminating t from (A) and (E), we have

$$\eta = (a + c) \log v + c \log p + c \log \frac{c}{a}. \tag{G}$$

If v is constant, equation (E) becomes

$$\eta = c \log t + \text{Const.},$$

i.e. the isometrics in the entropy-temperature diagram are logarithmic curves identical with one another in form,—a change in the value of v having only the effect of moving the curve parallel to the axis of η. If p is constant, equation (F) becomes

$$\eta = (a + c) \log t + \text{Const.},$$

so that the isopiestics in this diagram have similar properties. This identity in form diminishes greatly the labor of drawing any considerable number of these curves. For if a card or thin board be cut in the form of one of them, it may be used as a pattern or ruler to draw all of the same system.

The isodynamics are straight in this diagram (eq. B).

To find the form of the isothermals and isentropics in the volume-pressure diagram, we may make t and η constant in equations (A) and (G) respectively, which will then reduce to the well-known equations of these curves:—

$$pv = \text{Const.},$$

and
$$p^c v^{a+c} = \text{Const.}$$

The equation of the isodynamics is of course the same as that of the isothermals. None of these systems of lines have that property of identity of form which makes the systems of isometrics and isopiestics so easy to draw in the entropy-temperature diagram.

Case of Condensable Vapors.

The case of bodies which pass from the liquid to the gaseous condition is next to be considered. It is usual to assume of such a body, that when sufficiently superheated it approaches the condition of a perfect gas. If, then, in the entropy-temperature diagram of such a body we draw systems of isometrics, isopiestics and isodynamics, as if for a perfect gas, for proper values of the constants a and c, these will be asymptotes to the true isometrics, etc., of the vapor, and in many cases will not vary from them greatly in the part of the diagram which represents vapor unmixed with liquid, except in the vicinity of the line of saturation. In the volume-pressure diagram of the same body, the isothermals, isentropics and isodynamics, drawn for a perfect gas for the same values of a and c, will have the same relations to the true isothermals, etc.

In that part of any diagram which represents a mixture of vapor and liquid, the isopiestics and isothermals will be identical, as the pressure is determined by the temperature alone. In both the diagrams which we are now comparing, they will be straight and parallel to the axis of abscissas. The form of the isometrics and isodynamics in the entropy-temperature diagram, or that of the isentropics and isodynamics in the volume-pressure diagram, will depend upon the nature of the fluid, and probably cannot be expressed by any simple equations. The following property, however, renders it easy to construct equidifferent systems of these lines, viz: any such system will divide any isothermal (isopiestic) into equal segments.

It remains to consider that part of the diagram which represents the body when entirely in the condition of liquid. The fundamental characteristic of this condition of matter is that the volume is very nearly constant, so that variations of volume are generally entirely inappreciable when represented graphically on the same scale on which the volume of the body in the state of vapor is represented, and both the variations of volume and the connected variations of the connected quantities may be, and generally are, neglected by the side of the variations of the same quantities which occur when the body passes to the state of vapor.

Let us make, then, the usual assumption that v is constant, and see how the general equations (1), (2), (3) and (4) are thereby affected. We have first,

$$dv = 0,$$

then
$$dW = 0,$$

and
$$d\varepsilon = t\,d\eta.$$

If we add
$$dH = t\,d\eta,$$

these four equations will evidently be equivalent to the three independent equations (1), (2) and (3), combined with the assumption which we have just made. For a liquid, then, ε, instead of being a function of two quantities v and η, is a function of η alone,—t is also a function of η alone, being equal to the differential coefficient of the function ε; that is, the value of one of the three quantities t, ε and η, is sufficient to determine the other two. The value of v, moreover, is fixed without reference to the values of t, ε and η (so long as these do not pass the limits of values possible for liquidity); while p does not enter into the equations, i.e., p may have any value (within certain limits) without affecting the values of t, ε, η or v. If the body changes its state, continuing always liquid, the value of W for such a change is 0, and that of H is determined by the values of any one of the three quantities t, ε and η. It is, therefore, the relations between t, ε, η and H, for which a graphical expression is to be sought; a method, therefore, in which the co-ordinates of the diagram are made equal to the volume and pressure, is totally inapplicable to this particular case; v and p are indeed the only two of the five functions of the state of the body, v, p, t, ε and η, which have no relations either to each other, or to the other three, or to the quantities W and H, to be expressed.* The values of v and p do not really determine the state of an incompressible fluid,—the values of t, ε and η are still left undetermined, so that through every point in the volume-pressure diagram which represents the liquid there must pass (in general) an infinite number of isothermals, isodynamics and isentropics. The character of this part of the diagram is as follows:—the states of liquidity are represented by the points of a line parallel to the axis of pressures, and the isothermals, isodynamics and isentropics, which cross the field of partial vaporization and meet this line, turn upward and follow its course.†

In the entropy-temperature diagram the relations of t, ε and η are distinctly visible. The line of liquidity is a curve AB (fig. 5) determined by the relation

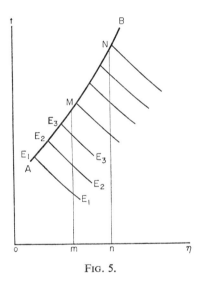

FIG. 5.

---

* That is, v and p have no such relations to the other quantities, as are expressible by equations; p, however, cannot be *less* than a certain function of t.

† All these difficulties are of course removed when the differences of volume of the liquid at different temperatures are rendered appreciable on the volume-pressure diagram. This can be done in various ways,—among others, by choosing as the body to which v, etc., refer, a sufficiently large quantity of the fluid. But, however we do it, we must evidently give up the possibility of representing the body in the state of vapor in the same diagram without making its dimensions enormous.

between t and η. This curve is also an isometric. Every point of it has a definite volume, temperature, entropy and energy. The latter is indicated by the isodynamics E_1E_1, E_2E_2, etc., which cross the region of partial vaporization and terminate in the line of liquidity. (They do not in this diagram turn and follow the line.) If the body passes from one state to another, remaining liquid, as from M to N in the figure, the heat received is represented as usual by the area MNnm. That the work done is nothing, is indicated by the fact that the line AB is an isometric. Only the isopiestics in this diagram are superposed in the line of fluidity, turning downward where they meet this line and following its course, so that for any point in this line the pressure is undetermined. This is, however, no inconvenience in the diagram, as it simply expresses the fact of the case, that when all the quantities v, t, ε and η are fixed, the pressure is still undetermined.

DIAGRAMS IN WHICH THE ISOMETRICS, ISOPIESTICS, ISOTHERMALS, ISODYNAMICS AND ISENTROPICS OF A PERFECT GAS ARE ALL STRAIGHT LINES.

There are many cases in which it is of more importance that it should be easy to draw the lines of equal volume, pressure, temperature, energy and entropy, than that work and heat should be represented in the simplest manner. In such cases it may be expedient to give up the condition that the scale (γ) of work and heat shall be constant, when by that means it is possible to gain greater simplicity in the form of the lines just mentioned.

In the case of a perfect gas, the three relations between the quantities v, p, t, ε and η are given on pages 53, 54, equations (A), (B) and (D). These equations may be easily transformed into the three

$$\log p + \log v - \log t = \log a, \tag{H}$$

$$\log \varepsilon - \log t = \log c, \tag{I}$$

$$\eta - c \log \varepsilon - a \log v = 0; \tag{J}$$

so that the three relations between the quantities $\log v$, $\log p$, $\log t$, $\log \varepsilon$, and η are expressed by linear equations, and it will be possible to make the five systems of lines all rectilinear in the same diagram, the distances of the isometrics being proportional to the differences of the logarithms of the volumes, the distances of the isopiestics being proportional to the differences of the logarithms of the pressures, and so with the isothermals and the isodynamics,—the distances of the isentropics, however, being proportional to the differences of entropy simply.

The scale of work and heat in such a diagram will vary inversely as the temperature. For if we imagine systems of isentropics and isothermals drawn throughout the diagram for equal small differences of entropy and temperature, the isentropics will be equidistant, but the distances of the isothermals will vary inversely as the temperature, and the small quadrilaterals into which the diagram is divided will vary in the same ratio: $\therefore \gamma \propto 1 \div t$. (See page 45.)

So far, however, the form of the diagram has not been completely defined. This may be done in various ways: e.g., if x and y be the rectangular coordinates, we may make

$$\begin{cases} x = \log v, \\ y = \log p; \end{cases} \quad \text{or} \quad \begin{cases} x = \eta, \\ y = \log t; \end{cases} \quad \text{or} \quad \begin{cases} x = \log v, \\ y = \eta; \end{cases} \quad \text{etc.}$$

Or we may set the condition that the logarithms of volume, of pressure and of temperature, shall be represented in the diagram on the same scale. (The logarithms of energy are necessarily represented on the same scale as those of temperature.) This will require that the isometrics, isopiestics and isothermals cut one another at angles of 60°.

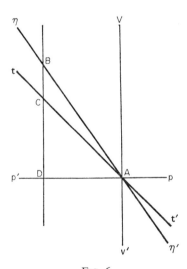

FIG. 6.

The general character of all these diagrams, which may be derived from one another by projection by parallel lines, may be illustrated by the case in which $x = \log v$, and $y = \log p$.

Through any point A (fig. 6) of such a diagram let there be drawn the isometric vv′, the isopiestic pp″, the isothermal tt′ and the isentropic $\eta\eta'$.

The lines pp and vv' are of course parallel to the axes. Also by equation (H)

$$\tan tAp = \left(\frac{dy}{dx}\right)_t = \left(\frac{d\log p}{d\log v}\right)_t = -1,$$

and by (G)

$$\tan \eta Ap = \left(\frac{dy}{dx}\right)_\eta = \left(\frac{d\log p}{d\log v}\right)_\eta = -\frac{c+a}{c}.$$

Therefore, if we draw another isometric, cutting $\eta\eta$, tt', and pp in B, C and D,

$$\frac{BD}{CD} = \frac{c+a}{c}, \qquad \frac{BC}{CD} = \frac{a}{c}, \qquad \frac{CD}{BC} = \frac{c}{a}.$$

Hence, in the diagrams of different gases, CD ÷ BC will be proportional to the specific heat determined for equal volumes and for constant volume.

As the specific heat, thus determined, has probably the same value for most simple gases, the isentropics will have the same inclination in diagrams of this kind for most simple gases. This inclination may easily be found by a method which is independent of any units of measurement, for

$$BD:CD::\left(\frac{d\log p}{d\log v}\right)_\eta : \left(\frac{d\log p}{d\log v}\right)_t :: \left(\frac{dp}{dv}\right)_\eta : \left(\frac{dp}{dv}\right)_t,$$

i.e., BD ÷ CD is equal to the quotient of the coefficient of elasticity under the condition of no transmission of heat divided by the coefficient of elasticity at constant temperature. This quotient for a simple gas is generally given as 1.408 or 1.421. As CA ÷ CD = $\sqrt{2}$ = 1.414, BD is very nearly equal to CA (for simple gases), which relation it may be convenient to use in the construction of the diagram.

In regard to compound gases the rule seems to be, that the specific heat (determined for equal volumes and for constant volume) is to the specific heat of a simple gas inversely as the volume of the compound is to the volume of its constituents (in the condition of gas); that is, the value of BC ÷ CD for a compound gas is to the value of BC ÷ CD for a simple gas, as the volume of the compound is to the volume of its constituents. Therefore, if we compare the diagrams (formed by this method) for a simple and a compound gas, the distance DA and therefore CD being the same in each, BC in the diagram of the compound gas will be to BC in the diagram of the simple gas, as the volume of the compound is to the volume of its constituents.

Although the inclination of the isentropics is independent of the quantity of gas under consideration, the rate of increase of η will vary with this quantity. In regard to the rate of increase of t, it is evident that if the whole diagram be divided into squares by isopiestics and isometrics drawn at equal distances, and isothermals be drawn as diagonals to these squares, the volumes of the

isometrics, the pressures of the isopiestics and the temperatures of the isothermals will each form a geometrical series, and in all these series the ratio of
two contiguous terms will be the same.

The properties of the diagrams obtained by the other methods mentioned
on page 59 do not differ essentially from those just described. For example,
in any such diagram, if through any point we draw an isentropic, an isothermal and an isopiestic, which cut any isometric not passing through the same
point, the ratio of the segments of the isometric will have the value which has
been found for BC:CD.

In treating the case of vapors also, it may be convenient to use diagrams in
which $x = \log v$ and $y = \log p$, or in which $x = \eta$ and $y = \log t$; but the
diagrams formed by these methods will evidently be radically different from
one another. It is to be observed that each of these methods is what may be
called a *method of definite scale* for work and heat; that is, the value of γ
in any part of the diagram is independent of the properties of the fluid con-
sidered. In the first method $\gamma = \dfrac{1}{e^{x+y}}$, in the second $\gamma = \dfrac{1}{e^{y}}$. In this respect
these methods have an advantage over many others. For example, if we should
make $x = \log v$, $y = \eta$, the value of γ in any part of the diagram would
depend upon the properties of the fluid, and would probably not vary in any
case, except that of a perfect gas, according to any simple law.

The conveniences of the entropy-temperature method will be found to
belong in nearly the same degree to the method in which the coordinates are
equal to the entropy and the logarithm of the temperature. No serious difficulty
attaches to the estimation of heat and work in a diagram formed on the latter
method on account of the variation of the scale on which they are represented,
as this variation follows so simple a law. It may often be of use to remember
that such a diagram may be reduced to an entropy-temperature diagram by a
vertical compression or extension, such that the distances of the isothermals
shall be made proportional to their differences of temperature. Thus if we wish
to estimate the work or heat of the circuit ABCD (fig. 7), we may draw a

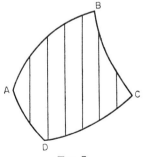

FIG. 7.

number of equidistant ordinates (isentropics) as if to estimate the included area, and for each of the ordinates take the differences of temperature of the points where it cuts the circuit; these differences of temperature will be equal to the lengths of the segments made by the corresponding circuit in the entropy-temperature diagram upon a corresponding system of equidistant ordinates, and may be used to calculate the area of the circuit in the entropy-temperature diagram, i.e., to find the work or heat required. We may find the work of any path by applying the same process to the circuit formed by the path, the iso-metric of the final state, the line of no pressure (or any isopiestic; see note on page 50), and the isometric of the initial state. And we may find the heat of any path by applying the same process to a circuit formed by the path, the ordinates of the extreme points and the line of absolute cold. That this line is at an infinite distance occasions no difficulty. The lengths of the ordinates in the entropy-temperature diagram which we desire are given by the temper-ature of points in the path determined (in either diagram) by equidistant ordinates.

The properties of the part of the entropy-temperature diagram representing a mixture of vapor and liquid, which are given on page 56, will evidently not be altered if the ordinates are made proportional to the logarithms of the temperatures instead of the temperatures simply.

The representation of specific heat in the diagram under discussion is pe-culiarly simple. The specific heat of any substance at constant volume or under constant pressure may be defined as the value of

$$\left(\frac{dH}{dt}\right)_v \quad \text{or} \quad \left(\frac{dH}{dt}\right)_p, \quad \text{i.e.,} \quad \left(\frac{d\eta}{d\log t}\right)_v \quad \text{or} \quad \left(\frac{d\eta}{d\log t}\right)_p,$$

for a certain quantity of the substance. Therefore, if we draw a diagram, in which $x = \eta$ and $y = \log t$, for that quantity of the substance which is used for the determination of the specific heat, the tangents of the angles made by the isometrics and the isopiestics with the ordinates in the diagram will be equal to the specific heat of the substance determined for constant volume and for constant pressure respectively. Sometimes, instead of the condition of constant volume or constant pressure, some other condition is used in the determination of specific heat. In all cases, the condition will be represented by a line in the diagram, and the tangent of the angle made by this line with an ordinate will be equal to the specific heat as thus defined. If the diagram be drawn for any other quantity of the substance, the specific heat for constant volume or constant pressure, or for any other condition, will be equal to the tangent of the proper angle in the diagram, multiplied by the ratio of the quantity of the substance for which the specific heat is determined to the quantity for which the diagram is drawn.*

* From this general property of the diagram, its character in the case of a perfect gas might be immediately deduced.

THE VOLUME-ENTROPY DIAGRAM.

The method of representation, in which the co-ordinates of the point in the diagram are made equal to the volume and entropy of the body, presents certain characteristics which entitle it to a somewhat detailed consideration, and for some purposes give it substantial advantages over any other method. We might anticipate some of these advantages from the simple and symmetrical form of the general equations of thermodynamics, when volume and entropy are chosen as independent variables, viz:—*

$$p = -\frac{d\varepsilon}{dv}, \tag{11}$$

$$t = \frac{d\varepsilon}{d\eta}, \tag{12}$$

$$dW = p\, dv,$$

$$dH = t\, d\eta.$$

Eliminating p and t we have also

$$dW = \frac{d\varepsilon}{dv}\, dv \tag{13}$$

$$dH = \frac{d\varepsilon}{d\eta}\, d\eta. \tag{14}$$

The geometrical relations corresponding to these equations are in the volume-entropy diagram extremely simple. To fix our ideas, let the axes of volume and entropy be horizontal and vertical respectively, volume increasing toward the right and entropy upward. Then the pressure taken negatively will equal the ratio of the difference of energy to the difference of volume of two adjacent points in the same horizontal line, and the temperature will equal the ratio of the difference of energy to the difference of entropy of two adjacent points in the same vertical line. Or, if a series of isodynamics be drawn for equal infinitesimal differences of energy, any series of horizontal lines will be divided into segments inversely proportional to the pressure, and any series of vertical lines into segments inversely proportional to the temperature. We see by equations (13) and (14), that for a motion parallel to the axis of volume,

---

* See page 43, equations (2), (3) and (4).
In general, in this article, where differential coefficients are used, the quantity which is constant in the differentiation is indicated by a subscript letter. In this discussion of the volume-entropy diagram, however, v and η are uniformly regarded as the independent variables, and the subscript letter is omitted.

the heat received is 0, and the work done is equal to the decrease of the energy, while for a motion parallel to the axis of entropy, the work done is 0, and the heat received is equal to the increase of the energy. These two propositions are true either for elementary paths or for those of finite length. In general, the work for any element of a path is equal to the product of the pressure in that part of the diagram into the horizontal projection of the element of the path, and the heat received is equal to the product of the temperature into the vertical projection of the element of the path.

If we wish to estimate the value of the integrals $\int p \, dv$ and $\int t \, d\eta$, which represent the work and heat of any path, by means of measurements upon the diagram, or if we wish to appreciate readily by the eye the approximate value of these expressions, or if we merely wish to illustrate their meaning by means of the diagram; for any of these purposes the diagram which we are now considering will have the advantage that it represents the differentials dv and $d\eta$ more simply and clearly than any other.

But we may also estimate the work and heat of any path by means of an integration extending over the elements of an area, viz: by the formulae of page 48,

$$W^C = H^C = \sum^C \frac{1}{\gamma} \, \delta A,$$

$$W^S = \sum^{[S,v'',v^0,v']} \frac{1}{\gamma} \, \delta A,$$

$$H^s = \sum^{[S,\eta'',t^0,\eta']} \frac{1}{\gamma} \, \delta A.$$

In regard to the limits of integration in these formulae, we see that for the work of any path which is not a circuit, the bounding line is composed of the path, the line of no pressure and two vertical lines, and for the heat of the path, the bounding line is composed of the path, the line of absolute cold and two horizontal lines.

As the sign of γ, as well as that of δA, will be indeterminate until we decide in which direction an area must be circumscribed in order to be considered positive, we will call an area positive which is circumscribed in the direction in which the hands of a watch move. This choice, with the positions of the axes of volume and entropy which we have supposed, will make the value of γ in most cases positive, as we shall see hereafter.

The value of γ, in a diagram drawn according to this method, will depend upon the properties of the body for which the diagram is drawn. In this respect, this method differs from all the others which have been discussed in detail in this article. It is easy to find an expression for γ depending simply upon the variations of the energy, by comparing the area and the work or heat of an infinitely small circuit in the form of a rectangle having its sides parallel to the two axes.

Let $N_1N_2N_3N_4$ (fig. 8) be such a circuit, and let it be described in the order of the numerals, so that the area is positive Also let ε_1, ε_2, ε_3, ε_4 represent the energy at the four corners. The work done in the four sides in order commen-

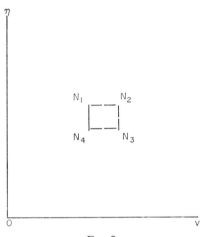

FIG. 8.

cing at N_1, will be $\varepsilon_1 - \varepsilon_2$, 0, $\varepsilon_3 - \varepsilon_4$, 0. The total work, therefore, for the rectangular circuit is

$$\varepsilon_1 - \varepsilon_2 + \varepsilon_3 - \varepsilon_4.$$

Now as the rectangle is infinitely small, if we call its sides dv and $d\eta$, the above expression will be equivalent to

$$-\frac{d^2\varepsilon}{dv\,d\eta}\,dv\,d\eta.$$

Dividing by the area $dv\,d\eta$, and writing $\gamma_{v.\eta}$ for the scale of work and heat in a diagram of this kind, we have

$$\frac{1}{\gamma_{v,\eta}} = -\frac{d^2\varepsilon}{dv\,d\eta} = \frac{dp}{d\eta} = -\frac{dt}{dv}. \tag{15}$$

The two last expressions for the value of $1 \div \gamma_{v,\eta}$ indicate that the value of $\gamma_{v,\eta}$ in different parts of the diagram will be indicated proportionally by the segments into which vertical lines are divided by a system of equidifferent isopiestics, and also by the segments into which horizontal lines are divided by a system of equidifferent isothermals. These results might also be derived directly from the propositions on page 46.

As, in almost all cases, the pressure of a body is increased when it receives heat without change of volume, $\dfrac{dp}{d\eta}$ is in general positive, and the same will be true of $\gamma_{v,\eta}$ under the assumptions which we have made in regard to the directions of the axes (page 63) and the definition of a positive area (page 64).

In the estimation of work and heat it may often be of use to consider the deformation necessary to reduce the diagram to one of constant scale for work and heat. Now if the diagram be so deformed, that each point remains in the same vertical line, but moves in this line so that all isopiestics become straight and horizontal lines, at distances proportional to their differences of pressure, it will evidently become a volume-pressure diagram. Again, if the diagram be so deformed that each point remains in the same horizontal line, but moves in it so that isothermals become straight and vertical lines at distances proportional to their differences of temperature, it will become an entropy-temperature diagram. These considerations will enable us to compute numerically the work or heat of any path which is given in a volume-entropy diagram, when the pressure and temperature are known for all points of the path, in a manner analogous to that explained on page 61.

The ratio of any element of area in the volume-pressure or the entropy-temperature diagrams, or in any other in which the scale of work and heat is unity, to the corresponding element in the volume-entropy diagram, is represented by $\dfrac{1}{\gamma_{v,\eta}}$ or $-\dfrac{d^2\varepsilon}{dv\,d\eta}$. The cases in which this ratio is 0, or changes its sign, demand especial attention, as in such cases the diagrams of constant scale fail to give a satisfactory representation of the properties of the body, while no difficulty or inconvenience arises in the use of the volume-entropy diagram.

As $-\dfrac{d^2\varepsilon}{dv\,d\eta} = \dfrac{dp}{d\eta}$, its value is evidently zero in that part of the diagram which represents the body when in part solid, in part liquid, and in part vapor. The properties of such a mixture are very simply and clearly exhibited in the volume-entropy diagram.

Let the temperature and the pressure of the mixture, which are independent of the proportions of vapor, solid and liquid, be denoted by t' and p'. Also let V, L and S (fig. 9) be points of the diagram which indicate the volume and entropy of the body in three perfectly defined states, viz: that of a vapor of temperature t' and pressure p', that of a liquid of the same temperature and pressure, and that of a solid of the same temperature and pressure. And let v_V, η_V, v_L, η_L, v_S, η_S denote the volume and entropy of these states. The position of the point which represents the body, when part is vapor, part

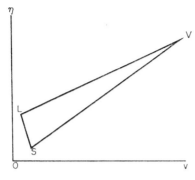

liquid, and part solid, these parts being as μ, ν, and $1 - \mu - \nu$, is determined by the equations

$$v = \mu v_V + \nu v_L + (1 - \mu - \nu)v_S,$$
$$\eta = \mu \eta_V + \nu \eta_L + (1 - \mu - \nu)\eta_S,$$

where v and η are the volume and entropy of the mixture. The truth of the first equation is evident. The second may be written

$$\eta - \eta_S = \mu(\eta_V - \eta_S) + \nu(\eta_L - \eta_S),$$

or multiplying by t',

$$t'(\eta - \eta_S) = \mu t'(\eta_V - \eta_S) + \nu t'(\eta_L - \eta_S).$$

The first member of this equation denotes the heat necessary to bring the body from the state S to the state of the mixture in question under the constant temperature t', while the terms of the second member denote separately the heat necessary to vaporize the part μ, and to liquefy the part ν of the body.

The values of v and η are such as would give the center of gravity of masses μ, ν and $1 - \mu - \nu$ placed at the points V, L and S.* Hence the part of the diagram which represents a mixture of vapor, liquid and solid, is the triangle VLS. The pressure and temperature are constant for this triangle, i.e., an isopiestic and also an isothermal here expand to cover a space. The isodynamics

---

* These points will not be in the same straight line unless

$$t'(\eta_V - \eta_S) : t'(\eta_L - \eta_S) :: v_V - v_S : v_L - v_S,$$

a condition very unlikely to be fulfilled by any substance. The first and second terms of this proportion denote the heat of vaporization (from the solid state) and that of liquefaction.

are straight and equidistant for equal differences of energy. For $\dfrac{d\varepsilon}{dv} = -p'$, and $\dfrac{d\varepsilon}{d\eta} = t'$, both of which are constant throughout the triangle.

This case can be but very imperfectly represented in the volume-pressure, or in the entropy-temperature diagram. For all points in the same vertical line in the triangle VLS will, in the volume-pressure diagram, be represented by a single point, as having the same volume and pressure. And all the points in the same horizontal line will be represented in the entropy-temperature diagram by a single point, as having the same entropy and temperature. In either diagram, the whole triangle reduces to a straight line. It must reduce to a line in any diagram whatever of constant scale, as its area must become 0 in such a diagram. This must be regarded as a defect in these diagrams, as essentially different states are represented by the same point. In consequence, any circuit within the triangle VLS will be represented in any diagram of constant scale by two paths of opposite directions superposed, the appearance being as if a body should change its state and then return to its original state by inverse processes, so as to repass through the same series of states. It is true that the circuit in question is like this combination of processes in one important particular, viz: that $W = H = 0$, i.e., there is no transformation of heat into work. But this very fact, that a circuit without transformation of heat into work is possible, is worthy of distinct representation.

A body may have such properties that in one part of the volume-entropy diagram $\dfrac{1}{\gamma_{v,\eta}}$, i.e., $\dfrac{dp}{d\eta}$ is positive and in another negative. These parts of the diagram may be separated by a line, in which $\dfrac{dp}{d\eta} = 0$, or by one in which $\dfrac{dp}{d\eta}$ changes abruptly from a positive to a negative value.* (In part, also, they may be separated by an area in which $\dfrac{dp}{d\eta} = 0$.) In the representation of such cases in any diagram of constant scale, we meet with a difficulty of the following nature.

Let us suppose that on the right of the line LL (fig. 10) in a volume-entropy diagram, $\dfrac{dp}{d\eta}$ is positive, and on the left negative. Then, if we draw any circuit ABCD on the right side of LL, the direction being that of the hands of a watch, the work and heat of the circuit will be positive. But if we draw any circuit EFGH in the same direction on the other side of the line LL, the work

---

* The line which represents the various states of water at its maximum density for various constant pressures is an example of the first case. A substance which as a liquid has no proper maximum density for constant pressure, but which expands in solidifying, affords an example of the second case.

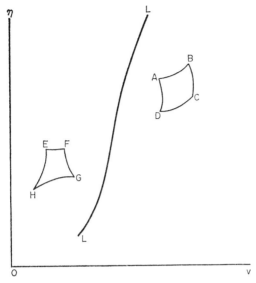

FIG. 10.

and heat will be negative. For

$$W = H = \sum \frac{1}{\gamma_{v,\eta}} \delta A = \sum \frac{dp}{d\eta} \delta A,$$

and the direction of the circuits makes the areas positive in both cases. Now if we should change this diagram into any diagram of constant scale, the areas of the circuits, as representing proportionally the work done in each case, must necessarily have opposite signs, i.e., the direction of the circuits must be opposite. We will suppose that the work done is positive in the diagram of constant scale, when the direction of the circuit is that of the hands of a watch. Then, in that diagram, the circuit ABCD would have that direction, and the circuit EFGH the contrary direction, as in figure 11. Now if we imagine an indefinite number of circuits on each side of LL in the volume-entropy diagram, it will be evident that to transform such a diagram into one of constant scale, so as to change the direction of all the circuits on one side of LL, and of none on the other, the diagram must be *folded over* along that line; so that the points on one side of LL in a diagram of constant scale do not represent any states of the body, while on the other side of this line, each point, for a certain distance at least, represents two different states of the body, which in the volume-entropy diagram are represented by points on opposite sides of the line LL. We have thus in a part of the field two diagrams superposed, which must be carefully distinguished. If this be done, as by the help of different colors, or of continuous and dotted lines, or otherwise, and it is remembered that there is no continuity between these superposed diagrams, except along the bounding line LL, all the general theorems which have been developed in this article can be readily applied to the diagram. But to the eye or to the

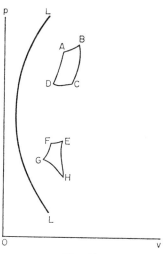

Fig. 11.

imagination, the figure will necessarily be much more confusing than a volume-entropy diagram.

If $\frac{dp}{d\eta} = 0$ for the line LL, there will be another inconvenience in the use of any diagram of constant scale, viz: in the vicinity of the line LL, $\frac{dp}{d\eta}$, i.e., $1 \div \gamma_{v,\eta}$ will have a very small value, so that areas will be very greatly reduced in the diagram of constant scale, as compared with the corresponding areas in the volume-entropy diagram. Therefore, in the former diagram, either the isometrics, or the isentropics, or both, will be crowded together in the vicinity of the line LL, so that this part of the diagram will be necessarily indistinct.

It may occur, however, in the volume-entropy diagram, that the same point must represent two different states of the body. This occurs in the case of liquids which can be vaporized. Let MM (fig. 12) be the line representing the states of the liquid bordering upon vaporization. This line will be near to the axis of entropy, and nearly parallel to it. If the body is in a state represented

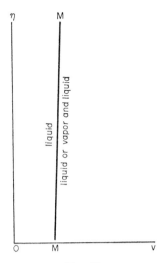

FIG. 12.

by a point of the line MM, and is compressed without addition or subtraction of heat, it will remain of course liquid. Hence, the points of the space immediately on the left of MM represent simple liquid. On the other hand, the body being in the original state, if its volume should be increased without addition or subtraction of heat, and if the conditions necessary for vaporization are present (conditions relative to the body enclosing the liquid in question, etc.), the liquid will become partially vaporized, but if these conditions are not present, it will continue liquid. Hence, every point on the right of MM and sufficiently near to it represents two different states of the body, in one of which it is partially vaporized, and in the other it is entirely liquid. If we take the points as representing the mixture of vapor and liquid, they form one diagram, and if we take them as representing simple liquid, they form a totally different diagram superposed on the first. There is evidently no continuity between these diagrams except at the line MM; we may regard them as upon separate sheets united only along MM. For the body cannot pass from the state of partial vaporization to the state of liquid except at this line. The reverse process is indeed possible; the body can pass from the state of superheated liquid to that of partial vaporization, if the conditions of vaporization alluded to above are supplied, or if the increase of volume is carried beyond a certain limit, but not by gradual changes or reversible processes. After such a change, the point representing the state of the body will be found in a different position from that which it occupied before, but the change of state cannot be properly represented by any path, as during the change the body does not satisfy that condition of uniform temperature and pressure which has been assumed throughout this article, and which is necessary for the graphical methods under discussion. (See note on page 42.)

Of the two superposed diagrams, that which represents simple liquid is a continuation of the diagram on the left of MM. The isopiestics, isothermals and isodynamics pass from one to the other without abrupt change of direction or curvature. But that which represents a mixture of vapor and liquid will be different in its character, and its isopiestics and isothermals will make angles in general with the corresponding lines in the diagram of simple liquid. The isodynamics of the diagram of the mixture, and those of the diagram of simple liquid, will differ in general in curvature at the line MM, but not in direction, for $\dfrac{d\varepsilon}{dv} = -p$ and $\dfrac{d\varepsilon}{d\eta} = t$.

The case is essentially the same with some substances, as water, for example, about the line which separates the simple liquid from a mixture of liquid and solid.

In these cases the inconvenience of having one diagram superposed upon another cannot be obviated by any change of the principle on which the diagram is based. For no distortion can bring the three sheets, which are united along the line MM (one on the left and two on the right), into a single plane surface without superposition. Such cases, therefore, are radically distinguished from those in which the superposition is caused by an unsuitable method of representation.

To find the character of a volume-entropy diagram of a perfect gas, we may make ε constant in equation (D) on page 54, which will give for the equation of an isodynamic and isothermal

$$\eta = a \log v + \text{Const.},$$

and we may make p constant in equation (G), which will give for the equation of an isopiestic

$$\eta = (a + c) \log v + \text{Const.}$$

It will be observed that all the isodynamics and isothermals can be drawn by a single pattern and so also with the isopiestics.

The case will be nearly the same with vapors in a part of the diagram. In that part of the diagram which represents a mixture of liquid and vapor, the isothermals, which of course are identical with the isopiestics, are straight lines. For when a body is vaporized under constant pressure and temperature, the quantities of heat received are proportional to the increments of volume; therefore, the increments of entropy are proportional to the increments of volume. As $\dfrac{d\varepsilon}{dv} = -p$ and $\dfrac{d\varepsilon}{d\eta} = t$, any isothermal is cut at the same angle by all the isodynamics, and is divided into equal segments by equidifferent isodynamics. The latter property is useful in drawing systems of equidifferent isodynamics.

ARRANGEMENT OF THE ISOMETRIC, ISOPIESTIC, ISOTHERMAL AND ISENTROPIC ABOUT A POINT.

The arrangement of the isometric, the isopiestic, the isothermal and the isentropic drawn through any same point, in respect to the order in which they succeed one another around that point, and in respect to the sides of these lines toward which the volume, pressure, temperature and entropy increase, is not altered by any deformation of the surface on which the diagram is drawn, and is therefore independent of the method by which the diagram is formed.* This arrangement is determined by certain of the most characteristic thermodynamic properties of the body in the state in question, and serves in turn to indicate these properties. It is determined, namely, by the value of $\left(\dfrac{dp}{d\eta}\right)_v$ as positive, negative, or zero, i.e., by the effect of heat as increasing or diminishing the pressure when the volume is maintained constant, and by the nature of the internal thermodynamic equilibrium of the body as stable or neutral,—an unstable equilibrium, except as a matter of speculation, is of course out of the question.

Let us first examine the case in which $\left(\dfrac{dp}{d\eta}\right)_v$ is positive and the equilibrium is stable. As $\left(\dfrac{dp}{d\eta}\right)_v$ does not vanish at the point in question, there is a definite isopiestic passing through that point, on one side of which the pressures are greater, and on the other less, than on the line itself. As $\left(\dfrac{dt}{dv}\right)_\eta = -\left(\dfrac{dp}{d\eta}\right)_v$, the case is the same with the isothermal. It will be convenient to distinguish the sides of the isometric, isopiestic, etc., on which the volume, pressure, etc., increase, as the *positive* sides of these lines. The condition of stability requires that, when the pressure is constant, the temperature shall increase with the heat received,—therefore with the entropy. This may be written $[dt:d\eta]_p > 0$.† It also requires that when there is no transmission of heat, the pressure

---

* It is here assumed that, in the vicinity of the point in question, each point in the diagram represents only one state of the body. The propositions developed in the following pages cannot be applied to points of the line where two superposed diagrams are united (see pages 69–72) without certain modifications.

† As the notation $\dfrac{dt}{d\eta}$ is used to denote the limit of the ratio of dt to $d\eta$, it would not be quite accurate to say that the condition of stability requires that $\left(\dfrac{dt}{d\eta}\right)_p > 0$. This condition requires that the ratio of the differences of temperature and entropy between the point in question and any other infinitely near to it and upon the same isopiestic should be positive. It is not necessary that the limit of this ratio should be positive.

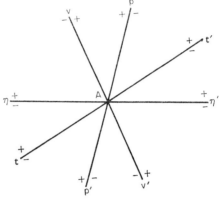

FIG. 13.

should increase as the volume diminishes, i.e., that $[dp:dv]_\eta < 0$. Through the point in question, A (fig. 13), let there be drawn the isometric vv' and the isentropic $\eta\eta'$, and let the positive sides of these lines be indicated as in the figure. The conditions $\left(\dfrac{dp}{d\eta}\right)_v > 0$ and $[dp:dv]_\eta < 0$ requires that the pressure at v and at η shall be greater than at A, and hence, that the isopiestic shall fall as pp' in the figure, and have its positive side turned as indicated. Again, the conditions

$$\left(\frac{dt}{dv}\right)_\eta < 0 \quad \text{and} \quad [dt:d\eta]_p > 0$$

require that the temperature at η and at p shall be greater than at A, and hence, that the isothermal shall fall as tt' and have its positive side turned as indicated. As it is not necessary that $\left(\dfrac{dt}{d\eta}\right)_p > 0$, the lines pp' and tt' may be tangent to one another at A, provided that they cross one another, so as to have the same order about the point A as is represented in the figure; i.e., they may have a contact of the second (or any even) order.* But the condition that $\left(\dfrac{dp}{d\eta}\right)_v > 0$,

* An example of this is doubtless to be found at the critical point of a fluid. See Dr. Andrews "On the continuity of the gaseous and liquid states of matter." *Phil. Trans.*, vol. 159, p. 575.

If the isothermal and isopiestic have a simple tangency at A, on one side of that point they will have such directions as will express an unstable equilibrium. A line drawn through all such points in the diagram will form a boundary to the *possible* part of the diagram. It may be that the part of the diagram of a fluid, which represents the superheated liquid state, is bounded on one side by such a line.

and hence $\left(\dfrac{dt}{dv}\right)_\eta < 0$, does not allow pp' to be tangent to vv', nor tt' to $\eta\eta'$.

If $\left(\dfrac{dp}{d\eta}\right)_v$ be still positive, but the equilibrium be neutral, it will be possible for the body to change its state without change either of temperature or of pressure; i.e., the isothermal and isopiestic will be identical. The lines will fall as in figure 13, except that the isothermal and isopiestic will be superposed.

In like manner, if $\left(\dfrac{dp}{d\eta}\right)_v < 0$, it may be proved that the lines will fall as in figure 14 for stable equilibrium, and in the same way for neutral equilibrium, except that pp' and tt' will be superposed.*

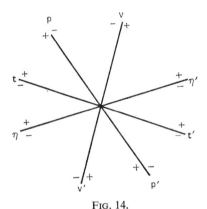

Fig. 14.

The case that $\left(\dfrac{dp}{d\eta}\right)_v = 0$ includes a considerable number of conceivable cases, which would require to be distinguished. It will be sufficient to mention those most likely to occur.

* When it is said that the arrangement of the lines in the diagram must be like that in figure 13 or in figure 14, it is not meant to exclude the case in which the figure (13 or 14) must be turned over, in order to correspond with the diagram. In the case, however, of diagrams formed by any of the methods mentioned in this article, if the directions of the axes be such as we have assumed, the agreement with figure 13 will be *without inversion*, and the agreement with figure 14 will also be *without inversion* for volume-entropy diagrams, but *with inversion* for volume-pressure or entropy-temperature diagrams, or those in which $x = \log v$ and $y = \log p$, or $x = \eta$ and $y = \log t$.

In a field of stable equilibrium it may occur that $\left(\dfrac{dp}{d\eta}\right)_v = 0$ along a line, on one side of which $\left(\dfrac{dp}{d\eta}\right)_v > 0$, and on the other side $\left(\dfrac{dp}{d\eta}\right)_v < 0$. At any point in such a line the isopiestics will be tangent to the isometrics and the isothermals to the isentropics. (See, however, note on page 73.)

In a field of neutral equilibrium representing a mixture of two different states of the substance, where the isothermals and isopiestics are identical, a line may occur which has the threefold character of an isometric, an isothermal and an isopiestic. For such a line $\left(\dfrac{dp}{d\eta}\right)_v = 0$. If $\left(\dfrac{dp}{d\eta}\right)_v$ has opposite signs on opposite sides of this line, it will be an isothermal of maximum or minimum temperature.*

The case in which the body is partly solid, partly liquid and partly vapor has already been sufficiently discussed. (See page 67.)

The arrangement of the isometric, isopiestic, etc., as given in figure 13, will indicate directly the sign of any differential coefficient of the form $\left(\dfrac{du}{dw}\right)_z$, where u, w and z may be any of the quantities v, p, t, η (and ε, if the isodynamic be added in the figure). The value of such a differential coefficient will be indicated when the rates of increase of v, p, etc., are indicated, as by isometrics, etc., drawn both for the values of v, etc., at the point A, and for values differing from these by a small quantity. For example, the value of $\left(\dfrac{dp}{dv}\right)_\eta$ will be indicated by the ratio of the segments intercepted upon an isentropic by a pair of isometrics and a pair of isopiestics, of which the differences of volume and pressure have the same numerical value. The case in which W or H appears in the numerator or denominator instead of a function of the state of the body, can be reduced to the preceding by the substitution of $p\,dv$ for dW, or that of $t\,d\eta$ for dH.

In the foregoing discussion, the equations which express the fundamental principles of thermodynamics in an analytical form have been assumed, and the aim has only been to show how the same relations may be expressed geometrically. It would, however, be easy, starting from the first and second laws of thermodynamics as usually enunciated, to arrive at the same results without the aid of analytical formulae,—to arrive, for example, at the conception

---

* As some liquids expand and others contract in solidifying, it is possible that there are some which will solidify either with expansion, or without change of volume, or with contraction, according to the pressure. If any such there are, they afford examples of the case mentioned above.

of energy, of entropy, of absolute temperature, in the construction of the diagram without the analytical definitions of these quantities, and to obtain the various properties of the diagram without the analytical expression of the thermodynamic properties which they involve. Such a course would have been better fitted to show the independence and sufficiency of a graphical method, but perhaps less suitable for an examination of the comparative advantages or disadvantages of different graphical methods.

The possibility of treating the thermodynamics of fluids by such graphical methods as have been described, evidently arises from the fact that the state of the body considered, like the position of a point in a plane, is capable of two and only two independent variations. It is perhaps, worthy of notice, that when the diagram is only used to demonstrate or illustrate general theorems, it is not necessary, although it may be convenient, to assume any particular method of forming the diagram; it is enough to suppose the different states of the body to be represented continuously by points upon a sheet.

(c) HETEROGENEOUS EQUILIBRIA

Gibbs' third paper on thermodynamics, his *magnum opus*, was essentially analytical; it consisted of a rigorous deduction of mathematical conditions for equilibrium and stability, particularly with respect to modifications introduced by (1) matter of different kinds and states, (2) gravitational forces, (3) effects of solid strain, (4) effects of surface tension at interfaces, and (5) effects of electrical forces. It was published in two parts: Part I, a quite condensed version of fluids; Part II, a detailed account of solid and surface phenomena. Its most significant impacts have been in the field of physical chemistry; starting with the two experimental laws of thermodynamics, Gibbs truly created a comprehensive physico-chemical thermodynamics, the implications of which have probably not yet been fully exploited. The British chemist Frederick George Donnan (1890–1956) called it "one of the mightiest works of genius the human mind has ever produced".[8] He regarded Gibbs' comprehensive and generalized memoir on thermodynamics as comparable to the developments in mechanics by the French mathematician Joseph Louis Lagrange (1736–1813) and by the Irish mathematician Sir William Rowan Hamilton (1805–65). Before considering a few of the highlights of this work, let us survey the author's own attempt to summarize it.

On the Equilibrium of Heterogeneous Substances

by J. WILLARD GIBBS.*

Abstract by the author.

(From the *American Journal of Sciences and Arts*, xvi, pp. 441–58 (1878)).

IT is an inference naturally suggested by the general increase of entropy which accompanies the changes occurring in any isolated material system that when the entropy of the system has reached a maximum, the system will be in a state of equilibrium. Although this principle has by no means escaped the attention of physicists, its importance does not appear to have been duly appreciated. Little has been done to develop the principle as a foundation for the general theory of thermodynamic equilibrium.

The principle may be formulated as follows, constituting a criterion of equilibrium:

I. *For the equilibrium of any isolated system it is necessary and sufficient that in all possible variations of the state of the system which do not alter its energy, the variation of its entropy shall either vanish or be negative.*

The following form, which is easily shown to be equivalent to the preceding, is often more convenient in application:

II. *For the equilibrium of any isolated system it is necessary and sufficient that in all possible variations of the state of the system which do not alter its entropy, the variation of its energy shall either vanish or be positive.*

If we denote the energy and entropy of the system by ε and η respectively, the criterion of equilibrium may be expressed by either of the formulae

$$(\delta\eta)_\varepsilon \leqq 0, \tag{1}$$

$$(\delta\varepsilon)_\eta \geqq 0. \tag{2}$$

Again, if we assume that the temperature of the system is uniform, and denote its absolute temperature by t, and set

$$\psi = \varepsilon - t\eta, \tag{3}$$

the remaining conditions of equilibrium may be expressed by the formula

$$(\delta\psi)_t \geqq 0, \tag{4}$$

the suffixed letter, as in the preceding cases, indicating that the quantity which it represents is constant. This condition, in connection with that of uniform temperature, may be shown to be equivalent to (1) or (2). The difference of the values of ψ for two different states of the system which have the same temperature represents the work which would be expended in bringing the system from one state to the other by a reversible process and without change of temperature.

If the system is incapable of thermal changes, like the systems considered in theoretical mechanics, we may regard the entropy as having the constant value zero. Conditions (2) and (4) may then be written

$$\delta\varepsilon \geqq 0, \qquad \delta\psi \geqq 0,$$

and are obviously identical in signification, since in this case $\psi = \varepsilon$.

Conditions (2) and (4), as criteria of equilibrium, may therefore both be regarded as extensions of the criterion employed in ordinary statics to the more general case of a thermodynamic system. In fact, each of the quantities $-\varepsilon$ and $-\psi$ (relating to a system without sensible motion) may be regarded as a kind of force-function for the system,—the former as the force-function *for constant entropy*, (i.e., when only such states of the system are considered as have the same entropy,) and the latter as the force-function *for constant temperature*, (i.e., when only such states of the system are considered as have the same uniform temperature).

In the deduction of the particular conditions of equilibrium for any system, the general formula (4) has an evident advantage over (1) or (2) with respect to the brevity of the processes of reduction, since the limitation of constant temperature applies to every part of the system taken separately, and diminishes by one the number of independent variations in the state of these parts which we have to consider. Moreover, the transition from the systems considered in ordinary mechanics to thermodynamic systems is most naturally made by this formula, since it has always been customary to apply the principles of theoretical mechanics to real systems on the supposition (more or less distinctly conceived and expressed) that the temperature of the system remains constant, the mechanical properties of a thermodynamic system maintained at a constant temperature being such as might be imagined to belong to a purely mechanical system, and admitting of representation by a force-function, as follows directly from the fundamental laws of thermodynamics.

Notwithstanding these considerations, the author has preferred in general to use condition (2) as the criterion of equilibrium, believing that it would be useful to exhibit the conditions of equilibrium of thermodynamic systems in connection with those quantities which are most simple and most general in their definitions, and which appear most important in the general theory of such systems. The slightly different form in which the subject would develop itself, if condition (4) has been chosen as a point of departure instead of (2), is occasionally indicated.

Equilibrium of masses in contact.—The first problem to which the criterion is applied is the determination of the conditions of equilibrium for different masses in contact, when uninfluenced by gravity, electricity, distortion of the solid masses, or capillary tensions. The statement of the result is facilitated by the following definition.

If to any homogeneous mass in a state of hydrostatic stress we suppose an infinitesimal quantity of any substance to be added, the mass remaining homogeneous and its entropy and volume remaining unchanged, the increase of the energy of the mass divided by the quantity of the substance added is the *potential* for that substance in the mass considered.

In addition to equality of temperature and pressure in the masses in contact, it is necessary for equilibrium that the potential for every substance which is an independently variable component of any of the different masses shall have the same value in all of which it is such a component, so far as they are in contact with one another. But if a substance, without being an actual component of a certain mass in the given state of the system, is capable of being absorbed by it, it is sufficient if the value of the potential for that substance in that mass is not less than in any contiguous mass of which the substance is an actual component. We may regard these conditions as sufficient for equilibrium with respect to infinitesimal variations in the composition and thermodynamic state of the different masses in contact. There are certain other conditions which relate to the possible formation of masses entirely different in composition or state from any initially existing. These conditions are best regarded as determining the stability of the system, and will be mentioned under that head.

Anything which restricts the free movement of the component substances, or of the masses as such, may diminish the number of conditions which are necessary for equilibrium.

Equilibrium of osmotic forces.—If we suppose two fluid masses to be separated by a diaphragm which is permeable to some of the component substances and not to others, of the conditions of equilibrium which have just been mentioned, those will still subsist which relate to temperature and the potentials for the substances to which the diaphragm is permeable, but those relating to the potentials for the substances to which the diaphragm is impermeable will no longer be necessary. Whether the pressure must be the same in the two fluids will depend upon the rigidity of the diaphragm. Even when the diaphragm is permeable to all the components without restriction, equality of pressure in the two fluids is not always necessary for equilibrium.

Effect of gravity.—In a system subject to the action of gravity, the potential for each substance, instead of having a uniform value throughout the system, so far as the substance actually occurs as an independently variable component, will decrease uniformly with increasing height, the difference of its values at different levels being equal to the difference of level multiplied by the force of gravity.

Fundamental equations.—Let ε, η, v, t and p denote respectively the energy, entropy, volume, (absolute) temperature, and pressure of a homogeneous mass, which may be either fluid or solid, provided that it is subject only to hydrostatic pressures, and let m_1, m_2, ... m_n denote the quantities of its independently variable components, and μ_1, μ_2, ... μ_n the potentials for these components. It is easily shown that ε is a function of η, v, m_1, m_2, ... m_n, and that the complete value of $d\varepsilon$ is given by the equation

$$d\varepsilon = t\, d\eta - p\, dv + \mu_1\, dm_1 + \mu_2\, dm_2 \cdots + \mu_n\, dm_n. \tag{5}$$

Now if ε is known in terms of η, v, m_1, ... m_n, we can obtain by differentiation t, p, μ_1, ... μ_n in terms of the same variables. This will make $n + 3$ independent known relations between the $2n + 5$ variables, ε, η, v, m_1, m_2, ... m_n, t, p, μ_1, μ_2, ... μ_n. These are all that exist, for of these variables, $n + 2$ are evidently independent. Now upon these relations depend a very large class of the properties of the compound considered,—we may say in general, all its thermal, mechanical, and chemical properties, so far as *active tendencies* are concerned, in cases in which the form of the mass does not require consideration. A single equation from which all these relations may be deduced may be called a fundamental equation. An equation between ε, η, v, m_1, m_2, ... m_n is a fundamental equation. But there are other equations which possess the same property.

If we suppose the quantity ψ to be determined for such a mass as we are considering by equation (3), we may obtain by differentiation and comparison with (5)

$$d\psi = -\eta\, dt - p\, dv + \mu_1\, dm_1 + m_2\, dm_2 \cdots + \mu_n\, dm_n. \tag{6}$$

If, then, ψ is known as a function of t, v, m_1, m_2, ... m_n, we can find η, p, μ_1, μ_2, ... μ_n in terms of the same variables. If we then substitute for ψ in our original equation its value taken from equation (3) we shall have again $n + 3$ independent relations between the same $2n + 5$ variables as before.

Let

$$\zeta = \varepsilon - t\eta + pv, \tag{7}$$

then, by (5),

$$d\zeta = -\eta\, dt + v\, dp + \mu_1\, dm_1 + \mu_2\, dm_2 \cdots + \mu_n\, dm_n. \tag{8}$$

If, then, ζ is known as a function of t, p, m_1, m_2, ... m_n, we can find η, v, μ_1, μ_2, ... μ_u in terms of the same variables. By eliminating ζ, we may obtain again $n + 3$ independent relations between the same $2n + 5$ variables as at first.[*]

---

[*] The properties of the quantities $-\psi$ and $-\zeta$ regarded as functions of the temperature and volume, and temperature and pressure, respectively, the composition of the body being regarded as invariable, have been discussed by M. Massieu in a memoir entitled "Sur les fonctions caractéristiques des divers fluides et sur la théorie des vapeurs" (*Mém. Savants Étrang.*, t. xxii.) A brief sketch of his method in a form

If we integrate (5), (6) and (8), supposing the quantity of the compound substance considered to vary from zero to any finite value, its nature and state remaining unchanged, we obtain

$$\varepsilon = t\eta - pv + \mu_1 m_1 + \mu_2 m_2 \cdots + \mu_n m_n \tag{9}$$

$$\psi = -pv + \mu_1 m_1 + \mu_2 m_2 \cdots + \mu_n m_n, \tag{10}$$

$$\zeta = \mu_1 m_1 + \mu_2 m_2 \cdots + \mu_n m_n. \tag{11}$$

If we differentiate (9) in the most general manner, and compare the result with (5), we obtain

$$-v \, dp + \eta \, dt + m_1 \, d\mu_1 + m_2 \, d\mu_2 \cdots + m_n \, d\mu_n = 0, \tag{12}$$

or

$$dp = \frac{\eta}{v} \, dt + \frac{m_1}{v} \, d\mu_1 + \frac{m_2}{v} \, d\mu_2 \cdots + \frac{m_n}{v} \, d\mu_n = 0. \tag{13}$$

Hence, there is a relation between the $n + 2$ quantities $t, p, \mu_1, \mu_2, \ldots \mu_n$, which, if known, will enable us to find in terms of these quantities all the ratios of the $n + 2$ quantities $\eta, v, m_1, m_2, \ldots m_n$. With (9), this will make $n + 3$ independent relations between the same $2n + 5$ variables as at first.

Any equation, therefore, between the quantities

$\varepsilon,$	$\eta,$	$v,$	$m_1,$	$m_2, \ldots m_n,$

or

$\psi,$	$t,$	$v,$	$m_1,$	$m_2, \ldots m_n,$

or

$\zeta,$	$t,$	$p,$	$m_1,$	$m_2, \ldots m_n,$

or

	$t,$	$p,$	$\mu_1,$	$\mu_2, \ldots \mu_n,$

is a fundamental equation, and any such is entirely equivalent to any other.

Coëxistent phases.—In considering the different homogeneous bodies which can be formed out of any set of component substances, it is convenient to have a term which shall refer solely to the composition and thermodynamic state of any such body without regard to its size or form. The word *phase* has been chosen for this purpose. Such bodies as differ in composition or state are called different phases of the matter considered, all bodies which differ only in size and form being regarded as different examples of the same phase. Phases which can exist together, the dividing surfaces being plain, in an equilibrium which does not depend upon passive resistances to change, are called coëxistent.

The number of independent variations of which a system of coëxistent phases is capable is $n + 2 - r$, where r denotes the number of phases, and n

---

slightly different from that ultimately adopted is given in *Comptes Rendus*, t. lxix, (1869) pp. 858 and 1057, and a report on his memoir by M. Bertrand in *Comptes Rendus*, t. lxix. p. 257. M. Massieu appears to have been the first to solve the problem of representing all the properties of a body of invariable composition which are concerned in reversible processes by means of a single function.

the number of independently variable components in the whole system. For the system of phases is completely specified by the temperature, the pressure, and the n potentials, and between these $n + 2$ quantities there are r independent relations (one for each phase), which characterize the system of phases.

When the number of phases exceeds the number of components by unity, the system is capable of a single variation of phase. The pressure and all the potentials may be regarded as functions of the temperature. The determination of these functions depends upon the elimination of the proper quantities from the fundamental equations in p, t, μ_1, μ_2, etc., for the several members of the system. But without a knowledge of these fundamental equations, the values of the differential coefficients such as $\dfrac{dp}{dt}$ may be expressed in terms of the entropies and volumes of the different bodies and the quantities of their several components. For this end we have only to eliminate the differentials of the potentials from the different equations of the form (12) relating to the different bodies. In the simplest case, when there is but one component, we obtain the well-known formula

$$\frac{dp}{dt} = \frac{\eta' - \eta''}{v' - v''} = \frac{Q}{t(v'' - v')}$$

in which v', v'', η', η'', denote the volumes and entropies of a given quantity of the substance in the two phases, and Q the heat which it absorbs in passing from one phase to the other.

It is easily shown that if the temperature of two coëxistent phases of two components is maintained constant, the pressure is in general a maximum or minimum when the composition of the phases is identical. In like manner, if the pressure of the phases is maintained constant, the temperature is in general a maximum or minimum when the composition of the phases is identical. The series of simultaneous values of t and p for which the composition of two coëxistent phases is identical separates those simultaneous values of t and p for which no coëxistent phases are possible from those for which there are two pairs of coëxistent phases.

If the temperature of three coëxistent phases of three components is maintained constant, the pressure is in general a maximum or minimum when the composition of one of the phases is such as can be produced by combining the other two. If the pressure is maintained constant, the temperature is in general a maximum or minimum when the same condition in regard to the composition of the phases is fulfilled.

Stability of fluids.—A criterion of the stability of a homogeneous fluid, or of a system of coëxistent fluid phases, is afforded by the expression

$$\varepsilon - t'\eta + p'v - \mu_1' m_1 - \mu_2' m_2 \cdots - \mu_n' m_n \qquad (14)$$

in which the values of the accented letters are to be determined by the phase or system of phases of which the stability is in question, and the values of the unaccented letters by any other phase of the same components, the possible formation of which is in question. We may call the former constants, and the latter variables. Now if the value of the expression, thus determined, is always positive for any possible values of the variables, the phase or system of phases will be stable with respect to the formation of any new phases of its components. But if the expression is capable of a negative value, the phase or system is at least *practically* unstable. By this is meant that, although, strictly speaking, an infinitely small disturbance or change may not be sufficient to destroy the equilibrium, yet a very small change in the initial state will be sufficient to do so. The presence of a small portion of matter in a phase for which the above expression has a negative value will in general be sufficient to produce this result. In the case of a system of phases, it is of course supposed that their contiguity is such that the formation of the new phase does not involve any transportation of matter through finite distances.

The preceding criterion affords a convenient point of departure in the discussion of the stability of homogeneous fluids. Of the other forms in which the criterion may be expressed, the following is perhaps the most useful.

If the pressure of a fluid is greater than that of any other phase of its independent variable components which has the same temperature and potentials, the fluid is stable with respect to the formation of any other phase of these components; but if its pressure is not as great as that of some such phase, it will be practically unstable.

Stability of fluids with respect to continuous changes of phase.—In considering the changes which may take place in any mass, we have often to distinguish between infinitesimal changes in existing phases, and the formation of entirely new phases. A phase of a fluid may be stable with respect to the former kind of change, and unstable with respect to the latter. In this case, it may be capable of continued existence in virtue of properties which prevent the commencement of discontinuous changes. But a phase which is unstable with respect to continuous changes is evidently incapable of permanent existence on a large scale except in consequence of passive resistances to change. To obtain the conditions of stability with respect to continuous changes, we have only to limit the application of the variables in (14) to phases adjacent to the given phase. We obtain results of the following nature.

The stability of any phase with respect to continuous changes depends upon the same conditions with respect to the second and higher differential coëfficients of the density of energy regarded as a function of the density of entropy and the densities of the several components, which would make the density of energy a minimum, if the necessary conditions with respect to the first differential coëfficients were fulfilled.

Again, it is necessary and sufficient for the stability with respect to continuous changes of all the phases within any given limits, that within those limits the same conditions should be fulfilled with respect to the second and higher differential coëfficients of the pressure regarded as a function of the temperature and the several potentials, which would make the pressure a minimum, if the necessary conditions with respect to the first differential coëfficients were fulfilled.

The equation of the limits of stability with respect to continuous changes may be written

$$\left(\frac{d\mu_n}{d\gamma_n}\right)_{t,\mu_1,\ldots\mu_{n-1}} = 0 \quad \text{or} \quad \left(\frac{d^2p}{d\mu_n^2}\right)_{t,\mu_1,\ldots\mu_{n-1}} = \infty, \tag{15}$$

where γ_n, denotes the density of the component specified or $m_u \div v$. It is in general immaterial to what component the suffix $_n$ is regarded as relating.

Critical phases.—The variations of two coëxistent phases are sometimes limited by the vanishing of the difference between them. Phases at which this occurs are called *critical phases.* A critical phase, like any other, is capable of $n + 1$ independent variations, n denoting the number of independently variable components. But when subject to the condition of remaining a critical phase, it is capable of only $n - 1$ independent variations. There are therefore two independent equations which characterize critical phases. These may be written

$$\left(\frac{d\mu_n}{d\gamma_n}\right)_{t,\mu_1,\ldots\mu_{n-1}} = 0,\left(\frac{d^2\mu_n}{d\gamma_n^2}\right)_{t,\mu_1,\ldots\mu_{n-1}} = 0. \tag{16}$$

It will be observed that the first of these equations is identical with the equation of the limit of stability with respect to continuous changes. In fact, stable critical phases are situated at that limit. They are also situated at the limit of stability with respect to discontinuous changes. These limits are in general distinct, but touch each other at critical phases.

Geometrical illustrations.—In an earlier paper,* the author has described a method of representing the thermodynamic properties of substances of invariable composition by means of surfaces. The volume, entropy, and energy of a constant quantity of the substance are represented by rectangular coördinates. This method corresponds to the first kind of fundamental equation described above. Any other kind of fundamental equation for a substance of invariable composition will suggest an analogous geometrical method. In the present paper, the method in which the coördinates represent temperature, pressure, and the potential, is briefly considered. But when the composition of the body is variable, the fundamental equation cannot be completely represented by any surface or finite number of surfaces. In the case of three components, if we regard the temperature and pressure as constant, as well as the

* *Transactions of the Connecticut Academy*, vol. ii, part 2.

total quantity of matter, the relations between ζ, m_1, m_2, m_3 may be represented by a surface in which the distances of a point from the three sides of a triangular prism represent the quantities m_1, m_2, m_3, and the distance of the point from the base of the prism represents the quantity ζ. In the case of two components, analogous relations may be represented by a plane curve. Such methods are especially useful for illustrating the combinations and separations of the components, and the changes in states of aggregation, which take place when the substances are exposed in varying proportions to the temperature and pressure considered.

Fundamental equations of ideal gases and gas-mixtures.—From the physical properties which we attribute to ideal gases, it is easy to deduce their fundamental equations. The fundamental equation in ε, η, v, and m for an ideal gas is

$$c \log \frac{\varepsilon - \mathrm{E}m}{cm} = \frac{\eta}{m} - \mathrm{H} + a \log \frac{m}{v} : \tag{17}$$

that in ψ, t, v, and m is

$$\psi = \mathrm{E}m + mt\left(c - \mathrm{H} - c \log t + a \log \frac{m}{v}\right) : \tag{18}$$

that in p, t, and μ is

$$p = ae^{(\mathrm{H}-c-a)/a}t^{(c+a)/a}e^{(\mu-\mathrm{E})/at}, \tag{19}$$

where e denotes the base of the Naperian system of logarithms. As for the other constants, c denotes the specific heat of the gas at constant volume, a denotes the constant value of $pv \div mt$, E and H depend upon the zeros of energy and entropy. The two last equations may be abbreviated by the use of different constants. The properties of fundamental equations mentioned above may easily be verified in each case by differentiation.

The law of Dalton respecting a mixture of different gases affords a point of departure for the discussion of such mixtures and the establishment of their fundamental equations. It is found convenient to give the law the following form:

The pressure in a mixture of different gases is equal to the sum of the pressures of the different gases as existing each by itself at the same temperature and with the same value of its potential.

A mixture of ideal gases which satisfies this law is called an *ideal gas-mixture*. Its fundamental equation in p, t, μ_1, μ_2, etc. is evidently of the form

$$p = \sum_1 (a_1 e^{(\mathrm{H}_1-c_1-a_1)/a_1}t^{(c_1+a_1)/a_1}e^{(\mu_1-\mathrm{E}_1)/a_1 t} \tag{20}$$

where Σ_1 denotes summation with respect to the different components of the mixture. From this may be deduced other fundamental equations for ideal gas-mixtures. That in ψ, t, v, m_1, m_2, etc. is

$$\psi = \sum_1 \left(E_1 m_1 + m_1 t \left(c_1 - H_1 - c_1 \log t + a_1 \log \frac{m_1}{v} \right) \right). \tag{21}$$

Phases of dissipated energy of ideal gas-mixtures.—When the proximate components of a gas-mixture are so related that some of them can be formed out of others, although not necessarily in the gas-mixture itself at the temperatures considered, there are certain phases of the gas-mixture which deserve especial attention. These are the *phases of dissipated energy*, i.e., those phases in which the energy of the mass has the least value consistent with its entropy and volume. An atmosphere of such a phase could not furnish a source of mechanical power to any machine or chemical engine working within it, as other phases of the same matter might do. Nor can such phases be affected by any catalytic agent. A *perfect catalytic agent* would reduce any other phase of the gas-mixture to a phase of dissipated energy. The condition which will make the energy a minimum is that the potentials for the proximate components shall satisfy an equation similar to that which expresses the relation between the units of weight of these components. For example, if the components were hydrogen, oxygen and water, since one gram of hydrogen with eight grams of oxygen are chemically equivalent to nine grams of water, the potentials for these substances in a phase of dissipated energy must satisfy the relation

$$\mu_H + 8\mu_0 = 9\mu_W.$$

Gas-mixtures with convertible components.—The theory of the phases of dissipated energy of an ideal gas-mixture derives an especial interest from its possible application to the case of those gas-mixtures in which the chemical composition and resolution of the components can take place in the gas-mixture itself, and actually do take place, so that the quantities of the proximate components are entirely determined by the quantities of a smaller number of ultimate components, with the temperature and pressure. These may be called *gas-mixtures with convertible components*. If the general laws of *ideal* gas-mixtures apply in any such case, it may easily be shown that the phases of dissipated energy are the only phases which can exist. We can form a fundamental equation which shall relate solely to these phases. For this end, we first form the equation in p, t, μ_1, μ_2, etc. for the gas-mixture, regarding its proximate components as *not* convertible. This equation will contain a potential for every proximate component of the gas-mixture. We then eliminate one (or more) of these potentials by means of the relations which exist between them in virtue of the convertibility of the components to which they relate, leaving the potentials which relate to those substances which naturally express the ultimate composition of the gas-mixture.

The validity of the results thus obtained depends upon the applicability of the laws of ideal gas-mixtures to cases in which chemical action takes place. Some of these laws are generally regarded as capable of such application, others are not so regarded. But it may be shown that in the very important case in which the components of a gas are convertible at certain temperatures, and not at others, the theory proposed may be established without other assumptions than such as are generally admitted.

It is, however, only by experiments upon gas-mixtures with convertible components, that the validity of any theory concerning them can be satisfactorily established.

The vapor of the peroxide of nitrogen appears to be a mixture of two different vapors, of one of which the molecular formula is double that of the other. If we suppose that the vapor conforms to the laws of an ideal gas-mixture in a state of dissipated energy, we may obtain an equation between the temperature, pressure, and density of the vapor, which exhibits a somewhat striking agreement with the results of experiment.

Equilibrium of stressed solids.—The second paper commences with a discussion of the conditions of internal and external equilibrium for solids in contact with fluids with regard to all possible states of strain of the solids. These conditions are deduced by analytical processes from the general condition of equilibrium (2). The condition of equilibrium which relates to the dissolving of the solid at a surface where it meets a fluid may be expressed by the equation

$$\mu_1 = \frac{\varepsilon - t\eta + pv}{m} , \qquad (22)$$

where ε, η, v, and m, denote respectively the energy, entropy, volume, and mass of the solid, if it is homogeneous in nature and state of strain,—otherwise, of any small portion which may be treated as thus homogeneous,—μ_1 the potential in the fluid for the substance of which the solid consists, p the pressure in the fluid and therefore one of the principal pressures in the solid, and t the temperature. It will be observed that when the pressure in the solid is isotropic, the second member of this equation will represent the potential in the solid for the substance of which it consists [see (9)], and the condition reduces to the equality of the potential in the two masses, just as if it were a case of two fluids. But if the stresses in the solid are not isotropic, the value of the second member of the equation is not entirely determined by the nature and state of the solid, but has in general three different values (for the same solid at the same temperature, and in the same state of strain) corresponding to the three principal pressures in the solid. If a solid in the form of a right parallelopiped is subject to different pressures on its three pairs of opposite sides by fluids in which it is soluble, it is in general necessary for equilibrium that the composition of the fluids shall be different.

The *fundamental equations* which have been described above are limited, in their application to solids, to the case in which the stresses in the solid are isotropic. An example of a more general form of fundamental equation for a solid, is afforded by an equation between the energy and entropy of a given quantity of the solid, and the quantities which express its state of strain, or by an equation between ψ [see (3)] as determined for a given quantity of the solid, the temperature, and the quantities which express the state of strain.

Capillarity.—The solution of the problems which precede may be regarded as a first approximation, in which the peculiar state of thermodynamic equilibrium about the surfaces of discontinuity is neglected. To take account of the condition of things at these surfaces, the following method is used. Let us suppose that two homogeneous fluid masses are separated by a surface of discontinuity, i.e., by a very thin non-homogeneous film. Now we may imagine a state of things in which each of the homogeneous masses extends without variation of the densities of its several components, or of the densities of energy and entropy, quite up to a geometrical surface (to be called the dividing surface) at which the masses meet. We may suppose this surface to be sensibly coincident with the physical surface of discontinuity. Now if we compare the actual state of things with the supposed state, there will be in the former in the vicinity of the surface a certain (positive or negative) excess of energy, of entropy, and of each of the component substances. These quantities are denoted by ε^S, η^S, m_1^S, m_2^S, etc. and are treated as belonging to the surface. The ^{S} is used simply as a distinguishing mark, and must not be taken for an algebraic exponent.

It is shown that the conditions of equilibrium already obtained relating to the temperature and the potentials of the homogeneous masses, are not affected by the surfaces of discontinuity, and that the complete value of $d\varepsilon^S$ is given by the equation

$$\delta\varepsilon^S = t\,\delta\eta^S + \sigma\,\delta s + \mu_1\,\delta m_1^S + \mu_2\,\delta m_2^S + \text{etc.} \tag{23}$$

in which s denotes the area of the surface considered, t the temperature, μ_1, μ_2, etc. the potentials for the various components in the adjacent masses. It may be, however, that some of the components are found only at the surface of discontinuity, in which case the letter μ with the suffix relating to such a substance denotes, as the equation shows, the rate of increase of energy at the surface per unit of the substance added, when the entropy, the area of the surface, and the quantities of the other components are unchanged. The quantity σ we may regard as defined by the equation itself, or by the following, which is obtained by integration:

$$\varepsilon^S = t\eta^S + \sigma s + \mu_1 m_1^S + \mu_2 m_2^S + \text{etc.} \tag{24}$$

There are terms relating to variations of the curvatures of the surface which might be added, but it is shown that we can give the dividing surface such a position as to make these terms vanish, and it is found convenient to regard its position as thus determined. It is always sensibly coincident with the physical surface of discontinuity. (Yet in treating of plane surfaces, this supposition in regard to the position of the dividing surface is unnecessary, and it is sometimes convenient to suppose that its position is determined by other considerations.)

With the aid of (23), the remaining condition of equilibrium for contiguous homogeneous masses is found, viz:

$$\sigma(c_1 + c_2) = p' - p'', \tag{25}$$

where p', p'' denote the pressures in the two masses, and c_1, c_2 the principal curvatures of the surface. Since this equation has the same form as if a tension equal to σ resided at the surface, the quantity σ is called (as is usual) the *superficial tension*, and the dividing surface in the particular position above mentioned is called the *surface of tension*.

By differentiation of (24) and comparison with (23), we obtain

$$d\sigma = -\eta_S \, dt - \Gamma_1 \, d\mu_1 - \Gamma_2 \, d\mu_2 - \text{etc.}, \tag{26}$$

Where η_S, Γ_1, Γ_2, etc. are written for $\dfrac{\eta^S}{s}$, $\dfrac{m_1{}^S}{s}$, $\dfrac{m_2{}^S}{s}$, etc., and denote the superficial densities of entropy and of the various substances. We may regard σ as a function of t, μ_1, μ_2, etc., from which if known η_S, Γ_1, Γ_2, etc. may be determined in terms of the same variables. An equation between σ, t, μ_1, μ_2, etc. may therefore be called a *fundamental equation for the surface of discontinuity*. The same may be said of an equation between ε^S, η^S, s, $m_1{}^S$, $m_2{}^S$, etc.

It is necessary for the stability of a surface of discontinuity that its tension shall be as small as that of any other surface which can exist between the same homogeneous masses with the same temperature and potentials. Beside this condition, which relates to the nature of the surface of discontinuity, there are other conditions of stability, which relate to the possible motion of such surfaces. One of these is that the tension shall be positive. The others are of a less simple nature, depending upon the extent and form of the surface of discontinuity, and in general upon the whole system of which it is a part. The most simple case of a system with a surface of discontinuity is that of two coexistent phases separated by a spherical surface, the outer mass being of indefinite extent. When the interior mass and the surface of discontinuity are formed entirely of substances which are components of the surrounding mass, the equilibrium is always unstable; in other cases, the equilibrium may be stable. Thus, the equilibrium of a drop of water in an atmosphere of vapor is unstable, but may be made stable by the addition of a little salt. The analytical conditions which determine the stability or instability of the system are easily found, when the temperature and potentials of the system are regarded as known, as well as the fundamental equations for the interior mass and the surface of discontinuity.

The study of surfaces of discontinuity throws considerable light upon the subject of the stability of such phases of fluids as have a less pressure than other phases of the same components with the same temperature and potentials. Let the pressure of the phase of which the stability is in question be denoted by p', and that of the other phase of the same temperature and potentials by p''. A spherical mass of the second phase and of a radius determined by the equation

$$2\sigma = (p'' - p')r, \tag{27}$$

would be in equilibrium with a surrounding mass of the first phase. This equilibrium, as we have just seen, is unstable, when the surrounding mass is indefinitely extended. A spherical mass a little larger would tend to increase indefinitely. The work required to form such a spherical mass, by a reversible process, in the interior of an infinite mass of the other phase, is given by the equation

$$W = \sigma s - (p'' - p')v''. \tag{28}$$

The term σs represents the work spent in forming the surface, and the term $(p'' - p')v''$ the work gained in forming the interior mass. The second of these quantities is always equal to two-thirds of the first. The value of W is therefore positive, and the phase is in strictness stable, the quantity W affording a kind of measure of its stability. We may easily express the value of W in a form which does not involve any geometrical magnitudes, viz:

$$W = \frac{16\pi\sigma^2}{3(p'' - p')^2}, \tag{29}$$

where p'', p' and σ may be regarded as functions of the temperature and potentials. It will be seen that the stability, thus measured, is infinite for an infinitesimal difference of pressures, but decreases very rapidly as the difference of pressures increases. These conclusions are all, however, practically limited to the case in which the value of r, as determined by equation (27), is of sensible magnitude.

With respect to the somewhat similar problem of the stability of the surface of contact of two phases with respect to the formation of a new phase, the following results are obtained. Let the phases (supposed to have the same temperature and potentials) be denoted by A, B, and C; their pressures by p_A, p_B and p_C; and the tensions of the three possible surfaces σ_{AB}, σ_{BC}, σ_{AC}. If p_C is less than

$$\frac{\sigma_{BC}p_A + \sigma_{AC}p_B}{\sigma_{BC} + \sigma_{AC}},$$

there will be no tendency toward the formation of the new phase at the surface between A and B. If the temperature or potentials are now varied until p_C is equal to the above expression, there are two cases to be distinguished. The tension σ_{AB} will be either equal to $\sigma_{AC} + \sigma_{BC}$ or less. (A greater value could only relate to an unstable and therefore unusual surface.) If $\sigma_{AB} = \sigma_{AC} + \sigma_{BC}$, a farther variation of the temperature or potentials, making p_C greater than the above expression, would cause the phase C to be formed at the surface between A and B. But if $\sigma_{AB} < \sigma_{AC} + \sigma_{BC}$, the surface between A and B would remain stable, but with rapidly diminishing stability, after p_C has passed the limit mentioned.

The conditions of stability for a line where several surfaces of discontinuity meet, with respect to the possible formation of a new surface, are capable of a very simple expression. If the surfaces A–B, B–C, C–D, D–A, separating the masses A, B, C, D, meet along a line, it is necessary for equilibrium that their tensions and directions at any point of the line should be such that a quadrilateral α, β, γ, δ may be formed with sides representing in direction and length the normals and tensions of the successive surfaces. For the stability of the system with reference to the possible formation of surfaces between A and C, or between B and D, it is farther necessary that the tensions σ_{AC} and σ_{BD} should be greater than the diagonals $\alpha\gamma$ and $\beta\delta$ respectively. The conditions of stability are entirely analogous in the case of a greater number of surfaces. For the conditions of stability relating to the formation of a new phase at a line in which three surfaces of discontinuity meet, or at a point where four different phases meet, the reader is referred to the original paper.

Liquid films.—When a fluid exists in the form of a very thin film between other fluids, the great inequality of its extension in different directions will give rise to certain peculiar properties, even when its thickness is sufficient for its interior to have the properties of matter in mass. The most important case is where the film is liquid and the contiguous fluids are gaseous. If we imagine the film to be divided into elements of the same order of magnitude as its thickness, each element extending through the film from side to side, it is evident that far less time will in general be required for the attainment of approximate equilibrium between the different parts of any such element and the contiguous gases than for the attainment of equilibrium between all the different elements of the film.

There will accordingly be a time, commencing shortly after the formation of the film, in which its separate elements may be regarded as satisfying the conditions of internal equilibrium, and of equilibrium with the contiguous gases, while they may not satisfy all the conditions of equilibrium with each other. It is when the changes due to this want of complete equilibrium take place so slowly that the film appears to be at rest, except so far as it accommodates itself to any change in the external conditions to which it is subjected, that the characteristic properties of the film are most striking and most sharply defined. It is from this point of view that these bodies are discussed. They are regarded as satisfying a certain well-defined class of conditions of equilibrium, but as not satisfying at all certain other conditions which would be necessary for complete equilibrium, in consequence of which they are subject to gradual changes, which ultimately determine their rupture.

The elasticity of a film (i.e., the increase of its tension when extended), is easily accounted for. It follows from the general relations given above that, when a film has more than one component, those components which diminish the tension will be found in greater proportion on the surfaces. When the film is extended, there will not be enough of these substances to keep up the same volume- and surface-densities as before, and the deficiency will cause a certain increase of tension. It does not follow that a thinner film has always a greater tension than a thicker formed of the same liquid. When the phases within the films as well as without are the same, and the surfaces of the films are also the same, there will be no difference of tension. Nor will the tension of the same film be altered, if a part of the interior drains away in the course of time, without affecting the surfaces. If the thickness of the film is reduced by evaporation, its tension may be either increased or diminished, according to the relative volatility of its different components.

Let us now suppose that the thickness of the film is reduced until the limit is reached at which the interior ceases to have the properties of matter in mass. The elasticity of the film, which determines its stability with respect to extension and contraction, does not vanish at this limit. But a certain kind of instability will generally arise, in virtue of which inequalities in the thickness of the film will tend to increase through currents in the interior of the film. This probably leads to the destruction of the film, in the case of most liquids. In a film of soap-water, the kind of instability described seems to be manifested in the breaking out of the black spots. But the sudden diminution in thickness which takes place in parts of the film is arrested by some unknown cause, possibly by viscous or gelatinous properties, so that the rupture of the film does not necessarily follow.

Electromotive force.—The conditions of equilibrium may be modified by electromotive force. Of such cases a galvanic or electrolytic cell may be regarded as the type. With respect to the potentials for the ions and the electrical potential the following relation may be noticed:

When all the conditions of equilibrium are fulfilled in a galvanic or electrolytic cell, the electromotive force is equal to the difference in the values of the potential for any ion at the surfaces of the electrodes multiplied by the electro-chemical equivalent of that ion, the greater potential of an anion being at the same electrode as the greater electrical potential, and the reverse being true of a cation.

The relation which exists between the electromotive force of a *perfect electrochemical apparatus* (i.e., a galvanic or electrolytic cell which satisfies the condition of reversibility), and the changes in the cell which accompany the passage of electricity, may be expressed by the equation

$$d\varepsilon = (V' - V'') \, de + t \, d\eta + dW_G + dW_P, \qquad (30)$$

in which $d\varepsilon$ denotes the increment of the intrinsic energy in the apparatus, $d\eta$ the increment of entropy, de the quantity of electricity which passes through it, V' and V" the electrical potentials in pieces of the same kind of metal connected with the anode and cathode respectively, dW_G the work done by gravity, and dW_P the work done by the pressures which act on the external surface of the apparatus. The term dW_G may generally be neglected. The same is true of dW_P, when gases are not concerned. If no heat is supplied or is withdrawn, the term $t\,d\eta$ will vanish. But in the calculation of electromotive forces, which is the most important application of the equation, it is convenient and customary to suppose that the temperature is maintained constant. Now this term $t\,d\eta$, which represents the heat absorbed by the cell, is frequently neglected in the consideration of cells of which the temperature is supposed to remain constant. In other words, it is frequently assumed that neither heat nor cold is produced by the passage of an electrical current through a perfect electrochemical apparatus (except that heat which may be indefinitely diminished by increasing the time in which a given quantity of electricity passes), unless it be by processes of a secondary nature, which are not immediately or necessarily connected with the process of electrolysis.

That this assumption is incorrect is shown by the electromotive force of a gas battery charged with hydrogen and nitrogen, by the currents caused by differences in the concentration of the electrolyte, by electrodes of zinc and mercury in a solution of sulphate of zinc, by *a priori* considerations based on the phenomena exhibited in the direct combination of the elements of water or of hydrochloric acid, by the absorption of heat which M. Favre has in many cases observed in a galvanic or electrolytic cell, and by the fact that the solid or liquid state of an electrode (at its temperature of fusion) does not affect the electromotive force.

1. *Fundamental Concepts*

Consider an isolated homogeneous thermodynamic system of volume v and constant mass m at uniform pressure p and absolute temperature t. The first law of thermodynamics states that an infinitesimal change in internal energy ϵ is given by

$$d\epsilon = dH - dW,$$

where dH and dW represent the heat absorbed *by* the system and the work done *by* it, respectively (in modern notation we would prefer δH and δW in order to emphasize that these changes are not perfect differentials of functions such as $d\epsilon$). For a reversible mechanical process

$$d\epsilon = dH - p\,dv.$$

The second law of thermodynamics for a reversible thermal change states that the change in entropy η is given by

$$d\eta = \frac{dH}{t}.$$

Hence $$d\epsilon = t\,d\eta - p\,dv.$$

The functions of state ϵ, η are more descriptive of a working substance than the operational quantities H, W.

Suppose the mass of the system changes while its pressure and temperature remain the same. Let the subscript zero indicate the values of unit mass m under the specific conditions of pressure and temperature. Then for a system with energy, entropy, and volume proportional to its mass, the total changes will be given by

$$d\epsilon = \Delta\epsilon + \varepsilon_0\,dm,$$
$$d\eta = \Delta\eta + \eta_0\,dm,$$
$$dv = \Delta v + v_0\,dm,$$

where Δ represents a change at constant mass.

Substituting these values in Clausius' equation, we obtain

$$d\epsilon = t\,d\eta - p\,dv + \mu\,dm,$$

where $$\mu \equiv \epsilon_0 - t\eta_0 + pv_0; \quad \text{i.e.} \quad \mu = \left(\frac{2\epsilon}{2\eta}\right)_{\eta v};$$

Gibbs called μ the potential of the system (nowadays it is sometimes called the *chemical potential* or partial potential). He extended this equation to a homogeneous mass of matter, i.e. a *phase*, consisting of any number n of independently variable components i thus:

$$d\epsilon = t\,d\eta - p\,dv + \sum_{i=1}^{n} \mu_i\,dm_i.$$

This *fundamental equation* makes it possible to consider the equilibrium resulting from mutual interactions of coexistent phases, i.e. a *heterogeneous* system—a typical example of Gibbs' ability to generalize.

In 1869 the French scientist M. Massieu had shown how all thermodynamic properties of a fluid can be deduced in two instances from a single so-called *characteristic function*. Gibbs proved that three such functions satisfy his fundamental equation, viz.

$$\psi \equiv \epsilon - t\eta,$$

$$\chi \equiv \epsilon + pv,$$

and $\qquad \zeta \equiv \epsilon - t\eta + pv = \chi - t\eta.$

These functions have subsequently been given various names by different investigators. The thermodynamic potential at constant volume $\psi(t, v, \eta)$ measures the energy of a simple substance available for mechanical work in an isothermal process. It has been widely used in physical chemistry (E. A. Guggenheim[10] and D. ter Haar[16] denote it by the symbol F, G. N. Lewis and A. A. Noyes by A, H. L. Helmholtz by H, which he designated "free energy"). "Gibbs' heat function for constant pressure" $\zeta(\eta, p, n)$ is commonly called the total heat by engineers; $d\epsilon$ is the heat taken in by a simple substance during a change at constant pressure ($d\epsilon(\eta, v, n)$ is the heat taken in during a change at constant volume). (It is denoted H by E. A. Guggenheim, G. N. Lewis and A. A. Noyes.) The function $\zeta(t, p, n)$ has been called the Gibbs "free energy" (symbol G by E. A. Guggenheim[10] and D. ter Haar,[16] symbol A by G. N. Lewis and A. A. Noyes); it remains constant for a simple substance undergoing an isothermal, isopiestic change. For an isothermal, isopiestic change in a phase

$$d\zeta = \sum_{i=1}^{n} \mu_i \, dm_i.$$

In equilibrium, for a mixture of r phases j at constant pressure and temperature

$$d\zeta = \sum_{i,j=1}^{m,r} u_i^j \, dm_i^j = 0.$$

But the total mass of each component is constant, hence, multiplying each of these i equations by λ_i Lagrangian multipliers (constant) and adding them to the one for $d\xi$; we now choose each λ_v so that the coefficients of the various differentials vanish, i.e.

$$u_i^j + \lambda_i = 0; \qquad i = 1, \ldots, n; i = 1, \ldots, r;$$

and $\qquad \mu_i^j = \mu_i^k; \qquad k \neq j, i = 1, \ldots, n; j = 1, \ldots, r.$

The chemical potentials of any component in each phase are the same for equilibrium. Otherwise a chemical substance tends to pass from a phase where it has a higher chemical potential to one where it has a lower one (*cf.* American chemist Gilbert Newton Lewis' (1875–1946) "fugacity" function (1901)). Recently[22] (1957–58) a generalization of Gibbs' chemical potential has led to a theory of density gradients for macromolecules which has contributed much to our detailed understanding of DNA replication.

Gibbs showed that the general condition (necessary and sufficient) of equilibrium can be expressed by either of the following variational forms:

$$(\delta \eta)_\epsilon \leq 0,$$

or

$$(\delta \epsilon)_\eta \geq 0,$$

where equality occurs in systems when, for any variation in η or ϵ, there corresponds an equal and opposite one.

In a section entitled "Geometrical Illustrations" Gibbs developed his geometrical techniques in conjunction with the analysis for heterogeneous equilibria. He paid particular attention to the t, p, ζ representation. The method was applied primarily in Holland (e.g. experimental work by the Dutch physical chemists H. W. B. Roozeboom and Jacobus Hendricus van't Hoff (1852–1911) and inorganic chemist F. A. H. Schreinemakers).

Gibbs was able to express also the chemical equilibrium in a homogeneous substance in an exact, general form. Suppose the components in such a closed phase are mutually convertible for equilibrium, then

$$\sum_{i=1}^{n} \mu_i \, dm_i = 0,$$

i.e. a restrictive condition that reduces the number of independently variable components. In the case of three components, for example, this becomes

$$\mu_1 \, dm_1 + \mu_2 \, dm_2 + \mu_3 \, dm_3 = 0.$$

But the chemical mass relations require that

$$\frac{dm_1}{c_1} = \frac{dm_2}{c_2} = \frac{dm_3}{c_3},$$

where the c's are positive. Hence for equilibrium

$$c_1 \mu_1 + c_2 \mu_2 = -c_3 \mu_3.$$

In the case of each pair t and η, p and v, μ_0 and η, there is an intensity factor and a capacity factor. The differential expressions can be integrated for constant values of the intensity factors. One thus obtains

$$\zeta = \epsilon - tn + pv = \sum_{i=1}^{n} \mu_i n_i,$$

where n_i is a number indicating the quantity of a substance i (e.g. number of moles, $n_0 = m_i/M_0$, where M_0 is the mass per mol). Now differentiating and comparing the result with

$$d\zeta = -n\,dt + v\,dp - \sum_{i=1}^{n} \mu_i\,dn_i = 0,$$

we obtain

$$-n\,dt + v\,dp - \sum_{i=1}^{n} n_i\,d\mu_i = 0.$$

For constant temperature and pressure

$$\sum_{i=1}^{n} n_i\,d\mu_i = 0,$$

a relation known as the *Gibbs–Duhem* formula.

On the Equilibrium of Heterogeneous Substances

By J. Willard Gibbs*

* From the *Transactions of the Connecticut Academy of Arts and Sciences*, III, pp. 108–248 and 343–524.

"Die Energie der Welt ist constant.
Die Entropie der Welt strebt einem Maximum zu."
Clausius.*

(From the *Transactions of the Connecticut Academy of Arts and Sciences*, III, pp. 108–24, 140–52 (1875–8)).

The comprehension of the laws which govern any material system is greatly facilitated by considering the energy and entropy of the system in the various states of which it is capable. As the difference of the values of the energy for

* *Pogg. Ann.* Bd. cxxv (1865), S. 400; or *Mechanische Wärmetheorie*, Abhand. ix., S. 44.

any two states represents the combined amount of work and heat received or yielded by the system when it is brought from one state to the other, and the difference of entropy is the limit of all the possible values of the integral $\int \frac{dQ}{t}$, (dQ denoting the element of the heat received from external sources, and t the temperature of the part of the system receiving it,) the varying values of the energy and entropy characterize in all that is essential the effects producible by the system in passing from one state to another. For by mechanical and thermodynamic contrivances, supposed theoretically perfect, any supply of work and heat may be transformed into any other which does not differ from it either in the amount of work and heat taken together or in the value of the integral $\int \frac{dQ}{t}$. But it is not only in respect to the external relations of a system that its energy and entropy are of predominant importance. As in the case of simply mechanical systems, (such as are discussed in theoretical mechanics,) which are capable of only one kind of action upon external systems, viz., the performance of mechanical work, the function which expresses the capability of the system for this kind of action also plays the leading part in the theory of equilibrium, the condition of equilibrium being that the variation of this function shall vanish, so in a thermodynamic system, (such as all material systems actually are,) which is capable of two different kinds of action upon external systems, the two functions which express the twofold capabilities of the system afford an almost equally simple criterion of equilibrium.

CRITERIA OF EQUILIBRIUM AND STABILITY.

The criterion of equilibrium for a material system which is isolated from all external influences may be expressed in either of the following entirely equivalent forms:

I. *For the equilibrium of any isolated system it is necessary and sufficient that in all possible variations of the state of the system which do not alter its energy, the variation of its entropy shall either vanish or be negative.* If ε denotes the energy, and η the entropy of the system, and we use a subscript letter after a variation to indicate a quantity of which the value is not to be varied, the condition of equilibrium may be written

$$(d\eta)_{\varepsilon} \leqq 0. \tag{1}$$

II. *For the equilibrium of any isolated system it is necessary and sufficient that in all possible variations in the state of the system which do not alter its entropy, the variation of its energy shall either vanish or be positive.* This condition may be written

$$(\delta\varepsilon)_{\eta} \geqq 0. \tag{2}$$

That these two theorems are equivalent will appear from the consideration that it is always possible to increase both the energy and the entropy of the system, or to decrease both together, viz., by imparting heat to any part of the system or by taking it away. For, if condition (1) is not satisfied, there must be some variation in the state of the system for which

$$\delta\eta > 0 \quad \text{and} \quad \delta\varepsilon = 0;$$

therefore, by diminishing both the energy and the entropy of the system *in its varied state*, we shall obtain a state for which (considered as a variation from the original state)

$$\delta\eta = 0 \quad \text{and} \quad \delta\varepsilon < 0;$$

therefore condition (2) is not satisfied. Conversely, if condition (2) is not satisfied, there must be a variation in the state of the system for which

$$\delta\varepsilon < 0 \quad \text{and} \quad \delta\eta = 0;$$

hence there must also be one for which

$$\delta\varepsilon = 0 \quad \text{and} \quad \delta\eta > 0;$$

therefore condition (1) is not satisfied.

The equations which express the condition of equilibrium, as also its statement in words, are to be interpreted in accordance with the general usage in respect to differential equations, that is, infinitesimals of higher orders than the first relatively to those which express the amount of change of the system are to be neglected. But to distinguish the different kinds of equilibrium in respect to stability, we must have regard to the absolute values of the variations. We will use Δ as the sign of variation in those equations which are to be construed *strictly*, i.e., in which infinitesimals of the higher orders are not to be neglected. With this understanding, we may express the necessary and sufficient conditions of the different kinds of equilibrium as follows;—for stable equilibrium

$$(\Delta\eta)_\varepsilon < 0, \quad \text{i.e.,} \quad (\Delta\varepsilon)_\eta > 0; \tag{3}$$

for neutral equilibrium there must be some variations in the state of the system for which

$$(\Delta\eta)_\varepsilon = 0, \quad \text{i.e.,} \quad (\Delta\varepsilon)_\eta = 0, \tag{4}$$

while in general

$$(\Delta\eta)_\varepsilon \leqq 0, \quad \text{i.e.,} \quad (\Delta\varepsilon)_\eta \geqq 0; \tag{5}$$

and for unstable equilibrium there must be some variations for which

$$(\Delta\eta)_\varepsilon > 0, \tag{6}$$

$$(\Delta \varepsilon)_\eta < 0, \tag{7}$$

while in general

$$(\delta \eta)_\varepsilon \leqq 0, \quad \text{i.e.,} \quad (\delta \varepsilon)_\eta \geqq 0. \tag{8}$$

In these criteria of equilibrium and stability, account is taken only of *possible* variations. It is necessary to explain in what sense this is to be understood. In the first place, all variations in the state of the system which involve the transportation of any matter through any finite distance are of course to be excluded from consideration, although they may be capable of expression by infinitesimal variations of quantities which perfectly determine the state of the system. For example, if the system contains two masses of the same substance, not in contact, nor connected by other masses consisting of or containing the same substance or its components, an infinitesimal increase of the one mass with an equal decrease of the other is not to be considered as a possible variation in the state of the system. In addition to such cases of essential impossibility, if heat can pass by conduction or radiation from every part of the system to every other, only those variations are to be rejected as impossible, which involve changes which are prevented by passive forces or analogous resistances to change. But, if the system consist of parts between which there is supposed to be no thermal communication, it will be necessary to regard as impossible any diminution of the entropy of any of these parts, as such a change can not take place without the passage of heat. This limitation may most conveniently be applied to the second of the above forms of the condition of equilibrium, which will then become

$$(\delta \varepsilon)_{\eta', \eta'', \text{etc.}} \geqq 0, \tag{9}$$

η', η'', etc., denoting the entropies of the various parts between which there is no communication of heat. When the condition of equilibrium is thus expressed, the limitation in respect to the conduction of heat will need no further consideration.

In order to apply to any system the criteria of equilibrium which have been given, a knowledge is requisite of its passive forces or resistances to change, in so far, at least, as they are capable of *preventing* change. (Those passive forces which only retard change, like viscosity, need not be considered.) Such properties of a system are in general easily recognized upon the most superficial knowledge of its nature. As examples, we may instance the passive force of friction which prevents sliding when two surfaces of solids are pressed together,—that which prevents the different components of a solid, and sometimes of a fluid, from having different motions one from another,—that resistance to change which sometimes prevents either of two forms of the same substance (simple or compound), which are capable of existing, from passing into the other,—that which prevents the changes in solids which imply plasticity, (in other words, changes of the form to which the solid tends to return), when the deformation does not exceed certain limits.

It is a characteristic of all these passive resistances that they prevent a certain kind of motion or change, however the initial state of the system may be modified, and to whatever external agencies of force and heat it may be subjected, within limits, it may be, but yet within limits which allow finite variations in the values of all the quantities which express the initial state of the system or the mechanical or thermal influences acting on it, without producing the change in question. The equilibrium which is due to such passive properties is thus widely distinguished from that caused by the balance of the active tendencies of the system, where an external influence, or a change in the initial state, infinitesimal in amount, is sufficient to produce change either in the positive or negative direction. Hence the ease with which these passive resistances are recognized. Only in the case that the state of the system lies so near the limit at which the resistances cease to be operative to prevent change, as to create a doubt whether the case falls within or without the limit, will a more accurate knowledge of these resistances be necessary.

To establish the validity of the criterion of equilibrium, we will consider first the sufficiency, and afterwards the necessity, of the condition as expressed in either of the two equivalent forms.

In the first place, if the system is in a state in which its entropy is greater than in any other state of the same energy, it is evidently in equilibrium, as any change of state must involve either a decrease of entropy or an increase of energy, which are alike impossible for an isolated system. We may add that this is a case of *stable* equilibrium, as no infinitely small cause (whether relating to a variation of the initial state or to the action of any external bodies) can produce a finite change of state, as this would involve a finite decrease of entropy or increase of energy.

We will next suppose that the system has the greatest entropy consistent with its energy, and therefore the least energy consistent with its entropy, but that there are other states of the same energy and entropy as its actual state. In this case, it is impossible that any motion of masses should take place; for if any of the energy of the system should come to consist of *vis viva* (of sensible motions), a state of the system identical in other respects but without the motion would have less energy and not less entropy, which would be contrary to the supposition. (But we cannot apply this reasoning to the motion within any mass of its different components in different directions, as in diffusion, when the momenta of the components balance one another.) Nor, in the case supposed, can any conduction of heat take place, for this involves an increase of entropy, as heat is only conducted from bodies of higher to those of lower temperature. It is equally impossible that any changes should be produced by the transfer of heat by radiation. The condition which we have supposed is therefore sufficient for equilibrium, so far as the motion of masses and the transfer of heat are concerned, but to show that the same is true in regard to the motions of diffusion and chemical or molecular changes, when these can occur without being accompanied or followed by the motions of masses or the transfer of heat, we must have recourse to considerations of a more general nature. The following considerations seem to justify the belief that the condition is sufficient for equilibrium in every respect.

Let us suppose, in order to test the tenability of such a hypothesis, that a system may have the greatest entropy consistent with its energy without being in equilibrium. In such a case, changes in the state of the system must take place, but these will necessarily be such that the energy and the entropy will remain unchanged and the system will continue to satisfy the same condition, as initially, of having the greatest entropy consistent with its energy. Let us consider the change which takes place in any time so short that the change may be regarded as uniform in nature throughout that time. This time must be so chosen that the change does not take place in it infinitely slowly, which is always easy, as the change which we suppose to take place cannot be infinitely slow except at particular moments. Now no change whatever in the state of the system, which does not alter the value of the energy, and which commences with the same state in which the system was supposed at the commencement of the short time considered, will cause an increase of entropy. Hence, it will generally be possible by some slight variation in the circumstances of the case to make all changes in the state of the system like or nearly like that which is supposed actually to occur, and not involving a change of energy, to involve a necessary decrease of entropy, which would render any such change impossible. This variation may be in the values of the variables which determine the state of the system, or in the values of the constants which determine the nature of the system, or in the form of the functions which express its laws,—only there must be nothing in the system as modified which is thermodynamically impossible. For example, we might suppose temperature or pressure to be varied, or the composition of the different bodies in the system, or, if no small variations which could be actually realized would produce the required result, we might suppose the properties themselves of the substances to undergo variation, subject to the general laws of matter. If, then, there is any tendency toward change in the system as first supposed, it is a tendency which can be entirely checked by an infinitesimal variation in the circumstances of the case. As this supposition cannot be allowed, we must believe that a system is always in equilibrium when it has the greatest entropy consistent with its energy, or, in other words, when it has the least energy consistent with its entropy.

The same considerations will evidently apply to any case in which a system is in such a state that $\Delta\eta \leqq 0$ for any possible infinitesimal variation of the state for which $\Delta\varepsilon = 0$, even if the entropy is not the least of which the system is capable with the same energy. (The term *possible* has here the meaning previously defined, and the character Δ is used, as before, to denote that the equations are to be construed strictly, i.e., without neglect of the infinitesimals of the higher orders.)

The only case in which the sufficiency of the condition of equilibrium which has been given remains to be proved is that in which in our notation $\delta \eta \leqq 0$ for all possible variations not affecting the energy, but for some of these variations $\Delta \eta > 0$, that is, when the entropy has in some respects the characteristics of a minimum. In this case the considerations adduced in the last paragraph will not apply without modification, as the change of state may be infinitely slow at first, and it is only in the initial state that the condition $\delta \eta_\varepsilon \leqq 0$ holds true. But the differential coefficients of all orders of the quantities which determine the state of the system, taken with respect of the time, must be functions of these same quantities. None of these differential coefficients can have any value other than 0, for the state of the system for which $\delta \eta_\varepsilon \leqq 0$. For otherwise, as it would generally be possible, as before, by some infinitely small modification of the case, to render impossible any change like or nearly like that which might be supposed to occur, this infinitely small modification of the case would make a finite difference in the value of the differential coefficients which had before the finite values, or in some of lower orders, which is contrary to that continuity which we have reason to expect. Such considerations seem to justify us in regarding such a state as we are discussing as one of theoretical equilibrium; although as the equilibrium is evidently unstable, it cannot be realized.

We have still to prove that the condition enunciated is in every case necessary for equilibrium. It is evidently so in all cases in which the active tendencies of the system are so balanced that changes of every kind, except those excluded in the statement of the condition of equilibrium, can take place *reversibly*, (i.e., both in the positive and the negative direction), in states of the system differing infinitely little from the state in question. In this case, we may omit the sign of inequality and write as the condition of such a state of equilibrium

$$(\delta \eta)_\varepsilon = 0, \quad \text{i.e.,} \quad (\delta \varepsilon)_\eta = 0. \tag{10}$$

But to prove that the condition previously enunciated is in every case necessary, it must be shown that whenever an isolated system remains without change, if there is any infinitesimal variation in its state, not involving a finite change of position of any (even an infinitesimal part) of its matter, which would diminish its energy by a quantity which is not infinitely small relatively to the variations of the quantities which determine the state of the system, without altering its entropy,—or, if the system has thermally isolated parts, without altering the entropy of any such part,—this variation involves changes in the system which are prevented by its passive forces or analogous resistances to change. Now, as the described variation in the state of the system diminishes its energy without altering its entropy, it must be regarded as theoretically possible to produce that variation by some process, perhaps a very indirect one, so as to gain a certain amount of work (above all expended on the system). Hence we may conclude that the active forces or tendencies of the system favor the variation in question, and that equilibrium cannot subsist unless the variation is prevented by passive forces.

The preceding considerations will suffice, it is believed, to establish the validity of the criterion of equilibrium which has been given. The criteria of stability may readily be deduced from that of equilibrium. We will now proceed to apply these principles to systems consisting of heterogeneous substances and deduce the special laws which apply to different classes of phenomena. For this purpose we shall use the second form of the criterion of equilibrium, both because it admits more readily the introduction of the condition that there shall be no thermal communication between the different parts of the system, and because it is more convenient, as respects the form of the general equations relating to equilibrium, to make the entropy one of the independent variables which determine the state of the system, than to make the energy one of these variables.

THE CONDITIONS OF EQUILIBRIUM FOR HETEROGENEOUS MASSES IN CONTACT WHEN UNINFLUENCED BY GRAVITY, ELECTRICITY, DISTORTION OF THE SOLID MASSES, OR CAPILLARY TENSIONS.

In order to arrive as directly as possible at the most characteristic and essential laws of chemical equilibrium, we will first give our attention to a case of the simplest kind. We will examine the conditions of equilibrium of a mass of matter of various kinds enclosed in a rigid and fixed envelop, which is impermeable to and unalterable by any of the substances enclosed, and perfectly non-conducting to heat. We will suppose that the case is not complicated by the action of gravity, or by any electrical influences, and that in the solid portions of the mass the pressure is the same in every direction. We will farther simplify the problem by supposing that the variations of the parts of the energy and entropy which depend upon the surfaces separating heterogeneous masses are so small in comparison with the variations of the parts of the energy and entropy which depend upon the quantities of these masses, that the former may be neglected by the side of the latter; in other words, we will exclude the considerations which belong to the theory of capillarity.

It will be observed that the supposition of a rigid and nonconducting envelop enclosing the mass under discussion involves no real loss of generality, for if any mass of matter is in equilibrium, it would also be so, if the whole or any part of it were enclosed in an envelop as supposed; therefore the conditions of equilibrium for a mass thus enclosed are the general conditions which must always be satisfied in case of equilibrium. As for the other suppositions which have been made, all the circumstances and considerations which are here excluded will afterward be made the subject of special discussion.

Conditions relating to the Equilibrium between the initially existing Homogeneous Parts of the given Mass.

Let us first consider the energy of any homogeneous part of the given mass, and its variation for any possible variation in the composition and state of this part. (By *homogeneous* is meant that the part in question is uniform throughout, not only in chemical composition, but also in physical state.) If we consider the amount and kind of matter in this homogeneous mass as fixed, its energy ε is a function of its entropy η, and its volume v, and the differentials of these quantities are subject to the relation

$$d\varepsilon = t \, d\eta - p \, dv, \qquad (11)$$

t denoting the (absolute) temperature of the mass, and p its pressure. For $t \, d\eta$ is the heat received, and $p \, dv$ the work done, by the mass during its change of state. But if we consider the matter in the mass as variable, and write m_1, $m_2, \ldots m_n$ for the quantities of the various substances $S_1, S_2, \ldots S_n$ of which the mass is composed, ε will evidently be a function of $\eta, v, m_1, m_2, \ldots m_n$, and we shall have for the complete value of the differential of ε

$$d\varepsilon = t \, d\eta - p \, dv + \mu_1 \, dm_1 + \mu_2 \, dm_2 \cdots + \mu_n \, dm_n, \qquad (12)$$

$\mu_1, \mu_2, \ldots \mu_n$ denoting the differential coefficients of ε taken with respect to $m_1, m_2, \ldots m_n$.

The substances $S_1, S_2, \ldots S_n$, of which we consider the mass composed, must of course be such that the value of the differentials $dm_1, dm_2, \ldots dm_n$ shall be independent, and shall express every possible variation in the composition of the homogeneous mass considered, including those produced by the absorption of substances different from any initially present. It may therefore be necessary to have terms in the equation relating to component substances which do not initially occur in the homogeneous mass considered, provided, of course, that these substances, or their components, are to be found in some part of the whole given mass.

If the conditions mentioned are satisfied, the choice of the substances which we are to regard as the components of the mass considered, may be determined entirely by convenience, and independently of any theory in regard to the internal constitution of the mass. The number of components will sometimes be greater, and sometimes less, than the number of chemical elements present. For example, in considering the equilibrium in a vessel containing water and free hydrogen and oxygen, we should be obliged to recognize three components in the gaseous part. But in considering the equilibrium of dilute sulphuric acid with the vapor which it yields, we should have only two components to consider in the liquid mass, sulphuric acid (anhydrous, or of any particular degree of concentration) and (additional) water. If, however, we are considering sulphuric acid in a state of maximum concentration in connection with substances which might possibly afford water to the acid, it must be noticed that the condition of the independence of the differentials will require that we consider the acid in the state of maximum concentration as one of the components. The quantity of this component will then be capable of variation both in the positive and in the negative sense, while the quantity of the other component can increase but cannot decrease below the value 0.

For brevity's sake, we may call a substance S_a an *actual component* of any homogeneous mass, to denote that the quantity m_a of that substance in the given mass may be either increased or diminished (although we may have so chosen the other component substances that $m_a = 0$); and we may call a substance S_b a *possible component* to denote that it may be combined with, but cannot be subtracted from the homogeneous mass in question. In this case, as we have seen in the above example, we must so choose the component substances that $m_b = 0$.

The units by which we measure the substances of which we regard the given mass as composed may each be chosen independently. To fix our ideas for the purpose of a general discussion, we may suppose all substances measured by weight or mass. Yet in special cases, it may be more convenient to adopt chemical equivalents as the units of the component substances.

It may be observed that it is not necessary for the validity of equation (12) that the variations of nature and state of the mass to which the equation refers should be such as do not disturb its homogeneity, provided that in all parts of the mass the variations of nature and state are infinitely small. For, if this last condition be not violated, an equation like (12) is certainly valid for all the infinitesimal parts of the (initially) homogeneous mass; i.e., if we write $D\varepsilon$, $D\eta$, etc., for the energy, entropy, etc., of any infinitesimal part,

$$dD\varepsilon = t \, dD\eta - p \, dDv + \mu_1 \, dDm_1 + \mu_2 \, dDm_2 \cdots + \mu_n \, dDm_n, \quad (13)$$

whence we may derive equation (12) by integrating for the whole initially homogeneous mass.

We will now suppose that the whole mass is divided into parts so that each part is homogeneous, and consider such variations in the energy of the system as are due to variations in the composition and state of the several parts remaining (at least approximately) homogeneous, and together occupying the whole space within the envelop. We will at first suppose the case to be such that the component substances are the same for each of the parts, each of the substances $S_1, S_2, \ldots S_n$ being an actual component of each part. If we distinguish the letters referring to the different parts by accents, the variation in the energy of the system may be expressed by $\delta\varepsilon' + \delta\varepsilon'' +$ etc., and the general condition of equilibrium requires that

$$\delta\varepsilon' + \delta\varepsilon'' + \text{etc.} \geqq 0 \quad (14)$$

for all variations which do not conflict with the *equations of condition*. These equations must express that the entropy of the whole given mass does not vary, nor its volume, nor the total quantities of any of the substances S_1, $S_2, \ldots S_n$. We will suppose that there are no other equations of condition. It will then be necessary for equilibrium that

$$t' \, \delta\eta' - p' \, \delta v' + \mu_1' \, \delta m_1' + \mu_2' \, \delta m_2' \cdots + \mu_n' \, \delta m_n'$$
$$+ t'' \, \delta\eta'' - p'' \, \delta v'' + \mu_1'' \, \delta m_1'' + \mu_2'' \, \delta m_2'' \cdots + \mu_n'' \, \delta m_n''$$
$$+ \text{etc.} \geqq 0 \tag{15}$$

for any values of the variations for which

$$\delta\eta' + \delta\eta'' + \delta\eta''' + \text{etc.} = 0, \tag{16}$$

$$\delta v' + \delta v'' + \delta v''' + \text{etc.} = 0, \tag{17}$$

$$\left. \begin{array}{l} \delta m_1' + \delta m_1'' + \delta m_1''' + \text{etc.} = 0, \\ \delta m_2' + \delta m_2'' + \delta m_2''' + \text{etc.} = 0, \\ \cdot \quad \cdot \quad \cdot \quad \cdot \quad \cdot \\ \delta m_n' + \delta m_n'' + \delta m_n''' + \text{etc.} = 0. \end{array} \right\} \tag{18}$$

and

For this it is evidently necessary and sufficient that

$$t' = t'' = t''' = \text{etc.} \tag{19}$$

$$p' = p'' = p''' = \text{etc.} \tag{20}$$

$$\left. \begin{array}{l} \mu_1' = \mu_1'' = \mu_1''' = \text{etc.} \\ \mu_2' = \mu_2'' = \mu_2''' = \text{etc.} \\ \cdot \quad \cdot \quad \cdot \quad \cdot \\ \mu_n' = \mu_n'' = \mu_n''' = \text{etc.} \end{array} \right\} \tag{21}$$

Equations (19) and (20) express the conditions of thermal and mechanical equilibrium, viz., that the temperature and the pressure must be constant throughout the whole mass. In equations (21) we have the conditions characteristic of chemical equilibrium. If we call a quantity μ_x, as defined by such an equation as (12), the *potential* for the substance S_z in the homogeneous mass considered, these conditions may be expressed as follows:

The potential for each component substance must be constant throughout the whole mass.

It will be remembered that we have supposed that there is no restriction upon the freedom of motion or combination of the component substances, and that each is an actual component of all parts of the given mass.

The state of the whole mass will be completely determined (if we regard as immaterial the position and form of the various homogeneous parts of which it is composed), when the values are determined of the quantities of which the variations occur in (15). The number of these quantities, which we may call the independent variables, is evidently $(n + 2)v$, v denoting the number of homogeneous parts into which the whole mass is divided. All the quantities which occur in (19), (20), (21), are functions of these variables, and may be regarded as known functions, if the energy of each part is known as a function of its entropy, volume, and the quantities of its components. (See eq. (12).) Therefore, equations (19), (20), (21), may be regarded as $(v - 1)$ $(n + 2)$ independent equations between the independent variables. The volume of the whole mass and the total quantities of the various substances being known afford $n + 1$ additional equations. If we also know the total energy of the given mass, or its total entropy, we will have as many equations as there are independent variables.

But if any of the substances S_1, $S_1 \cdots S_n$ are only possible components of some parts of the given mass, the variation δm of the quantity of such a substance in such a part cannot have a negative value, so that the general condition of equilibrium (15) does not require that the potential for that substance in that part should be equal to the potential for the same substance in the parts of which it is an actual component, but only that it shall not be less. In this case instead of (21) we may write

$$\mu_1 = M_1$$

for all parts of which S_1 is an actual component, and

$$\mu_1 \geqq M_1$$

for all parts of which S_1 is a possible (but not actual) component,

$$\mu_2 = M_2 \tag{22}$$

for all parts of which S_2 is an actual component, and

$$\mu_2 \geqq M_2$$

for all parts of which S_2 is a possible (but not actual) component,

etc.,

M_1, M_2, etc., denoting constants of which the value is only determined by these equations.

If we now suppose that the components (actual or possible) of the various homogeneous parts of the given mass are not the same, the result will be of the same character as before, provided that all the different components are *independent*, (i.e., that no one can be made out of the others); so that the total quantity of each component is fixed. The general condition of equilibrium (15) and the equations of condition (16), (17), (18) will require no change, except that, if any of the substances S_1, $S_2 \cdots S_n$ is not a component (actual or possible) of any part, the term $\mu \, \delta m$ for that substance and part will be wanting in the former, and the δm in the latter. This will require no change in the form of the particular conditions of equilibrium as expressed by (19), (20), (22); but the number of single conditions contained in (22) is of course less than if all the component substances were components of all the parts.

Whenever, therefore, each of the different homogeneous parts of the given mass may be regarded as composed of some or of all of the same set of substances, no one of which can be formed out of the others, the condition which (with equality of temperature and pressure) is necessary and sufficient for equilibrium between the different parts of the given mass may be expressed as follows:

The potential for each of the component substances must have a constant value in all parts of the given mass of which that substance is an actual component, and have a value not less than this in all parts of which it is a possible component.

The number of *equations* afforded by these conditions, after elimination of $M_1, M_2, \ldots M_n$, will be less than $(n + 2)(v - 1)$ by the number of terms in (15) in which the variation of the form δm is either necessarily nothing or incapable of a negative value. The number of variables to be determined is diminished by the same number, or, if we choose, we may write an equation of the form $m = 0$ for each of these terms. But when the substance is a possible component of the part concerned, there will also be a condition (expressed by $\geqq$) to show whether the supposition that the substance is not an actual component is consistent with equilibrium.

We will now suppose that the substances $S_1, S_2, \ldots S_n$ are not all independent of each other, i.e., that some of them can be formed out of others. We will first consider a very simple case. Let S_3 be composed of S_1 and S_2 combined in the ratio of a to b, S_1 and S_2 occurring as actual components in some parts of the given mass, and S_3 in other parts, which do not contain S_1 and S_2 as separately variable components. The general condition of equilibrium will still have the form of (15) with certain of the terms of the form $\mu\,\delta m$ omitted. It may be written more briefly

$$\sum (t\,\delta\eta) - \sum (p\,\delta v) + \sum (\mu_1\,\delta m_1) + \sum (\mu_2\,\delta m_2) \cdots + \sum (\mu_n\,\delta m_n) \geqq 0,$$

(23)

the sign $\sum$ denoting summation in regard to the different parts of the given mass. But instead of the three equations of condition,

$$\sum \delta m_1 = 0, \quad \sum \delta m_2 = 0, \quad \sum \delta m_3 = 0,$$

(24)

we shall have the two,

$$\left.\begin{aligned}
\sum \delta m_1 + \frac{a}{a + b}\sum \delta m_3 = 0,\\
\sum \delta m_2 + \frac{b}{a + b}\sum \delta m_3 = 0.
\end{aligned}\right\}$$

(25)

The other equations of condition,

$$\sum \delta\eta = 0, \quad \sum \delta v = 0, \quad \sum \delta m_4 = 0, \quad \text{etc.,}$$

(26)

will remain unchanged. Now as all values of the variations which satisfy equations (24) will also satisfy equations (25), it is evident that all the particular conditions of equilibrium which we have already deduced, (19), (20), (22), are necessary in this case also. When these are satisfied, the general condition (23) reduces to

$$M_1 \sum \delta m_1 + M_2 \sum \delta m_2 + M_3 \sum \delta m_3 \geqq 0. \tag{27}$$

For, although it may be that $\mu_1{}'$, for example, is greater than M_1, yet it can only be so when the following $\delta m_1{}'$ is incapable of a negative value. Hence, if (27) is satisfied, (23) must also be. Again, if (23) is satisfied, (27) must also be satisfied, so long as the variation of the quantity of every substance has the value 0 in all the parts of which it is not an actual component. But as this limitation does not affect the range of the possible values of $\sum \delta m_1$, $\sum \delta m_2$, and $\sum \delta m_3$, it may be disregarded. Therefore the conditions (23) and (27) are entirely equivalent, when (19), (20), (22) are satisfied. Now, by means of the equations of condition (25), we may eliminate $\sum \delta m_1$ and $\sum \delta m_2$ from (27), which becomes

$$- aM_1 \sum \delta m_3 - bM_2 \sum \delta m_3 + (a + b)M_3 \sum \delta m_3 \geqq 0, \tag{28}$$

i.e., as the value of $\sum \delta m_3$ may be either positive or negative,

$$aM_1 + bM_2 = (a + b)M_3, \tag{29}$$

which is the additional condition of equilibrium which is necessary in this case.

The relations between the component substances may be less simple than in this case, but in any case they will only affect the equations of condition, and these may always be found without difficulty, and will enable us to eliminate from the general condition of equilibrium as many variations as there are equations of condition, after which the coefficients of the remaining variations may be set equal to zero, except the coefficients of variations which are incapable of negative values, which coefficients must be equal to or greater than zero. It will be easy to perform these operations in each particular case, but it may be interesting to see the form of the resultant equations in general.

We will suppose that the various homogeneous parts are considered as having in all n components, $S_1, S_2, \ldots S_n$, and that there is no restriction upon their freedom of motion and combination. But we will so far limit the generality of the problem as to suppose that each of these components is an actual component of some part of the given mass.* If some of these

---

* When we come to seek the conditions of equilibrium relating to the formation of masses unlike any previously existing, we shall take up *de novo* the whole problem of the equilibrium of heterogeneous masses enclosed in a non-conducting envelop, and give it a more general treatment, which will be free from this limitation.

components can be formed out of others, all such relations can be expressed by equations such as

$$\alpha \mathfrak{S}_a + \beta \mathfrak{S}_b + \text{etc.} = \kappa \mathfrak{S}_k + \lambda \mathfrak{S}_l + \text{etc.} \tag{30}$$

where $\mathfrak{S}_a$, $\mathfrak{S}_b$, $\mathfrak{S}_k$, etc. denote the units of the substances S_a, S_b, S_k, etc., (that is, of certain of the substances $S_1, S_2, \ldots S_n,$) and α, β, κ, etc. denote numbers. These are not, it will be observed, equations between abstract quantities, but the sign $=$ denotes qualitative as well as quantitative equivalence. We will suppose that there are r independent equations of this character. The equations of condition relating to the component substances may easily be derived from these equations, but it will not be necessary to consider them particularly. It is evident that they will be satisfied by any values of the variations which satisfy equations (18); hence, the particular conditions of equilibrium (19), (20), (22) must be necessary in this case, and, if these are satisfied, the general equation of equilibrium (15) or (23) will reduce to

$$M_1 \sum \delta m_1 + M_2 \sum \delta m_2 \cdots + M_n \sum \delta m_n \geqq 0. \tag{31}$$

This will appear from the same considerations which were used in regard to equations (23) and (27). Now it is evidently possible to give to $\Sigma \ \delta m_a$, $\Sigma \ \delta m_b$, $\Sigma \ \delta m_k$, etc. values proportional to α, β, $-\kappa$, etc. in equation (30), and also the same values taken negatively, making $\Sigma \ \delta m = 0$ in each of the other terms; therefore

$$\alpha M_a + \beta M_b + \text{etc.} \cdots - \kappa M_k - \lambda M_l - \text{etc.} = 0, \tag{32}$$

or,

$$\alpha M_a + \beta M_b + \text{etc.} = \kappa M_k + \lambda M_l + \text{etc.} \tag{33}$$

It will be observed that this equation has the same form and coefficients as equation (30), M taking the place of $\mathfrak{S}$. It is evident that there must be a similar condition of equilibrium for every one of the r equations of which (30) is an example, which may be obtained simply by changing $\mathfrak{S}$ in these equations into M. When these conditions are satisfied, (31) will be satisfied with any possible values of $\Sigma \ \delta m_1, \Sigma \ \delta m_2, \cdots \Sigma \ \delta m_n$. For no values of these quantities are possible, except such that the equation

$$(\sum \delta m_1)\mathfrak{S}_1 + (\sum \delta m_2)\mathfrak{S}_2 \cdots + (\sum \delta m_n)\mathfrak{S}_n = 0 \tag{34}$$

after the substitution of these values, can be derived from the r equations like (30), by the ordinary processes of the reduction of linear equations. Therefore, on account of the correspondence between (31) and (34), and between the r equations like (33) and the r equations like (30), the conditions obtained by giving any possible values to the variations in (31) may also be derived from the r equations like (33); that is, the condition (31) is satisfied, if the r equations like (33) are satisfied. Therefore the r equations like (33) are with (19), (20), and (22) the equivalent of the general condition (15) or (23).

For determining the state of a given mass when in equilibrium and having a given volume and given energy or entropy, the condition of equilibrium affords an additional equation corresponding to each of the r independent relations between the n component substances. But the equations which express our knowledge of the matter in the given mass will be correspondingly diminished, being $n - r$ in number, like the equations of condition relating to the quantities of the component substances, which may be derived from the former by differentiation. . . .

DEFINITION AND PROPERTIES OF FUNDAMENTAL EQUATIONS.

The solution of the problems of equilibrium which we have been considering has been made to depend upon the equations which express the relations between the energy, entropy, volume, and the quantities of the various components, for homogeneous combinations of the substances which are found in the given mass. The nature of such equations must be determined by experiment. As, however, it is only *differences* of energy and of entropy that can be measured, or indeed, that have a physical meaning, the values of these quantities are so far arbitrary, that we may choose independently for each simple substance the state in which its energy and its entropy are both zero. The values of the energy and the entropy of any compound body in any particular state will then be fixed. Its energy will be the sum of the work and heat expended in bringing its components from the states in which their energies and their entropies are zero into combination and to the state in question; and its entropy is the value of the integral $\int \dfrac{dQ}{t}$ for any *reversible* process by which that change is effected (dQ denoting an element of the heat communicated to the matter thus treated, and t the temperature of the matter receiving it). In the determination both of the energy and of the entropy, it is understood that at the close of the process, all bodies which have been used, other than those to which the determinations relate, have been restored to their original state, with the exception of the sources of the work and heat expended, which must be used only as such sources.

We know, however, *a priori*, that if the quantity of any homogeneous mass containing n independently variable components varies and not its nature or state, the quantities ε, η, v, m_1, m_2, . . . m_n will all vary in the same proportion; therefore it is sufficient if we learn from experiment the relation between all but any one of these quantities for a given constant value of that one. Or, we may consider that we have to learn from experiment the relation subsisting between the $n + 2$ ratios of the $n + 3$ quantities ε, η, v, m_1, m_2, . . . m_n. To fix our ideas we may take for these ratios $\dfrac{\varepsilon}{v}$, $\dfrac{\eta}{v}$, $\dfrac{m_1}{v}$, $\dfrac{m_2}{v}$, etc., that is, the separate densities of the components, and the ratios $\dfrac{\varepsilon}{v}$ and $\dfrac{\eta}{v}$, which may be called the *densities of energy and entropy*. But when there is but one component, it may be more convenient to choose $\dfrac{\varepsilon}{m}, \dfrac{\eta}{m}, \dfrac{v}{m}$ as the three variables. In any case, it is only a function of $n + 1$ independent variables, of which the form is to be determined by experiment.

Now if ε is a known function of $\eta, v, m_1, m_2, \ldots m_n$, as by equation (12)

$$d\varepsilon = t\, d\eta - p\, dv + \mu_1\, dm_1 + \mu_2\, dm_2 \cdots + \mu_n\, dm_n, \qquad (86)$$

$t, p, \mu_1, \mu_2, \ldots \mu_n$ are functions of the same variables, which may be derived from the original function by differentiation, and may therefore be considered as known functions. This will make $n + 3$ independent known relations between the $2n + 5$ variables, $\varepsilon, \eta, v, m_1, m_2, \ldots m_n, t, p, \mu_1, \mu_2, \ldots \mu_n$. These are all that exist, for of these variables, $n + 2$ are evidently independent. Now upon these relations depend a very large class of the properties of the compound considered,—we may say in general, all its thermal, mechanical, and chemical properties, so far as *active tendencies* are concerned, in cases in which the form of the mass does not require consideration. A single equation from which all these relations may be deduced we will call a *fundamental equation* for the substance in question. We shall hereafter consider a more general form of the fundamental equation for solids, in which the pressure at any point is not supposed to be the same in all directions. But for masses subject only to isotropic stresses an equation between $\varepsilon, \eta, v, m_1, m_2, \ldots m_n$ is a fundamental equation. There are other equations which possess this same property.*

Let

$$\psi = \varepsilon - t\eta, \qquad (87)$$

then by differentiation and comparison with (86) we obtain

$$d\psi = -\eta\, dt - p\, dv + \mu_1\, dm_1 + m_2\, dm_2 \cdots + \mu_n\, dm_n. \qquad (88)$$

* M. Massieu (*Comptes Rendus*, T. lxix, 1869, p. 858 and p. 1057) has shown how all the properties of a fluid "which are considered in thermodynamics" may be deduced from a single function, which he calls a characteristic function of the fluid considered. In the papers cited, he introduces two different functions of this kind; viz., a function of the temperature and volume, which he denotes by ψ, the value of which in our notation would be $\dfrac{-\varepsilon + t\eta}{t}$ or $\dfrac{-\psi}{t}$; and a function of the temperature and pressure, which he denotes by ψ', the value of which in our notation would be $\dfrac{-\epsilon + t\eta - pv}{t}$ or $\dfrac{-\zeta}{t}$. In both cases he considers a constant quantity (one kilogram) of the fluid, which is regarded as invariable in composition.

If, then, ψ is known as a function of t, v, m_1, m_2, ... m_n, we can find η, p, μ_1, μ_2, ... μ_n in terms of the same variables. If we then substitute for ψ in our original equation its value taken from eq. (87), we shall have again $n + 3$ independent relations between the same $2n + 5$ variables as before.

Let
$$\chi = \varepsilon + pv, \tag{89}$$
then by (86),
$$d\chi = t\,d\eta + v\,dp + \mu_1\,dm_1 + \mu_2\,dm_2 \cdots + \mu_n\,dm_n. \tag{90}$$

If, then, χ be known as a function of η, p, m_1, m_2, ... m_n, we can find t, v, μ_1, μ_2, ... μ_n in terms of the same variables. By eliminating χ, we may obtain again $n + 3$ independent relations between the same $2n + 5$ variables as at first.

Let
$$\zeta = \varepsilon - t\eta + pv, \tag{91}$$
then, by (86)
$$d\zeta = -\eta\,dt + v\,dp + \mu_1\,dm_1 + \mu_2\,dm_2 \cdots + \mu_n\,dm_n. \tag{92}$$

If, then, ζ is known as a function of t, p, m_1, m_2, ... m_n, we can find η, v, μ_1, μ_2, ... μ_n in terms of the same variables. By eliminating ζ, we may obtain again $n + 3$ independent relations between the same $2n + 5$ variables as at first.

If we integrate (86), supposing the quantity of the compound substance considered to vary from zero to any finite value, its nature and state remaining unchanged, we obtain

$$\varepsilon = t\eta - pv + \mu_1 m_1 + \mu_2 m_2 \cdots + \mu_n m_n, \tag{93}$$

and by (87), (89), (91)

$$\psi = -pv + \mu_1 m_1 + \mu_2 m_2 \cdots + \mu_n m_n, \tag{94}$$
$$\chi = t\eta + \mu_1 m_1 + \mu_2 m_2 \cdots + \mu_n m_n, \tag{95}$$
$$\zeta = \mu_1 m_1 + \mu_2 m_2 \cdots + \mu_n m_n. \tag{96}$$

The last three equations may also be obtained directly by integrating (88), (90), and (92).

If we differentiate (93) in the most general manner, and compare the result with (86), we obtain

$$-v\,dp + \eta\,dt + m_1\,d\mu_1 + m_2\,d\mu_2 \cdots + m_n\,d\mu_n = 0, \tag{97}$$

or

$$dp = \frac{\eta}{v}\,dt + \frac{m_1}{v}\,d\mu_1 + \frac{m_2}{v}\,d\mu_2 \cdots + \frac{m_n}{v}\,d\mu_n = 0. \tag{98}$$

Hence, there is a relation between the $n + 2$ quantities t, p, μ_1, μ_2, ... μ_n, which, if known, will enable us to find in terms of these quantities all the ratios of the $n + 2$ quantities $\eta, v, m_1, m_2 \cdots m_n$. With (93), this will make $n + 3$ independent relations between the same $2n + 5$ variables as at first.

Any equation, therefore, between the quantities

	ε,	η,	v,	m_1,	$m_2, \ldots m_n$,	(99)
or	ψ,	t,	v,	m_1,	$m_2, \ldots m_n$,	(100)
or	χ,	η,	p,	m_1,	$m_2, \ldots m_n$,	(101)
or	ζ,	t,	p,	m_1,	$m_2, \ldots m_n$,	(102)
or		t,	p,	μ_1,	$\mu_2, \ldots \mu_n$,	(103)

is a fundamental equation, and any such is entirely equivalent to any other.* For any homogeneous mass whatever, considered (in general) as variable in composition, in quantity, and in thermodynamic state, and having n independently variable components, to which the subscript numerals refer, (but not excluding the case in which $n = 1$ and the composition of the body is invariable,) there is a relation between the quantities enumerated in any one of the above sets, from which, if known, with the aid only of *general* principles and relations, we may deduce all the relations subsisting for such a mass between the quantities $\varepsilon, \psi, \chi, \zeta, \eta, v, m_1, m_2, \ldots m_n, t, p, \mu_1, \mu_2, \ldots \mu_n$. It will be observed that, besides the equations which define ψ, χ, and ζ, there is one finite equation, (93), which subsists between these quantities independently of the form of the fundamental equation.

---

* The distinction between equations which are, and which are not, *fundamental*, in the sense in which the word is here used, may be illustrated by comparing an equation between

$$\varepsilon, \eta, v, m_1, m_2, \ldots m_n$$

with one between

$$\varepsilon, t, v, m_1, m_2, \ldots m_n.$$

As, by (86),

$$t = \left(\frac{d\varepsilon}{d\eta}\right)_{vm},$$

the second equation may evidently be derived from the first. But the first equation cannot be derived from the second; for an equation between

$$\varepsilon, \left(\frac{d\varepsilon}{d\eta}\right)_{vm}, v, m_1, m_2, \ldots m_n$$

is equivalent to one between

$$\left(\frac{d\eta}{d\varepsilon}\right)_{vm}, \varepsilon, v, m_1, m_2, \ldots m_n,$$

which is evidently not sufficient to determine the value of η in terms of the other variables.

Other sets of quantities might of course be added which possess the same property. The sets (100), (101), (102) are mentioned on account of the important properties of the quantities ψ, χ, ζ, and because the equations (88), (90), (92), like (86), afford convenient definitions of the potentials, viz.,

$$\mu_1 = \left(\frac{d\varepsilon}{dm_1}\right)_{\eta,v,m} = \left(\frac{d\psi}{dm_1}\right)_{t,v,m} = \left(\frac{d\chi}{dm_1}\right)_{\eta,p,m} = \left(\frac{d\zeta}{dm_1}\right)_{t,p,m} \tag{104}$$

etc., where the subscript letters denote the quantities which remain constant in the differentiation, m being written for brevity for all the letters m_1, m_2, $\ldots$ m_n except the one occurring in the denominator. It will be observed that the quantities in (103) are all independent of the quantity of the mass considered, and are those which must, in general, have the same value in contiguous masses in equilibrium.

On the quantities ψ, χ, ζ.

The quantity ψ has been defined for any homogeneous mass by the equation

$$\psi = \varepsilon - t\eta. \tag{105}$$

We may extend this definition to any material system whatever which has a uniform temperature throughout.

If we compare two states of the system of the same temperature, we have

$$\psi' - \psi'' = \varepsilon' - \varepsilon'' - t(\eta' - \eta''). \tag{106}$$

If we suppose the system brought from the first to the second of these states without change of temperature and by a reversible process in which W is the work done and Q the heat received by the system, then

$$\varepsilon' - \varepsilon'' = W - Q, \tag{107}$$

and

$$t(\eta'' - \eta') = Q. \tag{108}$$

Hence

$$\psi' - \psi'' = W; \tag{109}$$

and for an infinitely small reversible change in the state of the system, in which the temperature remains constant, we may write

$$-d\psi = dW. \tag{110}$$

Therefore, $-\psi$ is the force function of the system for constant temperature, just as $-\varepsilon$ is the force function for constant entropy. That is, if we consider ψ as a function of the temperature and the variables which express the distribution of the matter in space, for every different value of the temperature $-\psi$ is the different force function required by the system if maintained at that special temperature.

5

From this we may conclude that when a system has a uniform temperature throughout, the additional conditions which are necessary and sufficient for equilibrium may be expressed by

$$(\delta\psi)_t \geqq 0.* \tag{111}$$

When it is not possible to bring the system from one to the other of the states to which ψ' and ψ'' relate by a reversible process without altering the temperature, it will be observed that it is not necessary for the validity of (107)–(109) that the temperature of the system should remain constant during the reversible process to which W and Q relate, provided that the only source of heat or cold used has the same temperature as the system in its initial or final state. Any external bodies may be used in the process in any way not affecting the condition of reversibility, if restored to their original condition at the close of the process; nor does the limitation in regard to the use of heat apply to such heat as may be restored to the source from which it has been taken.

It may be interesting to show directly the equivalence of the conditions (111) and (2) when applied to a system of which the temperature in the given state is uniform throughout.

If there are any variations in the state of such a system which do not satisfy (2), then for these variations

$$\delta\varepsilon < 0 \quad \text{and} \quad \delta\eta = 0.$$

If the temperature of the system in its varied state is not uniform, we may evidently increase its entropy without altering its energy by supposing heat to pass from the warmer to the cooler parts. And the state having the greatest entropy for the energy $\varepsilon + \delta\varepsilon$ will necessarily be a state of uniform temperature. For this state (regarded as a variation from the original state)

$$\delta\varepsilon < 0 \quad \text{and} \quad \delta\eta > 0.$$

---

* This general condition of equilibrium might be used instead of (2) in such problems of equilibrium as we have considered and others which we shall consider hereafter with evident advantage in respect to the brevity of the formulae, as the limitation expressed by the subscript t in (111) applies to every part of the system taken separately, and diminishes by one the number of independent variations in the state of these parts which we have to consider. The more cumbersome course adopted in this paper has been chosen, among other reasons, for the sake of deducing *all* the particular conditions of equilibrium from one general condition, and of having the quantities mentioned in this general condition such as are most generally used and most simply defined; and because in the longer formulae as given, the reader will easily see in each case the form which they would take if we should adopt (111) as the general condition of equilibrium, which would be in effect to take the thermal condition of equilibrium for granted, and to seek only the remaining conditions. For example, in the problem treated on pages 116 ff., we would obtain from (111) by (88)a condition precisely like (15), except that the terms $t\,\delta\eta'$, $t\,\delta\eta''$, etc. would be wanting. Hence, as we may diminish both the energy and the entropy by cooling the system, there must be a state of uniform temperature for which (regarded as a variation of the original state)

$$\delta\varepsilon < 0 \quad \text{and} \quad \delta\eta = 0.$$

From this we may conclude that for systems of initially uniform temperature condition (2) will not be altered if we limit the variations to such as do not disturb the uniformity of temperature.

Confining our attention, then, to states of uniform temperature, we have by differentiation of (105)

$$\delta\varepsilon - t\,\delta\eta = \delta\psi + \eta\,\delta t. \tag{112}$$

Now there are evidently changes in the system (produced by heating or cooling) for which

$$\delta\varepsilon - t\,\delta\eta = 0 \quad \text{and therefore} \quad \delta\psi + \eta\,\delta t = 0, \tag{113}$$

neither $\delta\eta$ nor δt having the value zero. This consideration is sufficient to show that the condition (2) is equivalent to

$$\delta\varepsilon - t\,\delta\eta \geqq 0, \tag{114}$$

and that the condition (111) is equivalent to

$$\delta\psi + \eta\,\delta t \geqq 0 \tag{115}$$

and by (112) the two last conditions are equivalent.

In such cases as we have considered [from pages 105 on], in which the form and position of the masses of which the system is composed are immaterial, uniformity of temperature and pressure are always necessary for equilibrium, and the remaining conditions, when these are satisfied, may be conveniently expressed by means of the function ζ, which has been defined for a homogeneous mass on pages 114–115, and which we will here define for any mass of uniform temperature and pressure by the same equation

$$\zeta = \varepsilon - t\eta + pv. \tag{116}$$

For such a mass, the condition of (internal) equilibrium is

$$(\delta\zeta)_{t,p} \geqq 0. \tag{117}$$

That this condition is equivalent to (2) will easily appear from considerations like those used in respect to (111).

Hence, it is necessary for the equilibrium of two contiguous masses identical in composition that the values of ζ as determined for equal quantities of the two masses should be equal. Or, when one of three contiguous masses can be formed out of the other two, it is necessary for equilibrium that the value of ζ for any quantity of the first mass should be equal to the sum of the values of ζ for such quantities of the second and third masses as together contain the same matter. Thus, for the equilibrium of a solution composed of *a* parts of water and b parts of a salt which is in contact with vapor of water and crystals of the salt, it is necessary that the value of ζ for the quantity $a + b$ of the solution should be equal to the sum of the values of ζ for the quantities a of the vapor and b of the salt. Similar propositions will hold true in more complicated cases.

In like manner we may extend the definition of χ to any mass or combination of masses in which the pressure is everywhere the same, using ε for the energy and v for the volume of the whole and setting as before

$$\chi = \varepsilon + pv. \tag{118}$$

If we denote by Q the heat received by the combined masses from external sources in any process in which the pressure is not varied and distinguish the initial and final states of the system by accents we have

$$\chi'' - \chi' = \varepsilon'' - \varepsilon' + p(v'' - v') = Q. \tag{119}$$

This function may therefore be called the *heat function for constant pressure* (just as the energy might be called the heat function for constant volume), the diminution of the function representing in all cases in which the pressure is not varied the heat given out by the system. In all cases of chemical action in which no heat is allowed to escape the value of χ remains unchanged.

POTENTIALS.

In the definition of the potentials μ_1, μ_2, etc., the energy of a homogeneous mass was considered as a function of its entropy, its volume, and the quantities of the various substances composing it. Then the potential for one of these substances was defined as the differential coefficient of the energy taken with respect to the variable expressing the quantity of that substance. Now, as the manner in which we consider the given mass as composed of various substances is in some degree arbitrary, so that the energy may be considered as a function of various different sets of variables expressing quantities of component substances, it might seem that the above definition does not fix the value of the potential of any substance in the given mass, until we have fixed the manner in which the mass is to be considered as composed. For example, if we have a solution obtained by dissolving in water a certain salt containing water of crystallization, we may consider the liquid as composed of m_S weight-units of the hydrate and m_W of water, or as composed of m_s of the anhydrous salt and m_w of water. It will be observed that the values of m_S and m_s are not the same, nor those of m_W and m_w, and hence it might seem that the potential for water in the given liquid considered as composed of the hydrate and water, viz.,

$$\left(\frac{d\varepsilon}{dm_W} \right)_{\eta, v, m_S}$$

would be different from the potential for water in the liquid considered as composed of anhydrous salt and water, viz.,

$$\left(\frac{d\varepsilon}{dm_w}\right)_{\eta,v,m_s}.$$

The value of the two expressions is, however, the same, for, although m_W is not equal to m_w, we may of course suppose dm_W to be equal to dm_w, and then the numerators in the two fractions will also be equal, as they each denote the increase of energy of the liquid, when the quantity dm_W or dm_w of water is added without altering the entropy and volume of the liquid. Precisely the same considerations will apply to any other case.

In fact, we may give a definition of a potential which shall not presuppose any choice of a particular set of substances as the components of the homogeneous mass considered.

Definition.—If to any homogeneous mass we suppose an infinitesimal quantity of any substance to be added, the mass remaining homogeneous and its entropy and volume remaining unchanged, the increase of the energy of the mass divided by the quantity of the substance added is the *potential* for that substance in the mass considered. (For the purposes of this definition, any chemical element or combination of elements in given proportions may be considered a substance, whether capable or not of existing by itself as a homogeneous body.)

In the above definition we may evidently substitute for entropy, volume, and energy, respectively, either temperature, volume, and the function ψ; or entropy, pressure, and the function χ; or temperature, pressure, and the function ζ. (Compare equation (104).)

In the same homogeneous mass, therefore, we may distinguish the potentials for an indefinite number of substances, each of which has a perfectly determined value.

Between the potentials for different substances in the same homogeneous mass the same equations will subsist as between the units of these substances. That is, if the substances, S_a, S_b, etc., S_k, S_l, etc., are components of any given homogeneous mass, and are such that

$$\alpha\mathfrak{S}_a + \beta\mathfrak{S}_b + \text{etc.} = \kappa\mathfrak{S}_k + \lambda\mathfrak{S}_l + \text{etc.,} \tag{120}$$

$\mathfrak{S}_a$, $\mathfrak{S}_b$, etc., $\mathfrak{S}_k$, $\mathfrak{S}_l$, etc. denoting the units of the several substances, and α, β, etc., κ, λ, etc. denoting numbers, then if μ_a, μ_b, etc., μ_k, μ_l, etc. denote the potentials for these substances in the homogeneous mass,

$$\alpha\mu_a + \beta\mu_b + \text{etc.} = \kappa\mu_k + \lambda\mu_l + \text{etc.} \tag{121}$$

To show this, we will suppose the mass considered to be very large. Then, the first number of (121) denotes the increase of the energy of the mass produced by the addition of the matter represented by the first member of (120), and the second member of (121) denotes the increase of energy of the same mass produced by the addition of the matter represented by the second member of (120), the entropy and volume of the mass remaining in each case unchanged. Therefore, as the two members of (120) represent the same matter in kind and quantity, the two members of (121) must be equal.

But it must be understood that equation (120) is intended to denote equivalence of the substances represented *in the mass considered*, and not merely chemical identity; in other words, it is supposed that there are no passive resistances to change in the mass considered which prevent the substances represented by one member of (120) from passing into those represented by the other. For example, in respect to a mixture of vapor of water and free hydrogen and oxygen (at ordinary temperatures), we may not write

$$9\mathfrak{S}_{Aq} = 1\mathfrak{S}_H + 8\mathfrak{S}_O,$$

but water is to be treated as an independent substance, and no necessary relation will subsist between the potential for water and the potentials for hydrogen and oxygen.

The reader will observe that the relations expressed by equations (43) and (51) (which are essentially relations between the potentials for actual components in different parts of a mass in a state of equilibrium) are simply those which by (121) would necessary subsist between the same potentials in any homogeneous mass containing as variable components all the substances to which the potentials relate.

In the case of a body of invariable composition, the potential for the single component is equal to the value of ζ for one unit of the body, as appears from the equation

$$\zeta = \mu m \tag{122}$$

to which (96) reduces in this case. Therefore, when $n = 1$, the fundamental equation between the quantities in the set (102) (see page 116) and that between the quantities in (103) may be derived either from the other by simple substitution. But, with this single exception, an equation between the quantities in one of the sets (99)–(103) cannot be derived from the equation between the quantities in another of these sets without differentiation.

Also in the case of a body of variable composition, when all the quantities of the components except one vanish, the potential for that one will be equal to the value of ζ for one unit of the body. We may make this occur for any given composition of the body by choosing as one of the components the matter constituting the body itself, so that the value of ζ for one unit of a body may always be considered as a potential. Hence the relations between the values of ζ for contiguous masses given on page 119 may be regarded as relations between potentials.

The two following propositions afford definitions of a potential which may sometimes be convenient.

The potential for any substance in any homogeneous mass is equal to the amount of mechanical work required to bring a unit of the substance by a reversible process from the state in which its energy and entropy are both zero into combination with the homogeneous mass, which at the close of the process must have its original volume, and which is supposed so large as not to be sensibly altered in any part. All other bodies used in the process must by its close be restored to their original state, except those used to supply the work, which must be used only as the source of the work. For, in a reversible process, when the entropies of other bodies are not altered, the entropy of the substance and mass taken together will not be altered. But the original entropy of the substance is zero; therefore the entropy of the mass is not altered by the addition of the substance. Again, the work expended will be equal to the increment of the energy of the mass and substance taken together, and therefore equal, as the original energy of the substance is zero, to the increment of energy of the mass due to the addition of the substance, which by the definition on page 121 is equal to the potential in question.

The potential for any substance in any homogeneous mass is equal to the work required to bring a unit of the substance by a reversible process from a state in which $\psi = 0$ and the temperature is the same as that of the given mass into combination with this mass, which at the close of the process must have the same volume and temperature as at first, and which is supposed so large as not to be sensibly altered in any part. A source of heat or cold of the temperature of the given mass is allowed, with this exception, other bodies are to be used only on the same conditions as before. This may be shown by applying equation (109) to the mass and substance taken together.

2. *Phase Rule*

Consider the variation of the internal energy of a homogeneous body consisting of n independently variable components. The fundamental equation

$$d\epsilon = t\, d\eta - p\, dv + \sum_{i=1}^{n} \mu_i\, dm_i$$

contains $(2n + 5)$ variables, viz. ϵ, t, η, p, v, μ_i, m_i.

But

$$t = \left(\frac{\partial \epsilon}{\partial \eta}\right)_{v, m_1, \ldots, m_n,}$$

and

$$p = \left(\frac{\partial \epsilon}{\partial v}\right)_{n, m_1, \ldots, m_n,}$$

and

$$\mu_i = \left(\frac{\partial \epsilon}{\partial m_i}\right)_{n, v, m_1, \ldots, m_i, \ldots, m_{i+1}, \ldots, m_n,}$$

i.e. $n + 2$ independent relations, thus making a total of $n + 3$ known relations (including the fundamental equation). Hence $n + 2$ relations are independent. In addition, if the total mass remains constant, then any variation in the composition introduces another relation among the components so that the number of independent variations is $(n + 1)$. The thermodynamic or composition state of a body is regarded by Gibbs as defining its phase. The number of independent variations of a homogeneous body with n independent variations is $(n + 1)$.

Consider a heterogeneous system with r phases; the total number of independent variations is now $r(n + 1)$. For coexistence, the temperature and pressure must be uniform and the chemical potentials of any component in each phase must be the same—$(r - 1)(n + 2)$ conditions for the variations. The number of independent variations of phase, the so-called number of *degrees of freedom* of the system, is accordingly given by $r(n + 1) - (r - 1)(n + 2)$, or $(n - r + 2)$. This simple, qualitative, linear relation is called the *phase rule*; it has been a guiding star in the explorations of chemistry, particularly industrial applications. In 1878, no one, including Gibbs himself, could possibly have foreseen the domain of its usefulness, including geological phenomena and solid solutions, agricultural and physiological chemistry. For example, even W. H. Nernst regarded Gibbs' calculations as too generalized for appliation to particular problems. The phase rule has recently[22] been found useful in understanding petrology, which is concerned with the location of rocks and the conditions of pressure and temperature under which they were formed, and thus with the evolution of the earth throughout geologic time.

The detailed study of membrane (e.g., plasma membrane) structure is a difficult problem. In the last five years[22] by regarding the amphiphilic molecules (e.g., phospholipids) as a non-aqueous phase, scientists have been able to apply Gibbs' considerations of coexistent phases of matter.

On Coexistent Phases of Matter.

(From the *Transactions of the Connecticut Academy of Arts and Sciences*, III, pp. 152–6 (1875–8).)

In considering the different homogeneous bodies which can be formed out of any set of component substances, it will be convenient to have a term which shall refer solely to the composition and thermodynamic state of any such body without regard to its quantity or form. We may call such bodies as differ in composition or state different *phases* of the matter considered, regarding all

bodies which differ only in quantity and form as different examples of the same phase. Phases which can exist together, the dividing surfaces being plane, in an equilibrium which does not depend upon passive resistances to change, we shall call *coexistent*.

If a homogeneous body has n independently variable components, the phase of the body is evidently capable of $n + 1$ independent variations. A system of r coexistent phases, each of which has the same n independently variable components is capable of $n + 2 - r$ variations of phase. For the temperature, the pressure, and the potentials for the actual components have the same values in the different phases, and the variations of these quantities are by (97) subject to as many conditions as there are different phases. Therefore, the number of independent variations in the values of these quantities, i.e., the number of independent variations of phase of the system, will be $n + 2 - r$.

Or, when the r bodies considered have not the same independently variable components, if we still denote by n the number of independently variable components of the r bodies taken as a whole, the number of independent variations of phase of which the system is capable will still be $n + 2 - r$. In this case, it will be necessary to consider the potentials for more than n component substances. Let the number of these potentials be $n + h$. We shall have by (97), as before, r relations between the variations of the temperature, of the pressure, and of these $n + h$ potentials, and we shall also have by (43) and (51) h relations between these potentials, of the same form as the relations which subsist between the units of the different component substances.

Hence, if $r = n + 2$, no variation in the phases (remaining coexistent) is possible. It does not seem probable that r can ever exceed $n + 2$. An example of $n = 1$ and $r = 3$ is seen in the coexistent solid, liquid, and gaseous forms of any substance of invariable composition. It seems not improbable that in the case of sulphur and some other simple substances there is more than one triad of coexistent phases; but it is entirely improbable that there are four coexistent phases of any simple substance. An example of $n = 2$ and $r = 4$ is seen in a solution of a salt in water in contact with vapor of water and two different kinds of crystals of the salt.

Concerning $n + 1$ Coexistent Phases.

We will now seek the differential equation which expresses the relation between the variations of the temperature and the pressure in a system of $n + 1$ coexistent phases (n denoting, as before, the number of independently variable components in the system taken as a whole).

In this case we have $n + 1$ equations of the general form of (97) (one for each of the coexistent phases), in which we may distinguish the quantities η, v, m_1, m_2, etc. relating to the different phases by accents. But t and p will each have the same value throughout, and the same is true of μ_1, μ_2, etc., so far as each of these occurs in the different equations. If the total number of these potentials is $n + h$, there will be h independent relations between them, corresponding to the h independent relations between the units of the component substances to which the potentials relate, by means of which we may eliminate the variations of h of the potentials from the equations of the form of (97) in which they occur.

Let one of these equations be

$$v'\, dp = \eta'\, dt + m_a'\, d\mu_a + m_b'\, d\mu_b + \text{etc.,} \tag{124}$$

and by the proposed elimination let it become

$$v'\, dp = \eta'\, dt + A_1'\, d\mu_1 + A_2'\, d\mu_2 \cdots + A_n'\, d\mu_n. \tag{125}$$

It will be observed that μ_a, for example, in (124) denotes the potential in the mass considered for a substance S_a which may or may not be identical with any of the substances S_1, S_2, etc. to which the potentials in (125) relate. Now as the equations between the potentials by means of which the elimination is performed are similar to those which subsist between the units of the corresponding substances, (compare equations (38), (43), and (51),) if we denote these units by $\mathfrak{S}_a$, $\mathfrak{S}_b$, etc., $\mathfrak{S}_1$, $\mathfrak{S}_2$, etc., we must also have

$$m_a'\mathfrak{S}_a + m_b'\mathfrak{S}_b + \text{etc.} = A_1'\mathfrak{S}_1 + A_1'\mathfrak{S}_2 \cdots + A_n'\mathfrak{S}_n. \tag{126}$$

But the first member of this equation denotes (in kind and quantity) the matter in the body to which equations (124) and (125) relate. As the same must be true of the second member, we may regard this same body as composed of the quantity A_1' of the substance S_1, with the quantity A_2' of the substance S_2, etc. We will therefore, in accordance with our general usage, write m_1', m_2', etc. for A_1', A_2', etc. in (125), which will then become

$$v'\, dp = \eta'\, dt + m_1'\, d\mu_1 + m_2'\, d\mu_2 \cdots + m_n'\, d\mu_n. \tag{127}$$

But we must remember that the components to which the m_1', m_2', etc. of this equation relate are not necessarily independently variable, as are the components to which the similar expressions in (97) and (124) relate. The rest of the $n + 1$ equations may be reduced to a similar form, viz.,

$$v''\, dp = \eta''\, dt + m_1''\, d\mu_1 + m_2''\, d\mu_2 \cdots + m_n''\, d\mu_n, \tag{128}$$
etc.

By elimination of $d\mu_1, d\mu_2, \ldots d\mu_n$ from these equations we obtain

$$\begin{vmatrix} v' & m_1' & m_2' \cdots m_n' \\ v'' & m_1'' & m_2'' \cdots m_n'' \\ v''' & m_1''' & m_2''' \cdots m_n''' \\ \cdot & \cdot & \cdot \ \ \cdots \\ \cdot & \cdot & \cdot \ \ \cdots \end{vmatrix} dp = \begin{vmatrix} \eta' & m_1' & m_2' \cdots m_n' \\ \eta'' & m_1'' & m_2'' \cdots m_n'' \\ \eta''' & m_1''' & m_2''' \cdots m_n''' \\ \cdot & \cdot & \cdot \ \ \cdots \\ \cdot & \cdot & \cdot \ \ \cdots \end{vmatrix} dt. \tag{129}$$

In this equation we may make v', v'', etc. equal to unity. Then m_1', m_2', m_1'', etc. will denote the separate densities of the components in the different phases, and η', η'', etc. the densities of entropy.

When $n = 1$,

$$(m''v' - m'v'') \, dp = (m''\eta' - m'\eta'') \, dt, \tag{130}$$

or if we make $m' = 1$ and $m'' = 1$ we have the usual formula

$$\frac{dp}{dt} = \frac{\eta' - \eta''}{v' - v''} = \frac{Q}{t(v'' - v')}, \tag{131}$$

in which Q denotes the heat absorbed by a unit of the substance in passing from one state to the other without change of temperature or pressure.

Concerning Cases in which the Number of Coexistent Phases is less than $n + 1$.

When $n > 1$, if the quantities of all the components $S_1, S_2, \ldots S_n$ are proportional in two coexistent phases, the two equations of the form of (127) and (128) relating to these phases will be sufficient for the elimination of the variations of all the potentials. In fact, the condition of the coexistence of the two phases together with the condition of the equality of the $n - 1$ ratios of $m_1', m_2', \ldots m_n'$ with the $n - 1$ ratios of $m_1'', m_2'', \ldots m_n''$ is sufficient to determine p as a function of t if the fundamental equation is known for each of the phases. The differential equation in this case may be expressed in the form of (130), m' and m'' denoting either the quantities of any one of the components or the total quantities of matter in the bodies to which they relate. Equation (131) will also hold true in this case, if the total quantity of matter in each of the bodies is unity. But this case differs from the preceding in that the matter which absorbs the heat Q in passing from one state to another, and to which the other letters in the formula relate, although the same in quantity, is not in general the same in kind at different temperatures and pressures. Yet the case will often occur that one of the phases is essentially invariable in composition, especially when it is a crystalline body, and in this case the matter to which the letters in (131) relate will not vary with the temperature and pressure.

When $n = 2$, two coexistent phases are capable, when the temperature is constant, of a single variation in phase. But as (130) will hold true in this case when $m_1' : m_2' : : m_1'' : m_2''$, it follows that for constant temperature the pressure is in general a maximum or a minimum when the composition of the two phases is identical. In like manner, the temperature of the two coexistent phases is in general a maximum or a minimum, for constant pressure, when the composition of the two phases is identical. Hence, the series of simultaneous values of t and p for which the composition of two coexistent phases is identical separates those simultaneous values of t and p for which no coexistent phases are possible from those for which there are two pairs of coexistent phases. This may be applied to a liquid having two independently variable components in connection with the vapor which it yields, or in connection with any solid which may be formed in it.

When $n = 3$, we have for three coexistent phases three equations of the form of (127), from which we may obtain the following,

$$
\begin{vmatrix} v' & m_1' & m_2' \\ v'' & m_1'' & m_2'' \\ v''' & m_1''' & m_2''' \end{vmatrix} dp = \begin{vmatrix} \eta' & m_1' & m_2' \\ \eta'' & m_1'' & m_2'' \\ n''' & m_1''' & m_2''' \end{vmatrix} dt + \begin{vmatrix} m_1' & m_2' & m_3' \\ m_1'' & m_2'' & m_3'' \\ m_1''' & m_2''' & m_3''' \end{vmatrix} d\mu_3. \quad (132)
$$

Now the value of the last of these determinants will be zero, when the composition of one of the three phases is such as can be produced by combining the other two. Hence, the pressure of three coexistent phases will in general be a maximum or minimum for constant temperature, and the temperature a maximum or minimum for constant pressure, when the above condition in regard to the composition of the coexistent phases is satisfied. The series of simultaneous values of t and p for which the condition is satisfied separates those simultaneous values of t and p for which three coexistent phases are not possible, from those for which there are two triads of coexistent phases. These propositions may be extended to higher values of n, and illustrated by the boiling temperatures and pressures of saturated solutions of $n - 2$ different solids in solvents having two independently variable components.

3. Gas Mixtures

In 1662 the Irish physicist Robert Boyle (1627–91) found experimentally that the product of the pressure of a gas and its volume is constant at any particular room temperature, a law discovered independently in 1676 by the French physicist Edme Mariotte (1620–84). J. L. Gay-Lussac's investigations in 1802 showed that the product is directly proportional to the so-called absolute temperature. In 1845 J. P. Joule found that the temperature remains approximately unchanged for a freely expanding gas (from 1852–1868 he and W. Thomson (Kelvin) performed more precise experiments with a porous plug; slight cooling or heating was observed with different gases). Hence the internal energy must be essentially a function of temperature only. In 1842 the French physicist Henri Victor Regnault (1810–78) found that the specific heat of a gas at ordinary temperatures (neither too high, nor too low) is a constant so that the internal energy must be a linear function of absolute temperature. Gibbs adopted these three criteria of R. J. E. Clausius as the definition of an ideal gas. Deviations, to be sure, had already been found by H. V. Regnault; a more accurate (approximate) description of a real gas was given in 1873 by J. D. van der Waals. It has, however, been found quite convenient to utilize the simple ideal-gas law for theoretical calculations; although the results are only approximately descriptive of real gases. Gibbs used this method to discuss the physical behavior of a gas mixture.

The English physicist and chemist John Dalton (1766–1844) showed in 1802 that the pressure in a gas mixture is the same as if each constituent exerted the same pressure it would if it alone filled the whole volume. Gibbs generalized this law for a mixture of ideal gases with variable composition; it involves the proposition that all the thermodynamic functions, including internal energy and entropy, have the same value at the same temperature, as though each gas alone occupied the same volume as the mixture (sometimes called the *Gibbs–Dalton law*). He discussed also what has subsequently been called the *Gibbs' paradox* with respect to the constant entropy associated with mixing different portions of the same gas: if, however, the initially separated gases are not the same, there is the customary natural increase in entropy. Gibbs considered finally the case of gas mixtures whose components are chemically reactive.

Gibbs recognized that the equilibrium potential is the same for coexistent gaseous and liquid or solid phases of a given component in a mixture. He was thus able to establish the theoretical foundation for dilute solutions, which was rediscovered in 1888 by J. H. van't Hoff (cf. the *Gibbs–van't Hoff equation* $\mu = RT + \ln c + k$, where c is the concentration of the component and k is a function of the temperature as well as of the solute and of the solvent). In his discussion Gibbs assumed the law (1803) of the English chemist William Henry (1775–1836) that the solubility of a gas in a liquid is proportional to the pressure of the gas in the case of no chemical reactions. Later (1883) M. K. E. L. Planck deduced *Henry's Law* from the thermodynamic ζ function for a gas mixture. A related matter is the law of vapor pressure of a solution (e.g. depressed freezing point) with respect to that of the pure solvent, discovered in 1878 by the French chemist François Marie *Raoult* (1830–1901).

Fundamental Equations of Ideal Gases and Gas-mixtures

(From the *Transactions of the Connecticut Academy of Arts and Sciences*, III, pp. 210–18, 227–9 (1875–8)).

For a constant quantity of a perfect or ideal gas, the product of the volume and pressure is proportional to the temperature, and the variations of energy are proportional to the variations of temperature. For a unit of such a gas we may write

$$pv = at,$$
$$d\varepsilon = c\, dt,$$

a and c denoting constants. By integration, we obtain the equation

$$\varepsilon = ct + E,$$

in which E also denotes a constant. If by these equations we eliminate t and p from (11), we obtain

$$d\varepsilon = \frac{\varepsilon - E}{c}\, d\eta - \frac{a}{v}\frac{\varepsilon - E}{c}\, dv,$$

or

$$c\frac{d\varepsilon}{\varepsilon - E} = d\eta - a\frac{dv}{v}.$$

The integral of this equation may be written in the form

$$c\log\frac{\varepsilon - E}{c} = \eta - a\log v - H,$$

where H denotes a fourth constant. We may regard E as denoting the energy of a unit of the gas for $t = 0$; H its entropy for $t = 1$ and $v = 1$; a its pressure in the latter state, or its volume for $t = 1$ and $p = 1$; c its specific heat at constant volume. We may extend the application of the equation to any quantity of the gas, without altering the values of the constants, if we substitute $\frac{\varepsilon}{m}$, $\frac{\eta}{m}$, $\frac{v}{m}$ for ε, η, v, respectively. This will give

$$c\log\frac{\varepsilon - Em}{cm} = \frac{\eta}{m} - H + a\log\frac{m}{v}. \tag{255}$$

This is a fundamental equation (see pages 114–115) for an ideal gas of invariable composition. It will be observed that if we do not have to consider the properties of the matter which forms the gas as appearing in any other form or combination, but solely as constituting the gas in question (in a state of purity), we may without loss of generality give to E and H the value zero, or any other arbitrary values. But when the scope of our investigations is not thus limited, we may have determined the states of the substance of the gas for which $\varepsilon = 0$ and $\eta = 0$ with reference to some other form in which the substance appears, or, if the substance is compound, the states of its components for which $\varepsilon = 0$ and $\eta = 0$ may be already determined; so that the constants E and H cannot in general be treated as arbitrary.

We obtain from (255) by differentiation

$$\frac{c}{\varepsilon - Em} d\varepsilon = \frac{1}{m} d\eta - \frac{a}{v} dv + \left(\frac{cE}{\varepsilon - Em} + \frac{c + a}{m} - \frac{\eta}{m^2} \right) dm, \quad (256)$$

whence, in virtue of the general relation expressed by (86),

$$t = \frac{\varepsilon - Em}{cm}, \quad (257)$$

$$p = a \frac{\varepsilon - Em}{cv}, \quad (258)$$

$$\mu = E + \frac{\varepsilon - Em}{cm^2} (cm + am - \eta). \quad (259)$$

We may obtain the fundamental equation between ψ, t, v, and m from equations (87), (255), and (257). Eliminating ε we have

$$\psi = Em + cmt - t\eta,$$

and

$$c \log = \frac{\eta}{m} - H + a \log \frac{m}{v};$$

and eliminating η, we have the fundamental equation

$$\psi = Em + mt \left(c - H - c \log t + a \log \frac{m}{v} \right). \quad (260)$$

Differentiating this equation, we obtain

$$d\psi = -m \left(H + c \log t + a \log \frac{v}{m} \right) dt - \frac{amt}{v} dv$$

$$+ \left(E + t \left(c + a - H - c \log t + a \log \frac{m}{v} \right) \right) dm; \quad (261)$$

whence, by the general equation (88),

$$\eta = m\left(H + c \log t + a \log \frac{v}{m}\right), \tag{262}$$

$$p = \frac{amt}{v}, \tag{263}$$

$$\mu = E + t\left(c + a - H - c \log t + a \log \frac{m}{v}\right). \tag{264}$$

From (260), by (87) and (91), we obtain

$$\zeta = Em + mt\left(c - H - c \log t + a \log \frac{m}{v}\right) + pv,$$

and eliminating v by means of (263), we obtain the fundamental equation

$$\zeta = Em + mt\left(c + a - H - (c + a) \log t + a \log \frac{p}{a}\right) \tag{265}$$

From this, by differentiation and comparison with (92), we may obtain the equations

$$\eta = m\left(H + (c + a) \log t - a \log \frac{p}{a}\right), \tag{266}$$

$$v = \frac{amt}{p}, \tag{267}$$

$$\mu = E + t\left(c + a - H - (c + a) \log t + a \log \frac{p}{a}\right). \tag{268}$$

The last is also a fundamental equation. It may be written in the form

$$\log \frac{p}{a} = \frac{H - c - a}{a} + \frac{c + a}{a} \log t + \frac{\mu - E}{at}, \tag{269}$$

or, if we denote by e the base of the Naperian system of logarithms,

$$p = ae^{(H-c-a)/a}t^{(c+a)/a}e^{(\mu-E)/at} \tag{270}$$

The fundamental equation between χ, η, p, and m may also be easily obtained; it is

$$(c + a) \log \frac{\chi - Em}{(c + a)m} = \frac{\eta}{m} - H + a \log \frac{p}{a}, \tag{271}$$

which can be solved with respect to χ.

Any one of the fundamental equations (255), (260), (265), (270), and (271), which are entirely equivalent to one another, may be regarded as defining an ideal gas. It will be observed that most of these equations might be abbreviated by the use of different constants. In (270), for example, a single constant might be used for $ae^{(H-c-a)/a}$, and another for $\dfrac{c+a}{a}$. The equations have been given in the above form, in order that the relations between the constants occurring in the different equations might be most clearly exhibited. The sum $c + a$ is the specific heat for constant pressure, as appears if we differentiate (266) regarding p and m as constant.*

* We may easily obtain the equation between the temperature and pressure of a saturated vapor, if we know the fundamental equations of the substance both in the gaseous, and in the liquid or solid state. If we suppose that the density and the specific heat at constant pressure of the liquid may be regarded as constant quantities (for such moderate pressures as the liquid experiences while in contact with the vapor), and denote this specific heat by k, and the volume of a unit of the liquid by V, we shall have for a unit of the liquid

$$t\, d\eta = k\, dt,$$

whence

$$\eta = k \log t + H',$$

where H' denotes a constant. Also, from this equation and (97),

$$d\mu = -(k \log t + H')\, dt + V\, dp,$$

whence

$$\mu = kt - kt \log t - H't + Vp + E', \tag{A}$$

where E' denotes another constant. This is a fundamental equation for the substance in the liquid state. If (268) represents the fundamental equation for the same substance in the gaseous state, the two equations will both hold true of coexistent liquid and gas. Eliminating μ we obtain

$$\log \frac{p}{a} = \frac{H - H' + k - c - a}{a} - \frac{k - c - a}{a} \log t - \frac{E - E'}{at} + \frac{V}{a}\frac{p}{t}.$$

If we neglect the last term, which is evidently equal to the density of the vapor divided by the density of the liquid, we may write

$$\log p = A - B \log t - \frac{C}{t},$$

A, B, and C denoting constants. If we make similar suppositions in regard to the substance in the solid state, the equation between the pressure and temperature of coexistent solid and gaseous phases will of course have the same form.

A similar equation will also apply to the phases of an ideal gas which are coexistent with two different kinds of solids, one of which can be formed by the combination of the gas with the other, each being of invariable composition and of constant specific heat and density. In this case we may write for one solid

$$\mu_1 = k't - k't \log t - H't + V'p + E',$$

and for the other

$$\mu_2 = k''t - k''t \log t - H''t + V''p + E'',$$

and for the gas

$$\mu_3 = E + t\left(c + a - H - (c + a) \log t + a \log \frac{p}{a}\right).$$

Now if a unit of the gas unites with the quantity λ of the first solid to form the quantity $1 + \lambda$ of the second it will be necessary for equilibrium (see pages 110, 111) that

$$\mu_3 + \lambda\mu_1 = (1 + \lambda)\mu_2.$$

Substituting the values of μ_1, μ_2, μ_3, given above, we obtain after arranging the terms and dividing by at

$$\log \frac{p}{a} = A - B \log t - \frac{C}{t} + D\frac{p}{t},$$

when

$$A = \frac{H + \lambda H' - (1 + \lambda)H'' - c - a - \lambda k' + (1 + \lambda)k''}{a},$$

$$B = \frac{(1 + \lambda)k'' - \lambda k' - c - a}{a},$$

$$C = \frac{E + \lambda E' - (1 + \lambda)E''}{a}, \qquad D = \frac{(1 + \lambda)V'' - \lambda V'}{a}.$$

We may conclude from this that an equation of the same form may be applied to an ideal gas in equilibrium with a liquid of which it forms an independently variable component, when the specific heat and density of the liquid are entirely determined by its composition, except that the letters A, B, C, and D must in this case be understood to denote quantities which vary with the composition of the liquid. But to consider the case more in detail, we have for the liquid by (A)

$$\frac{\zeta}{m} = \mu = kt - kt \log t - H't + Vp + E',$$

where k, H', V, E' denote quantities which depend only upon the composition of the liquid. Hence, we may write

$$\zeta = \mathbf{k}t - \mathbf{k}t \log t - \mathbf{H}t + \mathbf{V}p + \mathbf{E},$$

where $\mathbf{k}$, $\mathbf{H}$, $\mathbf{V}$, and $\mathbf{E}$ denote functions of m_1, m_2, etc. (the quantities of the several components of the liquid). Hence, by (92),

$$\mu_1 = \frac{d\mathbf{k}}{dm_1} t - \frac{d\mathbf{k}}{dm_1} t \log t - \frac{d\mathbf{H}}{dm_1} t + \frac{d\mathbf{V}}{dm_1} p + \frac{d\mathbf{E}}{dm_1}.$$

If the component to which this potential relates is that which also forms the gas, we shall have by (269)

$$\log \frac{p}{a} = \frac{H - c - a}{a} + \frac{c + a}{a} \log t + \frac{\mu_1 - E}{at}.$$

The preceding fundamental equations all apply to gases *of constant composition*, for which the matter is entirely determined by a single variable (m). We may obtain corresponding fundamental equations for a mixture of gases, in which the proportion of the components shall be variable, from the following considerations.

It is a rule which admits of a very general and in many cases very exact experimental verification, that if several liquid or solid substances which yield different gases or vapors are simultaneously in equilibrium with a mixture of these gases (cases of chemical action between the gases being excluded,) the pressure in the gas-mixture is equal to the sum of the pressures of the gases yielded at the same temperature by the various liquid or solid substances taken separately. Now the potential in any of the liquids or solids for the substance which it yields in the form of gas has very nearly the same value when the liquid or solid is in equilibrium with the gas-mixture as when it is in equilibrium with its own gas alone. The difference of the pressure in the two cases will cause a certain difference in the values of the potential, but that this difference will be small, we may infer from the equation

$$\left(\frac{d\mu_1}{dp}\right)_{t,m} = \left(\frac{dv}{dm_1}\right)_{t,p,m}, \tag{272}$$

which may be derived from equation (92). In most cases, there will be a certain absorption by each liquid of the gases yielded by the others, but as it is well

---

Eliminating μ_1, we obtain the equation

$$\log\frac{p}{a} = A - B\log t - \frac{C}{t} + D\frac{p}{t},$$

in which A, B, C, and D denote quantities which depend only upon the composition of the liquid, viz:

$$A = \frac{1}{a}\left(H - \frac{d\mathbf{H}}{dm_1} - c - a + \frac{d\mathbf{k}}{dm_1}\right),$$

$$B = \frac{1}{a}\left(\frac{d\mathbf{k}}{dm_1} - c - a\right),$$

$$C = \frac{1}{a}\left(E - \frac{d\mathbf{E}}{dm_1}\right) \qquad D = \frac{1}{a}\frac{d\mathbf{V}}{dm_1}.$$

With respect to some of the equations which have here been deduced, the reader may compare Professor Kirchhoff "Ueber die Spannung des Dampfes von Mischungen aus Wasser und Schwefelsäure," *Pogg. Ann.*, vol. civ. (1858), p. 612; and Dr. Rankine "On Saturated Vapors," *Phil. Mag.*, vol. xxxi. (1866), p. 199.

known that the above rule does not apply to cases in which such absorption takes place to any great extent, we may conclude that the effect of this circumstance in the cases with which we have to do is of secondary importance. If we neglect the slight differences in the values of the potentials due to these circumstances, the rule may be expressed as follows:

The pressure in a mixture of different gases is equal to the sum of the pressures of the different gases as existing each by itself at the same temperature and with the same value of its potential.

To form a precise idea of the practical significance of the law as thus stated with reference to the equilibrium of two liquids with a mixture of the gases which they emit, when neither liquid absorbs the gas emitted by the other, we may imagine a long tube closed at each end and bent in the form of a W to contain in each of the descending loops one of the liquids, and above these liquids the gases which they emit, viz., the separate gases at the ends of the tube, and the mixed gases in the middle. We may suppose the whole to be in equilibrium, the difference of the pressures of the gases being balanced by the proper heights of the liquid columns. Now it is evident from the principles established prior to this section that the potential for either gas will have the same value in the mixed and in the separate gas *at the same level*, and therefore according to the rule in the form which we have given, the pressure in the gas-mixture is equal to the sum of the pressures in the separate gases, *all these pressures being measured at the same level.* Now the experiments by which the rule has been established relate rather to the gases in the vicinity of the surfaces of the liquids. Yet, although the differences of level in these surfaces may be considerable, the corresponding differences of pressure in the columns of gas will certainly be very small in all cases which can be regarded as falling under the laws of ideal gases, for which very great pressures are not admitted.

If we apply the above law to a mixture of ideal gases and distinguish by subscript numerals the quantities relating to the different gases, and denote by $\sum_1$ the sum of all similar terms obtained by changing the subscript numerals we shall have by (270)

$$p = \sum_1 (a_1 e^{(H_1 - c_1 - a)/a_1 t}(c_1 + a_1)/a_1 e^{(\mu_1 - E_1)/a_1 t}). \tag{273}$$

It will be legitimate to assume this equation provisionally as the fundamental equation defining an ideal gas-mixture, and afterwards to justify the suitableness of such a definition by the properties which may be deduced from it. In particular, it will be necessary to show that an ideal gas-mixture as thus defined, when the proportion of its components remains constant, has all the properties which have already been assumed for an ideal gas of invariable composition; it will also be desirable to consider more rigorously and more in detail the equilibrium of such a gas-mixture with solids and liquids, with respect to the above rule.

By differentiation and comparison with (98) we obtain

$$\frac{\eta}{v} = \sum_1 \left(\left(c_1 + a_1 - \frac{\mu_1 - E_1}{t} \right) e^{(H_1 - c_1 - a_1)/a_1} t^{c_1/a_1} e^{(\mu_1 - E_1)/a_1 t} \right), \quad (274)$$

$$\left. \begin{aligned} \frac{m_1}{v} &= e^{(H_1 - c_1 - a_1)/a_1} t^{c_1/a_1} e^{(\mu_1 - E_1)/a_1 t}, \\[2mm] \frac{m_2}{v} &= e^{(H_2 - c_2 - a_2)/a_2} t^{c_2/a_2} e^{(\mu_2 - E_2)/a_2 t}, \end{aligned} \right\} \quad (275)$$

etc.

Equations (275) indicate that the relation between the temperature, the density of any component, and the potential for that component, is not affected by the presence of the other components. They may also be written

$$\left. \mu_1 = E_1 + t \left(c_1 + a_1 - H_1 - c_1 \log t + a_1 \log \frac{m_1}{v} \right), \right\} \quad (276)$$

etc.

Eliminating μ_1, μ_2, etc. from (273) and (274) by means of (275) and (276), we obtain

$$p = \sum_1 \frac{a_1 m_1 t}{v}, \quad (277)$$

$$\eta = \sum_1 \left(m_1 H_1 + m_1 c_1 \log t + m_1 a_1 \log \frac{v}{m_1} \right). \quad (278)$$

Equation (277) expresses the familiar principle that the pressure in a gas-mixture is equal to the sum of the pressures which the component gases would possess if existing separately with the same volume at the same temperature. Equation (278) expresses a similar principle in regard to the entropy of the gas-mixture.

From (276) and (277) we may easily obtain the fundamental equation between ψ, t, v, m_1, m_2, etc. For by substituting in (94) the values of p, μ_1, μ_2, etc. taken from these equations, we obtain

$$\psi = \sum_1 \left(E_1 m_1 + m_1 t \left(c_1 - H_1 - c_1 \log t + a_1 \log \frac{m_1}{v} \right) \right). \quad (279)$$

If we regard the proportion of the various components as constant, this equation may be simplified by writing

$$m \quad \text{for} \quad \sum_1 m_1,$$

$$cm \quad \text{for} \quad \sum_1 (c_1 m_1),$$

$$am \quad \text{for} \quad \sum_1 (a_1 m_1),$$

$$Em \quad \text{for} \quad \sum_1 (E_1 m_1),$$

and $\quad Hm - am \log m \quad$ for $\quad \sum_1 (H_1 m_1 - a_1 m_1 \log m_1).$

The values of c, a, E, and H, will then be constant and m will denote the total quantity of gas. As the equation will thus be reduced to the form of (260), it is evident that an ideal gas-mixture, as defined by (273) or (279), when the proportion of its components remains unchanged, will have all the properties which we have assumed for an ideal gas of invariable composition. The relations between the specific heats of the gas-mixture at constant volume and at constant pressure and the specific heats of its components are expressed by the equations

$$c = \sum_1 \frac{m_1 c_1}{m}, \tag{280}$$

and

$$c + a = \sum_1 \frac{m_1(c_1 + a_1)}{m}. \tag{281}$$

We have already seen that the values of t, v, m_1, μ_1 in a gas-mixture are such as are possible for the component G_1 (to which m_1 and μ_1 relate) existing separately. If we denote by p_1, η_1, ψ_1, ε_1, χ_1, ζ_1 the connected values of the several quantities which the letters indicate determined for the gas G_1 as thus existing separately, and extend this notation to the other components, we shall have by (273), (274), and (279)

$$p = \sum_1 p_1, \qquad \eta = \sum_1 \eta_1, \qquad \psi = \sum_1 \psi_1; \tag{282}$$

whence by (87), (89), and (91)

$$\varepsilon = \sum_1 \varepsilon_1, \qquad \chi = \sum_1 \chi_1, \qquad \zeta = \sum_1 \zeta_1. \tag{283}$$

The quantities p, η, ψ, ε, χ, ζ relating to the gas-mixture may therefore be regarded as consisting of parts which may be attributed to the several components in such a manner that between the parts of these quantities which are assigned to any component, the quantity of that component, the potential for that component, the temperature, and the volume, the same relations shall subsist as if that component existed separately. It is in this sense that we should understand the law of Dalton, that every gas is as a vacuum to every other gas . . .

Considerations relating to the Increase of Entropy due to the Mixture of Gases by Diffusion.

From equation (278) we may easily calculate the increase of entropy which takes place when two different gases are mixed by diffusion, at a constant temperature and pressure. Let us suppose that the quantities of the gases are such that each occupies initially one half of the total volume. If we denote this volume by V, the increase of entropy will be

$$m_1 a_1 \log V + m_2 a_2 \log V - m_1 a_1 \log \frac{V}{2} - m_2 a_2 \log \frac{V}{2},$$

or
$$(m_1 a_1 + m_2 a_2) \log 2.$$

Now
$$m_1 a_1 = \frac{pV}{2t}, \quad \text{and} \quad m_2 a_2 = \frac{pV}{2t}.$$

Therefore the increase of entropy may be represented by the expression

$$\frac{pV}{t} \log 2. \tag{297}$$

It is noticeable that the value of this expression does not depend upon the kinds of gas which are concerned, if the quantities are such as has been supposed, except that the gases which are mixed must be of different kinds. If we should bring into contact two masses of the same kind of gas, they would also mix, but there would be no increase of entropy. But in regard to the relation which this case bears to the preceding, we must bear in mind the following considerations. When we say that when two different gases mix by diffusion, as we have supposed, the energy of the whole remains constant, and the entropy receives a certain increase, we mean that the gases could be separated and brought to the same volume and temperature which they had at first by means of certain changes in external bodies, for example, by the passage of a certain amount of heat from a warmer to a colder body. But when we say that when two gas-masses of the same kind are mixed under similar circumstances there is no change of energy or entropy, we do not mean that the gases which have been mixed can be separated without change to external bodies. On the contrary, the separation of the gases is entirely impossible. We call the energy and entropy of the gas-masses when mixed the same as when they were unmixed, because we do not recognize any difference in the substance of the two masses. So when gases of different kinds are mixed, if we ask what changes in external bodies are necessary to bring the system to its original state, we do not mean a state in which each particle shall occupy more or less exactly the same position as at some previous epoch, but only a state which shall be undistinguishable from the previous one in its sensible properties. It is to states of systems thus incompletely defined that the problems of thermodynamics relate.

But if such considerations explain why the mixture of gas-masses of the same kind stands on a different footing from the mixture of gas-masses of different kinds, the fact is not less significant that the increase of entropy due to the mixture of gases of different kinds, in such a case as we have supposed, is independent of the nature of the gases.

Now we may without violence to the general laws of gases which are embodied in our equations suppose other gases to exist than such as actually do exist, and there does not appear to be any limit to the resemblance which there might be between two such kinds of gas. But the increase of entropy due to the mixing of given volumes of the gases at a given temperature and pressure would be independent of the degree of similarity or dissimilarity between them. We might also imagine the case of two gases which should be absolutely identical in all the properties (sensible and molecular) which come into play while they exist as gases either pure or mixed with each other, but which should differ in respect to the attractions between their atoms and the atoms of some other substances, and therefore in their tendency to combine with such substances. In the mixture of such gases by diffusion an increase of entropy would take place, although the process of mixture, dynamically considered, might be absolutely identical in its minutest details (even with respect to the precise path of each atom) with processes which might take place without any increase of entropy. In such respects, entropy stands strongly contrasted with energy. Again, when such gases have been mixed, there is no more impossibility of the separation of the two kinds of molecules in virtue of their ordinary motions in the gaseous mass without any especial external influence, than there is of the separation of a homogeneous gas into the same two parts into which it has once been divided, after these have once been mixed. In other words, the impossibility of an uncompensated decrease of entropy seems to be reduced to improbability.

There is perhaps no fact in the molecular theory of gases so well established as that the number of molecules in a given volume at a given temperature and pressure is the same for every kind of gas when in a state to which the laws of ideal gases apply. Hence the quantity $\frac{pV}{t}$ in (297) must be entirely determined by the number of molecules which are mixed. And the increase of entropy is therefore determined by the number of these molecules and is independent of their dynamical condition and of the degree of difference between them.

4. *Osmotic Pressure*

The German botanist Wilhelm Pfeffer (1845–1920) discovered in 1877 that solutes exercise a so-called osmotic pressure on a semi-permeable membrane which is impenetrable to them but which lets the solvent through freely. J. H. van't Hoff gave a theory of this phenomenon in 1887. Ten years later Gibbs showed how van't Hoff's law could be derived from his own basic theory of 1875–8. As F. G. Donnan, who himself developed in 1911 a Theory of Membranes confessed later, "Many of the results which he [Gibbs] obtained have been made, unconsciously or subconsciously, the starting points of investigations by later workers in the field of thermochemistry".[8]

Effect of a Diaphragm (Equilibrium of Osmotic Forces).

(From the *Transactions of the Connecticut Academy of Arts and Sciences*, III, pp. 138–40 (1875–8).)

If the given mass, enclosed as before, is divided into two parts, each of which is homogeneous and fluid, by a diaphragm which is capable of supporting an excess of pressure on either side, and is permeable to some of the components and impermeable to others, we shall have the equations of condition

$$\delta\eta' + \delta\eta'' = 0, \tag{72}$$

$$\delta v' = 0, \quad \delta v'' = 0, \tag{73}$$

and for the components which cannot pass the diaphragm

$$\delta m_a' = 0, \quad \delta m_a'' = 0, \quad \delta m_b' = 0, \quad \delta m_b'' = 0, \quad \text{etc.}. \tag{74}$$

and for those which can

$$\delta m_h' + \delta m_h'' = 0, \quad \delta m_i' + \delta m_i'' = 0, \quad \text{etc.} \tag{75}$$

With these equations of condition, the general condition of equilibrium (see (15)) will give the following particular conditions:

$$t' = t'', \tag{76}$$

and for the components which can pass the diaphragm, if actual components of both masses,

$$\mu_h' = \mu_h'', \quad \mu_i' = \mu_i'', \quad \text{etc.}, \tag{77}$$

but not

$$p' = p'',$$

nor

$$\mu_a' = \mu_a'', \quad \mu_b' = \mu_b'', \quad \text{etc.}$$

Again, if the diaphragm is permeable to the components in certain proportions only, or in proportions not entirely determined yet subject to certain conditions, these conditions may be expressed by equations of condition, which will be linear equations between $\delta m_1'$, $\delta m_2'$, etc., and if these be known the deduction of the particular conditions of equilibrium will present no difficulties. We will however observe that if the components S_1, S_2, etc. (being actual components on each side) can pass the diaphragm simultaneously in the proportions a_1, a_2, etc. (without other resistances than such as vanish with the velocity of the current), values proportional to a_1, a_2, etc. are possible for $\delta m_1'$, $\delta m_2'$, etc. in the general condition of equilibrium, $\delta m_1''$, $\delta m_2''$, etc. having the same values taken negatively, so that we shall have for one particular condition of equilibrium

$$a_1\mu_1' + a_2\mu_2' + \text{etc.} = a_1\mu_1'' + a_2\mu_2'' + \text{etc.} \tag{78}$$

There will evidently be as many independent equations of this form as there are independent combinations of the elements which can pass the diaphragm.

These conditions of equilibrium do not of course depend in any way upon the supposition that the volume of each fluid mass is kept constant, if the diaphragm is in any case supposed immovable. In fact, we may easily obtain the same conditions of equilibrium, if we suppose the volumes variable. In this case, as the equilibrium must be preserved by forces acting upon the external surfaces of the fluids, the variation of the energy of the sources of these forces must appear in the general condition of equilibrium, which will be

$$\delta\varepsilon' + \delta\varepsilon'' + P'\,\delta v' + P''\,\delta v'' \gtreqless 0, \tag{79}$$

P' and P'' denoting the external forces per unit of area. (Compare (14).) From this condition we may evidently derive the same internal conditions of equilibrium as before, and in addition the external conditions

$$p' = P', \quad p'' = P''. \tag{80}$$

In the preceding paragraphs it is assumed that the permeability of the diaphragm is perfect, and its impermeability absolute, i.e., that it offers no resistance to the passage of the components of the fluids in certain proportions, except such as vanishes with the velocity, and that in other proportions the components cannot pass at all. How far these conditions are satisfied in any particular case is of course to be determined by experiment.

If the diaphragm is permeable to all the n components without restriction, the temperature and the potentials for all the components must be the same on both sides. Now, as one may easily convince himself, a mass having n components is capable of only $n + 1$ independent variations in nature and state. Hence, if the fluid on one side of the diaphragm remains without change, that on the other side cannot (in general) vary in nature or state. Yet the pressure will not necessarily be the same on both sides. For, although the pressure is a function of the temperature and the n potentials, it may be a many-valued function (or any one of several functions) of these variables. But when the pressures are different on the two sides, the fluid which has the less pressure will be *practically unstable*, in the sense in which the term has been used. For

$$\varepsilon'' = t''\eta'' + p''v'' - \mu_1''m_1'' - \mu_2''m_2'' \cdots - \mu_n''m_n'' = 0, \qquad (81)$$

as appears from equation (12) if integrated on the supposition that the nature and state of the mass remain unchanged. Therefore, if $p' < p''$ while $t' = t''$, $\mu_1' = \mu_1''$, etc.,

$$\varepsilon'' - t'\eta'' + p'v'' - \mu_1'm_1'' - \mu_2'm_2'' \cdots - \mu_n'm_n'' < 0. \qquad (82)$$

This relation indicates the instability of the fluid to which the single accents refer.

But independently of any assumption in regard to the permeability of the diaphragm, the following relation will hold true in any case in which each of the two fluid masses may be regarded as uniform throughout in nature and state. Let the character D be used with the variables which express the nature, state, and quantity of the fluids to denote the increments of the values of these quantities actually occurring in a time either finite or infinitesimal. Then, as the heat received by the two masses cannot exceed $t'\,\mathrm{D}\eta' + t''\,\mathrm{D}\eta''$, and as the increase of their energy is equal to the difference of the heat they receive and the work they do,

$$\mathrm{D}\varepsilon' + \mathrm{D}\varepsilon'' \leqq t'\,\mathrm{D}\eta' + t''\,\mathrm{D}\eta'' - p'\,\mathrm{D}v' - p''\,\mathrm{D}v'', \qquad (83)$$

i.e., by (12),

$$\mu_1'\,\mathrm{D}m_1' + \mu_1''\,\mathrm{D}m_1'' + \mu_2'\,\mathrm{D}m_2' + \mu_2''\,\mathrm{D}m_2'' + \text{etc.} \leqq 0, \qquad (84)$$

or

$$(\mu_1'' - \mu_1')\,\mathrm{D}m_1'' + (\mu_2'' - \mu_2')\,\mathrm{D}m_2'' + \text{etc.} \leqq 0. \qquad (85)$$

It is evident that the sign $=$ holds true only in the limiting case in which no motion takes place.

Semi-Permeable Films and Osmotic Pressure

(From *Nature*, lv, pp. 461–2 (1897).)

Lord Kelvin's very interesting problem concerning molecules which differ only in their power of passing a diaphragm (see Nature for January 21, p. 272), seems only to require for its solution the relation between density and pressure for the fluid at the temperature of the experiment, when this relation for small densities becomes that of an ideal gas; in other cases, a single numerical constant in addition to the relation between density and pressure is sufficient.

This will, perhaps, appear most readily if we imagine each of the vessels A and B connected with a vertical column of the fluid which it contains, these columns extending upwards until the state of an ideal gas is reached. The equilibrium which we suppose to subsist will not be disturbed by communications between the columns at as many levels as we choose, if these communications are always made through the same kind of semi-permeable diaphragm as that which separates the vessels A and B. It will be observed that the difference of level at which any same pressure is found in the two columns is a constant quantity, easily determined in the upper parts (where the fluids are in the ideal gaseous state) as a function of the composition of the fluid in the A-column, and giving at once the height above the vessel A, where in the A-column we find a pressure equal to that in the vessel B.

In fact, we have in either column

$$dp = -g\gamma \, dz,$$

where the letters denote respectively pressure, force of gravity, density, and vertical elevation. If we set

$$\frac{1}{\gamma} = F'(p),$$

we have

$$F'(p) \, dp = -g \, dz.$$

Integrating, with a different constant for each column, we get

$$F(p_A) = -g(z - C_A)$$
$$F(p_B) = -g(z - C_B)$$
$$F(p_A) - F(p_B) = g(C_A - C_B).$$

In the upper regions,

$$F'(p) = \frac{1}{\gamma} = \frac{at}{p}$$

$$\therefore \quad F(p) = at \log p,$$

where t denotes temperature, and a the constant of the law of Boyle and Charles. Hence,

$$at \log p_A - at \log p_B = g(C_A - C_B).$$

Moreover, if $1:n$ represents the constant ratio in which the S- and D-molecules are mixed in the A-column, we shall have in the upper regions, where the S-molecules have the same density in the two columns,

$$\gamma_A = (1 + n)\gamma_B \qquad p_A = (1 + n)p_B$$
$$g(C_A - C_B) = at \log (1 + n).$$

Therefore, at any height,

$$F(p_A) - F(p_B) = at \log (1 + n).$$

This equation gives the required relation between the pressures in A and B and the composition of the fluid in A. It agrees with van't Hoff's law, for when n is small the equation may be written

$$F'(p_A)(p_A - p_B) = atn$$

or

$$p_A - p_B = atn\gamma_A.$$

But we must not suppose, in any literal sense, that this difference of pressure represents the part of the pressure in A which is exerted by the D-molecules, for that would make the total pressure calculable by the law of Boyle and Charles.

To show that the case is substantially the same, at least for any one temperature, when the fluid is not volatile, we may suppose that we have many kinds of molecules, A, B, C, &c., which are identical in all properties except in regard to passing diaphragms. Let us imagine a row of vertical cylinders or tubes closed at both ends. Let the first contain A-molecules sufficient to give the pressure p' at a certain level. Then let it be connected with the second cylinder through a diaphragm impermeable to B-molecules, freely permeable to all others. Let the second cylinder contain such quantities of A- and B-molecules as to be in equilibrium with the first cylinder, and to have a certain pressure p'' at the level of p' in the first cylinder. At a higher level this second cylinder will have the pressure which we have called p'. There let it be connected with the third cylinder through a diaphragm impermeable to C-molecules, and to them alone. Let this third cylinder contain such quantities of A-, B-, and C-molecules as to be in equilibrium with the second cylinder, and have the pressure p'' at the diaphragm; and so on, the connections being so made, and the quantities of the several kinds of molecules so regulated, that the pressures at all the diaphragms shall have the same two values.

It is evident that the vertical distance between successive connections must be everywhere the same, say l; also, that at all the diaphragms, on the side of the greater pressure, the proportion of molecules which can and which cannot pass the diaphragm must be the same. Let the ratio be $1:n$. If we write γ_A, β_B, &c., for the densities of the several kinds of molecules, and γ for total density, we have for the second cylinder

$$\frac{\gamma_A + \gamma_B}{\gamma_A} = 1 + n.$$

For the third cylinder we have this equation, and also

$$\frac{\gamma_A + \gamma_B + \gamma_C}{\gamma_A + \gamma_B} = 1 + n$$

which gives

$$\frac{\gamma_A + \gamma_B + \gamma_C}{\gamma_A} = (1 + n)^2.$$

In this way, we have for the rth cylinder

$$\frac{\gamma}{\gamma_A} = (1 + n)^{r-1}.$$

Now the vertical distance between equal pressures in the first and rth cylinders, is

$$(r - 1)l.$$

Now the equilibrium will not be destroyed if we connect all the cylinders with the first through diaphragms impermeable to all except A-molecules. And the last equation shows that as γ/γ_A increases geometrically, the vertical distance between any pressure in the column when this ratio of densities is found, and the same pressure in the first cylinder increases arithmetically. This distance, therefore, may be represented by log (γ/γ_A) multiplied by a constant. This is identical with our result for a volatile liquid, except that for that case we found the value of the constant to be at/g.

The following demonstration of van't Hoff's law, which is intended to apply to existing substances, requires only that the solutum, *i.e.* dissolved substance, should be capable of the ideal gaseous state, and that its molecules, as they occur in the gas, should not be broken up in the solution, nor united to one another in more complex molecules.

It will be convenient to use certain quantities which may be called the *potentials* of the solvent and of the solutum, the term being thus defined:— In any sensibly homogeneous mass, the *potential* of any independently variable component substance is the differential coefficient of the thermodynamic energy of the mass taken with respect to that component, the entropy and volume of the mass and the quantities of its other components remaining constant. The advantage of using such *potentials* in the theory of semi-permeable diaphragms consists partly in the convenient form of the conditions of equilibrium, the potential for any substance to which a diaphragm is freely permeable having the same value on both sides of the diaphragm, and partly in our ability to express van't Hoff's law as a relation between the quantities characterising the state of the solution, without reference to any experimental arrangement (see *Transactions of the Connecticut Academy*, vol. iii. pp. 116, 138, 148, 194).

Let there be three reservoirs, R', R'', R''', of which the first contains the solvent alone, maintained in a constant state of temperature and pressure, the second the solution, and the third the solutum alone. Let R' and R'' be connected through a diaphragm freely permeable to the solvent, but impermeable to the solutum, and let R'' and R''' be connected through a diaphragm impermeable to the solvent, but freely permeable to the solutum. We have then, if we write μ_1 and μ_2 for the potentials of the solvent and the solutum, and distinguished by accents, quantities relating to the several reservoirs,

$$\mu_1'' = \mu_1' = \text{const.}, \qquad \mu_2'' = \mu_2'''.$$

Now if the quantity of the solutum in the apparatus be varied, the ratio in which it is divided in equilibrium between the reservoirs R'' and R''' will be constant, so long as its densities in the two reservoirs, γ_2'', γ_2''', are small. For let us suppose that there is only a single molecule of the solutum. It will wander through R'' and R''', and in a time sufficiently long the parts of the time spent respectively in R'' and R''', which for convenience we may suppose of equal volume, will approach a constant ratio, say $1:B$. Now if we put in the apparatus a considerable number of molecules, they will divide themselves between R' and R'' sensibly in the ratio $1:B$, so long as they do not sensibly interfere with one another *i.e.* so long as the number of molecules of the solutum which are within the spheres of action of other molecules of the solutum is a negligible part of the whole both in R'' and R'''. With the limitation we have, therefore,

$$\gamma_2''' = B\gamma_2''.$$

Now in R''' let the solutum have the properties of an ideal gas, which give for any constant temperature (*ibid.* p. 212)

$$\mu_2''' = a_2 t \log \gamma_2''' + C,$$

where a_2 is the constant of the law of Boyle and Charles, and C another constant. Therefore,

$$\mu_2'' = a_2 t \log (B\gamma_2'') + C.$$

This equation, in which a single constant may evidently take the place of B and C, may be regarded as expressing the property of the solution implied in vant' Hoff's law. For we have the general thermodynamic relation (*ibid.* p. 143)

$$v \, dp = \eta \, dt + m_1 \, d\mu_1 + m_2 \, d\mu_2,$$

where v and η denote the volume and entropy of the mass considered, and m_1 and m_2 the quantities of its components. Applied to this case, since t and μ_1 are constant, this becomes

$$dp'' = \gamma_2'' \, d\mu_2''.$$

Substituting the value of $d\mu_2''$ derived from the last finite equation, we have

$$dp'' = a_2 t \, d\gamma_2''$$

whence, integrating from $\gamma_2'' = 0$ and $p'' = p'$, we get

$$p'' - p' = a_2 t \gamma_2'',$$

which evidently expresses van't Hoff's law.

We may extend this proof to cases in which the solutum is not volatile by supposing that we give to its molecules mutually repulsive molecular forces, which, however, are entirely inoperative with respect to any other kind of molecules. In this way we may make the solutum capable of the ideal gaseous state. But the relations pertaining to the contents of R″ will not be affected by these new forces, since we suppose that only a negligible part of the molecules of the solutum are within the range of such forces. Therefore these relations cannot depend on the new forces, and must exist without them.

To give up the condition that the molecules of the solutum shall not be broken up in the solution, nor united to one another in more complex molecules, would involve the consideration of a good many cases, which it would be difficult to unite in a brief demonstration. The result, however, seems to be that the increase of pressure is to be estimated by Avogadro's law from the number of molecules in the solution which contain any part of the solutum, without reference to the quantity in each.

J. WILLARD GIBBS.

New Haven, Connecticut, February 18.

5. Surfaces of Discontinuity

Consider very thin non-homogeneous films which separate approximately homogeneous materials—what Gibbs called surfaces of discontinuity. His discussion of this subject comprised about one-third of his article on heterogeneous equilibria; it treated adsorption phenomena, stability of such surfaces, formation of new phases and new surfaces—and a brief portion on liquid films and surfaces. Gibbs may be said to have created the thermodynamic theory of capillarity. Introducing concepts of superficial densities of energy, entropy, and the component substances, he arrived at a fundamental equation for equilibrium at the interface; in general, it is

$$\Gamma = -\frac{d\sigma}{d\mu_i},$$

where Γ represents the superficial excess of a component with respect to the dividing surface and σ is the interfacial tension. It has been used subsequently by various investigators of adsorption phenomena. (A similar equation of more limited scope was obtained independently in 1888 by J. J. Thomson.) Gibbs paid particular attention to soap films and noted a ring that is formed when a film of soap solution is drawn up from the mouth of a cup—called the *Gibbs ring*. In 1924 F. G. Donnan commented about surfaces of discontinuity: "Even today not a hundredth part of the rich crop has yet been harvested."[8]

Influence of Surfaces of Discontinuity upon the Equilibrium of Heterogeneous Masses— Theory of Capillarity

(From the *Transactions of the Connecticut Academy of Arts and Sciences*, III, pp. 380–93 (1875–8).)

We have hitherto supposed, in treating of heterogeneous masses in contact, that they might be considered as separated by mathematical surfaces, each mass being unaffected by the vicinity of the others, so that it might be homogeneous quite up to the separating surfaces both with respect to the density of each of its various components and also with respect to the densities of energy and entropy. That such is not rigorously the case is evident from the consideration that if it were so with respect to the densities of the components it could not be so in general with respect to the density of energy, as the sphere of molecular action is not infinitely small. But we know from observation that it is only within very small distances of such a surface that any mass is sensibly affected by its vicinity,—a natural consequence of the exceedingly small sphere of sensible molecular action,—and this fact renders possible a simple method of taking account of the variations in the densities of the component substances and of energy and entropy, which occur in the vicinity of surfaces of discontinuity. We may use this term, for the sake of brevity, without implying that the discontinuity is absolute, or that the term distinguishes any surface with mathematical precision. It may be taken to denote the non-homogeneous film which separates homogeneous or nearly homogeneous masses.

Let us consider such a surface of discontinuity in a fluid mass which is in equilibrium and uninfluenced by gravity. For the precise measurement of the quantities with which we have to do, it will be convenient to be able to refer to a geometrical surface, which shall be sensibly coincident with the physical surface of discontinuity, but shall have a precisely determined position. For this end, let us take some point in or very near to the physical surface of discontinuity, and imagine a geometrical surface to pass through this point and all other points which are similarly situated with respect to the condition of the adjacent matter. Let this geometrical surface be called the *dividing surface*, and designated by the symbol S. It will be observed that the position of this surface is as yet to a certain extent arbitrary, but that the directions of its normals are already everywhere determined, since all the surfaces which can be formed in the manner described are evidently parallel to one another. Let us also imagine a closed surface cutting the surface S and including a part of the homogeneous mass on each side. We will so far limit the form of this closed surface as to suppose that on each side of S, as far as there is any want of perfect homogeneity in the fluid masses, the closed surface is such as may be generated by a moving normal to S. Let the portion of S which is included by the closed surface be denoted by **s**, and the area of this portion by s. Moreover, let the mass contained within the closed surface be divided into three parts by two surfaces, one on each side of S, and very near to that surface, although at such distance as to lie entirely beyond the influence of the discontinuity in its vicinity. Let us call the part which contains the surface **s** (with the physical surface of discontinuity) M, and the homogeneous parts M$'$ and M$''$, and distinguish by ε, ε', ε'', η, η', η'', m_1, m_1', m_1'', m_2, m_2', m_2'', etc., the energies and entropies of these masses, and the quantities which they contain of their various components.

It is necessary, however, to define more precisely what is to be understood in cases like the present by the energy of masses which are only separated from other masses by imaginary surfaces. A part of the total energy which belongs to the matter in the vicinity of the separating surface, relates to pairs of particles which are on different sides of the surface, and such energy is not in the nature of things referable to either mass by itself. Yet, to avoid the necessity of taking separate account of such energy, it will often be convenient to include it in the energies which we refer to the separate masses. When there is no break in the homogeneity at the surface, it is natural to treat the energy as distributed with a uniform density. This is essentially the case with the initial state of the system which we are considering, for it has been divided by surfaces passing in general through homogeneous masses. The only exception—that of the surface which cuts at right angles the non-homogeneous film—(apart from the consideration that without any important loss of generality we may regard the part of this surface within the film as very small compared with the other surfaces) is rather apparent than real, as there is no change in the state of the matter *in the direction perpendicular to this surface.* But in the variations to be considered in the state of the system, it will not be convenient to limit ourselves to such as do not create any discontinuity at the surfaces bounding the masses M, M$'$, M$''$: we must therefore determine how we will estimate the energies of the masses in cases of such infinitesimal discontinuities as may be supposed to arise. Now the energy of each mass will be most easily estimated by neglecting the discontinuity, i.e., if we estimate the energy on the supposition that beyond the bounding surface the phase is identical with that within the surface. This will evidently be allowable, if it does not affect the total amount of energy. To show that it does not affect this quantity, we have only to observe that, if the energy of the mass on one side of a surface where there is an infinitesimal discontinuity of phase is greater as determined by this rule than if determined by any other (suitable) rule, the energy of the mass on the other side must be less by the same amount when determined by the first rule than when determined by the second, since the discontinuity relative to the second mass is equal but opposite in character to the discontinuity relative to the first.

If the entropy of the mass which occupies any one of the spaces considered is not in the nature of things determined without reference to the surrounding masses, we may suppose a similar method to be applied to the estimation of entropy.

With this understanding, let us return to the consideration of the equilibrium of the three masses M, M′, and M″. We shall suppose that there are no limitations to the possible variations of the system due to any want of perfect mobility of the components by means of which we express the composition of the masses, and that these components are independent, i.e., that no one of them can be formed out of the others.

With regard to the mass M, which includes the surface of discontinuity, it is necessary for its internal equilibrium that when its boundaries are considered constant, and when we consider only *reversible* variations (i.e., those of which the opposite are also possible), the variation of its energy should vanish with the variations of its entropy and of the quantities of its various components. For changes within the mass will not affect the energy or the entropy of the surrounding masses (when these quantities are estimated on the principle which we have adopted) and it may therefore be treated as an isolated system. For fixed boundaries of the mass M, and for reversible variations, we may therefore write

$$\delta\varepsilon = A_0\, \delta\eta + A_1\, \delta m_1 + A_2\, \delta m_2 + \text{etc.} \tag{476}$$

where A_0, A_1, A_2, etc., are quantities determined by the initial (unvaried) condition of the system. It is evident that A_0 is the temperature of the lamelliform mass to which the equation relates, or the *temperature at the surface of discontinuity*. By comparison of this equation with (12) it will be seen that the definition of A_1, A_2, etc., is entirely analogous to that of the potentials in homogeneous masses, although the mass to which the former quantities relate is not homogeneous, while in our previous definition of potentials, only homogeneous masses were considered. By a natural extension of the term *potential*, we may call the quantities A_1, A_2, etc., the *potentials at the surface of discontinuity*. This designation will be farther justified by the fact, which will appear hereafter, that the value of these quantities is independent of the thickness of the lamina (M) to which they relate. If we employ our ordinary symbols for temperature and potentials, we may write

$$\delta\varepsilon = t\, \delta\eta + \mu_1\, \delta m_1 + \mu_2\, \delta m_2 + \text{etc.} \tag{477}$$

If we substitute $\geq$ for $=$ in this equation, the formula will hold true of all variations whether reversible or not;* for if the variation of energy could have

---

* To illustrate the difference between variations which are reversible, and those which are not, we may conceive of two entirely different substances meeting in equilibrium at a mathematical surface without being at all mixed. We may also conceive of them as mixed in a thin film about the surface where they meet, and then the amount of mixture is capable of variation both by increase and by diminution. But when they are absolutely unmixed, the amount of mixture can be increased, but

a value less than that of the second member of the equation, there must be variation in the condition of M in which its energy is diminished without change of its entropy or of the quantities of its various components.

It is important, however, to observe that for any given values of $\delta\eta$, δm_1, δm_2, etc., while there *may* be possible variations of the nature and state of M for which the value of $\delta\varepsilon$ is greater than that of the second member of (477), there *must* always be possible variations for which the value of $\delta\varepsilon$ is equal to that of the second member. It will be convenient to have a notation which will enable us to express this by an equation. Let $\mathfrak{d}\varepsilon$ denote the smallest value (i.e., the value nearest to $-\infty$) of $\delta\varepsilon$ consistent with given values of the other variations, then

$$\mathfrak{d}\varepsilon = t\,\delta\eta + \mu_1\,\delta m_1 + \mu_2\,\delta m_2 + \text{etc.} \tag{478}$$

For the internal equilibrium of the whole mass which consists of the parts M, M', M'', it is necessary that

$$\delta\varepsilon + \delta\varepsilon' + \delta\varepsilon'' \geqq 0 \tag{479}$$

for all variations which do not affect the enclosing surface or the total entropy or the total quantity of any of the various components. If we also regard the surfaces separating M, M', and M'' as invariable, we may derive from this condition, by equations (478) and (12), the following as a *necessary* condition of equilibrium:

$$t\,\delta\eta + \mu_1\,\delta m_1 + \mu_2\,\delta m_2 + \text{etc.}$$
$$+\; t'\,\delta\eta' + \mu_1'\,\delta m_1' + \mu_2'\,\delta m_2' + \text{etc.}$$
$$+\; t''\,\delta\eta'' + \mu_1''\,\delta m_1'' + \mu_2''\,\delta m_2'' + \text{etc.} \geqq 0, \tag{480}$$

---

is incapable of diminution, and it is then consistent with equilibrium that the value of $\delta\varepsilon$ (for a variation of the system in which the substances commence to mix) should be greater than the second member of (477). It is not necessary to determine whether precisely such cases actually occur; but it would not be legitimate to overlook the possible occurrence of cases in which variations may be possible while the opposite variations are not.

It will be observed that the sense in which the term *reversible* is here used is entirely different from that in which it is frequently used in treatises on thermodynamics, where a process by which a system is brought from a state A to a state B is called reversible, to signify that the system may also be brought from the state B to the state A through the same series of intermediate states taken in the reverse order by means of external agencies of the opposite character. The variation of a system from a state A to a state B (supposed to differ infinitely little from the first) is here called reversible when the system is capable of another state B' which bears the same relation to the state A that A bears to B.

the variations being subject to the equations of conditions

$$
\left.
\begin{aligned}
\delta\eta + \delta\eta' + \delta\eta'' &= 0, \\
\delta m_1 + \delta m_1' + \delta m_1'' &= 0, \\
\delta m_2 + \delta m_2' + \delta m_2'' &= 0, \\
\text{etc.}
\end{aligned}
\right\}
\tag{481}
$$

It may also be the case that some of the quantities $\delta m_1'$, $\delta m_1''$, $\delta m_2'$, $\delta m_2''$, etc., are incapable of negative values or can only have the value zero. This will be the case when the substances to which these quantities relate are not actual or possible components of M' or M''. (See page 107.) To satisfy the above condition it is necessary and sufficient that

$$
t = t' = t'',
\tag{482}
$$

$$
\mu_1' \, \delta m_1' \geqq \mu_1 \, \delta m_1', \quad \mu_2' \, \delta m_2' \geqq \mu_2 \, \delta m_2', \quad \text{etc.,}
\tag{483}
$$

$$
\mu_1'' \, \delta m_1'' \geqq \mu_1 \, \delta m_1'', \quad \mu_2'' \, \delta m_2'' \geqq \mu_2 \, \delta m_2'', \quad \text{etc.}
\tag{484}
$$

It will be observed that, if the substance to which μ_1, for instance, relates is an actual component of each of the homogeneous masses, we shall have $\mu_1 = \mu_1' = \mu_1''$. If it is an actual component of the first only of these masses, we shall have $\mu_1 = \mu_1'$. If it is also a possible component of the second homogeneous mass, we shall also have $\mu_1 \geqq \mu_1''$. If this substance occurs only at the surface of discontinuity, the value of the potential μ_1 will not be determined by any equation, but cannot be greater than the potential for the same substance in either of the homogeneous masses in which it may be a possible component.

It appears, therefore, that the particular conditions of equilibrium *relating to temperature and the potentials* which we have before obtained by neglecting the influence of the surfaces of discontinuity (pp. 108, 109, *et al.*) are not invalidated by the influence of such discontinuity in their application to homogeneous parts of the system bounded like M' and M'' by imaginary surfaces lying within the limits of homogeneity,—a condition which may be fulfilled by surfaces very near to the surfaces of discontinuity. It appears also that similar conditions will apply to the non-homogeneous films like M', which separate such homogeneous masses. The properties of such films, which are of course different from those of homogeneous masses, require our farther attention.

The volume occupied by the mass M is divided by the surface s into two parts, which we will call v''' and v'''', v''' lying next to M', and v'''' to M''. Let us imagine these volumes filled by masses having throughout the same temperature, pressure and potentials, and the same densities of energy and entropy, and of the various components, as the masses M' and M'' respectively. We shall then have, by equation (12), if we regard the volumes as constant,

$$\delta\varepsilon''' = t' \, \delta\eta'' + \mu_1' \, \delta m_1''' + \mu_2' \, \delta m_2''' + \text{etc.}, \qquad (485)$$

$$\delta\varepsilon'''' = t'' \, \delta\eta''' + \mu_1'' \, \delta m_1'''' + \mu_2'' \, \delta m_2'''' + \text{etc.}; \qquad (486)$$

whence, by (482)–(484), we have for reversible variations

$$\delta\varepsilon''' = t \, \delta\eta''' + \mu_1 \, \delta m_1''' + \mu_2 \, \delta m_2''' + \text{etc.}, \qquad (487)$$

$$\delta\varepsilon'''' = t \, \delta\eta'''' + \mu_1 \, \delta m_1'''' + \mu_2 \, \delta m_2'''' + \text{etc.} \qquad (488)$$

From these equations and (477), we have for reversible variations

$$\delta(\varepsilon - \varepsilon''' - \varepsilon'''') = t \, \delta(\eta - \eta''' - \eta'''') + \mu_1 \, \delta(m_1 - m_1''' - m_1'''')$$
$$+ \mu_2 \, \delta(m_2 - m_2''' - m_2'''') + \text{etc.} \qquad (489)$$

Or, if we set*

$$\varepsilon^s = \varepsilon - \varepsilon''' - \varepsilon'''', \qquad \eta^s = \eta - \eta''' - \eta'''', \qquad (490)$$

$$m_1^s = m_1 - m_1''' - m_1'''', \qquad m_2^s = m_2 - m_2''' - m_2'''', \text{ etc.}, \qquad (491)$$

we may write

$$\delta\varepsilon^s = t \, \delta\eta^s + \mu_1 \, \delta m_1^s + \mu_2 \, \delta m_2^s + \text{etc.} \qquad (492)$$

This is true of reversible variations in which the surfaces which have been considered are fixed. It will be observed that ε^s denotes the excess of the energy of the actual mass which occupies the total volume which we have considered over that energy which it would have, if on each side of the surface S the density of energy had the same uniform value quite up to that surface which it has at a sensible distance from it; and that η^s, m_1^s, m_2^s, etc., have analogous significations. It will be convenient, and need not be a source of any misconception, to call ε^s and η^s the energy and entropy *of the surface* (or the *superficial* energy and entropy), $\dfrac{\varepsilon^s}{s}$ and $\dfrac{\eta^s}{s}$ the *superficial densities* of energy and entropy, $\dfrac{m_1^s}{s}$, $\dfrac{m_2^s}{s}$, etc., the *superficial densities* of the several components.

Now these quantities (ε^s, η^s, m_1^s, etc.) are determined partly by the state of the physical system which we are considering, and partly by the various imaginary surfaces by means of which these quantities have been defined. The position of these surfaces, it will be remembered, has been regarded as fixed in the variation of the system. It is evident, however, that the form of that portion of these surfaces, which lies in the region of homogeneity on either side of the surface of discontinuity, cannot affect the values of these quantities. To obtain the complete value of $\delta\varepsilon^s$ for reversible variations, we have therefore

* It will be understood that the ^{s} here used is not an algebraic exponent, but is only intended as a distinguishing mark. The Roman letter S has not been used to denote any *quantity.*

only to regard variations in the position and form of the limited surface s, as this determines all of the surfaces in question lying within the region of non-homogeneity. Let us first suppose the form of s to remain unvaried and only its position in space to vary, either by translation or rotation. No change in (492) will be necessary to make it valid in this case. For the equation is valid if s remains fixed and the material system is varied in position; also, if the material system and s are both varied in position, while their relative position remains unchanged. Therefore, it will be valid if the surface alone varies its position.

But if the form of s be varied, we must add to the second member (492) terms which shall represent the value of

$$\delta \varepsilon^s - t\, \delta \eta^s - \mu_1\, \delta m_1{}^s - \mu_2\, \delta m_2{}^s - \text{etc.}$$

due to such variation in the form of s. If we suppose s to be sufficiently small to be considered uniform throughout in its curvatures and in respect to the state of the surrounding matter, the value of the above expression will be determined by the variation of its area δs and the variations of its principal curvatures δc_1 and δc_2, and we may write

$$\delta \varepsilon^s = t\, \delta \eta^s + \mu_1\, \delta m_1{}^s + \mu_2\, \delta m_2{}^s + \text{etc.} + \sigma\, \delta s + C_1\, \delta c_1 + C_2\, \delta c_2, \quad (493)$$

or

$$\delta \varepsilon^s = t\, \delta \eta^s + \mu_1\, \delta m_1{}^s + \mu_2\, \delta m_2{}^s + \text{etc.} + \sigma\, \delta s$$
$$+ \tfrac{1}{2}(C_1 + C_2)\, \delta(c_1 + c_2) + \tfrac{1}{2}(C_1 - C_2)\, \delta(c_1 - c_2), \quad (494)$$

σ, C_1, and C_2 denoting quantities which are determined by the initial state of the system and position and form of s. The above is the complete value of the variation of ε^s for reversible variations of the system. But it is always possible to give such a position to the surface s that $C_1 + C_2$ shall vanish.

To show this, it will be convenient to write the equation in the longer form [see (490), (491)]

$$\delta \varepsilon - t\, \delta \eta - \mu_1\, \delta m_1 - \mu_2\, \delta m_2 - \text{etc.}$$
$$- \delta \varepsilon''' + t\, \delta \eta''' + \mu_1\, \delta m_1''' + \mu_2\, \delta m_1''' + \text{etc.}$$
$$- \delta \varepsilon'''' + t\, \delta \eta'''' + \mu_1\, \delta m_1'''' + \mu_2\, \delta m_2'''' + \text{etc.}$$
$$= \sigma\, \delta s + \tfrac{1}{2}(C_1 + C_2)\, \delta(c_1 + c_2) + \tfrac{1}{2}(C_1 - C_2)\, \delta(c_1 - c_2), \quad (495)$$

i.e., by (482)–(484) and (12),

$$\delta \varepsilon - t\, \delta \eta - \mu_1\, \delta m_1 - \mu_2\, \delta m_2 - \text{etc.} + p'\, \delta v''' + p''\, \delta v''''$$
$$= \sigma\, \delta s + \tfrac{1}{2}(C_1 + C_2)\, \delta(c_1 + c_2) + \tfrac{1}{2}(C_3 - C_2)\, \delta(c_1 - c_2). \quad (496)$$

From this equation it appears in the first place that the pressure is the same in the two homogeneous masses separated by a plane surface of discontinuity.

For let us imagine the material system to remain unchanged, while the plane surface **s** without change of area or of form moves in the direction of its normal. As this does not affect the boundaries of the mass M,

$$\delta\varepsilon - t\,\delta\eta - \mu_1\,\delta m_1 - \mu_2\,\delta m_2 - \text{etc.} = 0.$$

Also $\delta s = 0$, $\delta(c_1 + c_2) = 0$, $\delta(c_1 - c_2) = 0$, and $\delta v''' = -\delta v''''$. Hence $p' = p''$, when the surface of discontinuity is plane.

Let us now examine the effect of different positions of the surface **s** in the same material system upon the value of $C_1 + C_2$, supposing at first that in the initial state of the system the surface of discontinuity is plane. Let us give the surface **s** some particular position. In the initial state of the system this surface will of course be plane like the physical surface of discontinuity, to which it is parallel. In the varied state of the system, let it become a portion of a spherical surface having positive curvature; and at sensible distances from this surface let the matter be homogeneous and with the same phases as in the initial state of the system; also at and about the surface let the state of the matter so far as possible be the same as at and about the plane surface in the initial state of the system. (Such a variation in the system may evidently take place negatively as well as positively, as the surface may be curved toward either side. But whether such a variation is consistent with the maintenance of equilibrium is of no consequence, since in the preceding equations only the initial state is supposed to be one of equilibrium.) Let the surface **s**, placed as supposed, whether in the initial or the varied state of the surface, be distinguished by the symbol **s′**. Without changing either the initial or the varied state of the material system, let us make another supposition with respect to the imaginary surface **s**. In the unvaried system let it be parallel to its former position but removed from it a distance λ on the side on which lie the centers of positive curvature. In the varied state of the system, let it be spherical and concentric with **s′**, and separated from it by the same distance λ. It will of course lie on the same side of **s′** as in the unvaried system. Let the surface **s**, placed in accordance with this second supposition, be distinguished by the symbol **s″**. Both in the initial and the varied state, let the perimeters of **s′** and **s″** be traced by a common normal. Now the value of

$$\delta\varepsilon = t\,\delta\eta - \mu_1\,\delta m_1 - \mu_2\,\delta m_2 - \text{etc.}$$

in equation (496) is not affected by the position of **s**, being determined simply by the body M: the same is true of $p'\,\delta v''' + p''\,\delta v''''$ or $p'\,\delta(v''' + v'''')$, $v''' + v''''$ being the volume of M. Therefore the second member of (496) will have the same value whether the expressions relate to **s′** or **s″**. Moreover, $\delta(c_1 - c_2) = 0$ both for **s′** and **s″**. If we distinguish the quantities determined for **s′** and for **s″** by the marks ′ and ″, we may therefore write

$$\sigma'\,\delta s' + \tfrac{1}{2}(C_1' + C_2')\,\delta(c_1' + c_2') = \sigma''\,\delta s'' + \tfrac{1}{2}(C_1'' + C_2'')\,\delta(c_1'' + c_2'').$$

Now if we make
$$\delta s'' = 0,$$
we shall have by geometrical necessity
$$\delta s' = s\lambda \, \delta(c_1'' + c_2'').$$
Hence
$$\delta' s\lambda \, \delta(c_1'' + c_2'') + \tfrac{1}{2}(C_1' + C_2') \, \delta(c_1' + c_2') = \tfrac{1}{2}(C_2'' + C_2'') \, \delta(c_1'' + c_2'').$$

But
$$\delta(c_1' + c_2') = \delta(c_1'' + c_2'').$$
Therefore,
$$C_1' + C_2' + 2\sigma' s\lambda = C_1'' + C_2''.$$

This equation shows that we may give a positive or negative value to $C_1'' + C_2''$ by placing $\mathbf{s}''$ a sufficient distance on one or on the other side of $\mathbf{s}'$. Since this is true when the (unvaried) surface is plane, it must also be true when the surface is nearly plane. And for this purpose a surface may be regarded as nearly plane, when the radii of curvature are very large in proportion to the thickness of the non-homogeneous film. This is the case when the radii of curvature have any sensible size. In general, therefore, whether the surface of discontinuity is plane or curved it is possible to place the surface $\mathbf{s}$ so that $C_1 + C_2$ in equation (494) shall vanish.

Now we may easily convince ourselves by equation (493) that if $\mathbf{s}$ is placed within the non-homogeneous film, and $s = 1$, the quantity σ is of the same order of magnitude as the values of ε^s, η^s, $m_1{}^s$, $m_2{}^s$, etc., while the values of C_1 and C_2 are of the same order of magnitude as the changes in the values of the former quantities caused by increasing the curvature of $\mathbf{s}$ by unity. Hence, on account of the thinness of the non-homogeneous film, since it can be very little affected by such a change of curvature in $\mathbf{s}$, the values of C_1 and C_2 must in general be very small relatively to σ. And hence, if $\mathbf{s}'$ be placed within the non-homogeneous film, the value of λ which will make $C_1'' + C_2''$ vanish must be very small (of the same order of magnitude as the thickness of the non-homogeneous film). The position of $\mathbf{s}$, therefore, which will make $C_1 + C_2$ in (494) vanish, will in general be sensibly coincident with the physical surface of discontinuity.

We shall hereafter suppose, when the contrary is not distinctly indicated that the surface $\mathbf{s}$, in the unvaried state of the system, has such a position as to make $C_1 + C_2 = 0$. It will be remembered that the surface $\mathbf{s}$ is a part of a larger surface $\mathbf{S}$, which we have called the *dividing surface*, and which is co-extensive with the physical surface of discontinuity. We may suppose that the position of the dividing surface is everywhere determined by similar considerations. This is evidently consistent with the suppositions made on page 149 with regard to this surface.

We may therefore cancel the term
$$\tfrac{1}{2}(C_1 + C_2) \, \delta(c_1 + c_2)$$

in (494). In regard to the following term, it will be observed that C_1 must necessarily be equal to C_2, when $c_1 = c_2$, which is the case when the surface of discontinuity is plane. Now on account of the thinness of the non-homogeneous film, we may always regard it as composed of parts which are approximately plane. Therefore, without danger of sensible error, we may also cancel the term

$$\tfrac{1}{2}(C_1 - C_2)\, \delta(c_1 - c_2).$$

Equation (494) is thus reduced to the form

$$\delta \varepsilon^s = t\, \delta \eta^s + \sigma\, \delta s + \mu_1\, \delta m_1{}^s + \mu_2\, \delta m_2{}^s + \text{etc.} \tag{497}$$

We may regard this as the complete value of $\delta \varepsilon^s$, for all reversible variations in the state of the system supposed initially in equilibrium, when the dividing surface has its initial position determined in the manner described.

The above equation is of fundamental importance in the theory of capillarity. It expresses a relation with regard to surfaces of discontinuity analogous to that expressed by equation (12) with regard to homogeneous masses. From the two equations may be directly deduced the conditions of equilibrium of heterogeneous masses in contact, subject or not to the action of gravity, without disregard of the influence of the surfaces of discontinuity. The general problem, including the action of gravity, we shall take up hereafter: at present we shall only consider, as hitherto, a small part of a surface of discontinuity with a part of the homogeneous mass on either side, in order to deduce the additional condition which may be found when we take account of the motion of the dividing surface.

We suppose as before that the mass especially considered is bounded by a surface of which all that lies in the region of non-homogeneity is such as may be traced by a moving normal to the dividing surface. But instead of dividing the mass as before into four parts, it will be sufficient to regard it as divided into two parts by the dividing surface. The energy, entropy, etc., of these parts, estimated on the supposition that its nature (including density of energy, etc.) is uniform quite up to the dividing surface, will be denoted by ε', η', etc., ε'', η'', etc. Then the total energy will be $\varepsilon^s + \varepsilon' + \varepsilon''$, and the general condition of internal equilibrium will be that

$$\delta \varepsilon^s + \delta \varepsilon' + \delta \varepsilon'' \geqq 0, \tag{498}$$

when the bounding surface is fixed, and the total entropy and total quantities of the various components are constant. We may suppose η, η', η'', $m_1{}^s$, $m_1{}'$, $m_1{}''$, $m_2{}^s$, $m_2{}'$, $m_2{}''$, etc., to be all constant. Then by (497) and (12) the condition reduces to

$$\sigma\, \delta s - p'\, \delta v' - p''\, \delta v'' = 0. \tag{499}$$

(We may set $=$ for $\geqq$, since changes in the position of the dividing surface can evidently take place in either of two opposite directions.) This equation has evidently the same form as if a membrane without rigidity and having a tension σ, uniform in all directions, existed at the dividing surface. Hence, the particular position which we have chosen for this surface may be called the surface of tension, and σ the superficial tension. If all parts of the dividing surface move a uniform normal distance δN, we shall have

$$\delta s = (c_1 + c_2)s\, \delta N, \quad \delta v' = s\, \delta N, \quad \delta v'' = -s\, \delta N;$$

whence
$$\sigma(c_1 + c_2) = p' - p'', \tag{500}$$

the curvatures being positive when their centers lie on the side to which p' relates. This is the condition which takes the place of that of equality of pressure (see pp. 108, *et al.*) for heterogeneous fluid masses in contact, when we take account of the influence of the surfaces of discontinuity. We have already seen that the conditions relating to temperature and the potentials are not affected by these surfaces.

Fundamental Equations for Surfaces of Discontinuity.

In equation (497) the initial state of the system is supposed to be one of equilibrium. The only limitation with respect to the varied state is that the variation shall be reversible, i.e., that an opposite variation shall be possible. Let us now confine our attention to variations in which the system remains in equilibrium. To distinguish this case, we may use the character d instead of δ, and write

$$d\varepsilon^s = t\, d\eta^s + d\sigma\, s + \mu_1\, dm_1{}^s + \mu_2\, dm_2{}^s + \text{etc.} \tag{501}$$

Both the states considered being states of equilibrium, the limitation with respect to the reversibility of the variations may be neglected, since the variations will always be reversible in at least one of the states considered.

If we integrate this equation, supposing the area s to increase from zero to any finite value s, while the material system to a part of which the equation relates remains without change, we obtain

$$\varepsilon^s = t\eta^s + \sigma s + \mu_1 m_1{}^s + \mu_2 m_2{}^s + \text{etc.}, \tag{502}$$

which may be applied to any portion of any surface of discontinuity (in equilibrium) which is of the same nature throughout, or throughout which the values of t, σ, μ_1, μ_2, etc. are constant.

If we differentiate this equation, regarding all the quantities as variable, and compare the result with (501), we obtain

$$\eta^s\, dt + s\, d\sigma + m_1{}^s\, d\mu_1 + m_2{}^s\, d\mu_2 + \text{etc.} = 0. \tag{503}$$

If we denote the *superficial densities* of energy, of entropy, and of the several component substances (see page 154) by ε_s, η_s, Γ_1, Γ_2, etc., we have

$$\varepsilon_\mathrm{s} = \frac{\varepsilon^\mathrm{s}}{s}, \qquad \eta_\mathrm{s} = \frac{\eta^\mathrm{s}}{s}, \tag{504}$$

$$\Gamma_1 = \frac{m_1{}^\mathrm{s}}{s}, \qquad \Gamma_2 = \frac{m_2{}^\mathrm{s}}{s}, \qquad \text{etc.,} \tag{505}$$

and the preceding equations may be reduced to the form:—

$$d\varepsilon_\mathrm{s} = t\, d\eta_\mathrm{s} + \mu_1\, d\Gamma_1 + \mu_2\, d\Gamma_2 + \text{etc.,} \tag{506}$$

$$\varepsilon_\mathrm{s} = t\eta_\mathrm{s} + \sigma + \mu_1\Gamma_1 + \mu_2\Gamma_2 + \text{etc.,} \tag{507}$$

$$d\sigma = -\eta_\mathrm{s}\, dt - \Gamma_1\, d\mu_1 - \Gamma_2\, d\mu_2 - \text{etc.} \tag{508}$$

Now the contact of the two homogeneous masses does not impose any restriction upon the variations of phase of either, except that the temperature and the potentials for actual components shall have the same value in both. [See (482)–(484) and (500).] For however the values of the pressures in the homogeneous masses may vary (on account of arbitrary variations of the temperature and potentials), and however the superficial tension may vary, equation (500) may always be satisfied by giving the proper curvature to the surface of tension, so long, at least, as the difference of pressures is not great. Moreover, if any of the potentials μ_1, μ_2, etc. relate to substances which are found only at the surface of discontinuity, their values may be varied by varying the superficial densities of those substances. The values of t, μ_1, μ_2, etc. are therefore independently variable, and it appears from equation (508) that σ is a function of these quantities. If the form of this function is known, we may derive from it by differentiation $n + 1$ equations (n denoting the total number of component substances) giving the values of η_s, Γ_1, Γ_2, etc. in terms of the variables just mentioned. This will give us, with (507), $n + 3$ independent equations between the $2n + 4$ quantities which occur in that equation. These are all that exist, since $n + 1$ of these quantities are independently variable. Or, we may consider that we have $n + 3$ independent equations between the $2n + 5$ quantities occurring in equation (502), of which $n + 2$ are independently variable.

An equation, therefore, between

$$\sigma, \quad t, \quad \mu_1, \quad \mu_2, \quad \text{etc.,} \tag{509}$$

may be called a fundamental equation for the surface of discontinuity. An equation between

$$s^\mathrm{s}, \quad \eta^\mathrm{s}, \quad s, \quad m_1{}^\mathrm{s}, \quad m_2{}^\mathrm{s}, \quad \text{etc.,} \tag{510}$$

or between

$$\varepsilon_\mathrm{s}, \quad \eta_\mathrm{s}, \quad \Gamma_1, \quad \Gamma_2, \quad \text{etc.,} \tag{511}$$

may also be called a fundamental equation in the same sense. For it is evident from (501) that an equation may be regarded as subsisting between the variables (510), and if this equation be known, since $n + 2$ of the variables may be regarded as independent (viz., $n + 1$ for the $n + 1$ variations in the nature of the surface of discontinuity, and one for the area of the surface considered), we may obtain by differentiation and comparison with (501), $n + 2$ additional equations between the $2n + 5$ quantities occurring in (502). Equation (506) shows that equivalent relations can be deduced from an equation between the variables (511). It is moreover quite evident that an equation between the variables (510) must be reducible to the form of an equation between the ratios of these variables, and therefore to an equation between the variables (511).

The same designation may be applied to any equation from which, by differentiation and the aid only of general principles and relations, $n + 3$ independent relations between the same $2n + 5$ quantities may be obtained.

If we set
$$\psi^s = \varepsilon^s, - t\eta^s, \tag{512}$$

we obtain by differentiation and comparison with (501)

$$d\psi^s = -\eta^s \, dt + \sigma \, ds + \mu_1 \, dm_1{}^s + \mu_2 \, dm_2{}^s + \text{etc.} \tag{513}$$

An equation, therefore, between ψ^s, t, s, $m_1{}^s$, $m_2{}^s$, etc., is a fundamental equation, and is to be regarded as entirely equivalent to either of the other fundamental equations which have been mentioned.

The reader will not fail to notice the analogy between these fundamental equations, which relate to surfaces of discontinuity, and those relating to homogeneous masses.

6. *Electrochemical Thermodynamics*

In 1851 W. Thomson (Kelvin) calculated the electromotive force of a so-called Daniell cell (a constant cell invented in 1836 by the English chemist John Frederic Daniell (1790–1845), initially concentrated copper sulphate and dilute sulphuric acid separated by an animal membrane). There was apparent agreement with the results of inaccurate experiments, but it involved the same error committed earlier by J. R. Mayer, namely, the possibility of heat being developed from the internal energy of the system, inasmuch as measurements were made at constant temperature—not at constant entropy. It was corrected in 1882 by H. L. Helmholtz via the Carnot cycle. Meanwhile, the correction had already been made by Gibbs in his implicit treatment in "Heterogeneous Equilibria". In a letter to O. Lodge in 1887, Gibbs deduced Helmholtz' equation from his own formulation of the problem, i.e. the electrical work done by the cell is equal to the decrease in the thermodynamic function ψ (not that of the internal energy of the cell). The so-called *Gibbs–Helmholtz equation* has been termed the cornerstone of electrochemical thermodynamics, viz.

$$\left(\frac{\partial \epsilon}{\partial e}\right)_t = \epsilon - \left(\frac{\partial \epsilon}{\partial t}\right)_e,$$

where e represents the quantity of electricity passing through the electric circuit.

On the Equilibria of Heterogeneous Substances.

(From the *Transactions of the Connecticut Academy of Arts and Sciences*, III, pp. 508–13 (1825–8).)

General Properties of a Perfect Electro-chemical Apparatus.

When an electrical current passes through a galvanic or electrolytic cell, the state of the cell is altered. If no changes take place in the cell except during the passage of the current, and all changes which accompany the current can be reversed by reversing the current, the cell may be called a perfect electrochemical apparatus. The electromotive force of the cell may be determined by the equations which have just been given. But some of the general relations to which such an apparatus is subject may be conveniently stated in a form in which the ions are not explicitly mentioned.

In the most general case, we may regard the cell as subject to external action of four different kinds. (1) The supply of electricity at one electrode and the withdrawal of the same quantity at the other. (2) The supply or withdrawal of a certain quantity of heat. (3) The action of gravity. (4) The motion of the surfaces enclosing the apparatus, as when its volume is increased by the liberation of gases.

The increase of the energy in the cell is necessarily equal to that which it receives from external sources. We may express this by the equation

$$d\varepsilon = (V' - V'') \, de + dQ + dW_{\mathrm{G}} + dW_{\mathrm{P}}, \tag{691}$$

in which $d\varepsilon$ denotes the increment of the intrinsic energy of the cell, de the quantity of electricity which passes through it, V' and V'' the electrical potentials in masses of the same kind of metal connected with the anode and cathode respectively, dQ the heat received from external bodies, dW_{G} the work done by gravity, and dW_P the work done by the pressures which act on the external surface of the apparatus.

The conditions under which we suppose the processes to take place are such that the increase of the entropy of the apparatus is equal to the entropy which it receives from external sources. The only external source of entropy is the heat which is communicated to the cell by the surrounding bodies. If we write $d\eta$ for the increment of entropy in the cell, and t for the temperature, we have

$$d\eta = \frac{dQ}{t} . \qquad (692)$$

Eliminating dQ, we obtain

$$d\varepsilon = (V' - V'') de + t \, d\eta + dW_G + dW_P, \qquad (693)$$

or

$$V'' - V' = -\frac{d\varepsilon}{de} + t \frac{d\eta}{de} + \frac{dW_G}{de} + \frac{dW_P}{de} . \qquad (694)$$

It is worth while to notice that if we give up the condition of the reversibility of the processes, so that the cell is no longer supposed to be a perfect electrochemical apparatus, the relation (691) will still subsist. But, if we still suppose, for simplicity, that all parts of the cell have the same temperature, which is *necessarily* the case with a perfect electro-chemical apparatus, we shall have, instead of (692),

$$d\eta \geqq \frac{dQ}{t} , \qquad (695)$$

and instead of (693), (694)

$$(V'' - V') de \leqq -d\varepsilon + t \, d\eta + dW_G + dW_P. \qquad (696)$$

The values of the several terms of the second member of (694), for a given cell, will vary with the external influences to which the cell is subjected. If the cell is enclosed (with the products of electrolysis) in a rigid envelop, the last term will vanish. The term relating to gravity is generally to be neglected. If no heat is supplied or withdrawn, the term containing $d\eta$ will vanish. But in the calculation of the electromotive force, which is the most important application of the equation, it is generally more convenient to suppose that the temperature remains constant.

The quantities expressed by the terms containing dQ and $d\eta$ in (691), (693), (694), and (696) are frequently neglected in the consideration of cells of which the temperature is supposed to remain constant. In other words, it is frequently assumed that neither heat nor cold is produced by the passage of an electrical current through a perfect electro-chemical combination (except that heat which may be indefinitely diminished by increasing the time in which a given quantity of electricity passes), and that only heat can be produced in any cell, unless it be by processes of a secondary nature, which are not immediately or necessarily connected with the process of electrolysis.

It does not appear that this assumption is justified by any sufficient reason. In fact, it is easy to find a case in which the electromotive force is determined entirely by the term $t\dfrac{d\eta}{de}$ in (694), all the other terms in the second member of the equation vanishing. This is true of a Grove's gas battery charged with hydrogen and nitrogen. In this case, the hydrogen passes over to the nitrogen,—a process which does not alter the energy of the cell, when maintained at a constant temperature. The work done by external pressures is evidently nothing, and that done by gravity is (or may be) nothing. Yet an electrical current is produced. The work done (or which may be done) by the current outside of the cell is the equivalent of the work (or of a part of the work) which might be gained by allowing the gases to mix in other ways. This is equal, as has been shown by Lord Rayleigh,* to the work which may be gained by allowing each gas separately to expand at constant temperature from its initial volume to the volume occupied by the two gases together. The same work is equal, as appears from equations (278), (279) on page 137, to the increase of the entropy of the system multiplied by the temperature.

It is possible to vary the construction of the cell in such a way that nitrogen or other neutral gas will not be necessary. Let the cell consist of a U-shaped tube of sufficient height, and have pure hydrogen at each pole under very unequal pressures (as of one and two atmospheres respectively) which are maintained constant by properly weighted pistons, sliding in the arms of the tube. The difference of the pressures in the gas-masses at the two electrodes must of course be balanced by the difference in the height of the two columns of acidulated water. It will hardly be doubted that such an apparatus would have an electromotive force acting in the direction of a current which would carry the hydrogen from the denser to the rarer mass. Certainly the gas could not be carried in the opposite direction by an external electromotive force without the expenditure of as much electromotive work as is equal to the mechanical work necessary to pump the gas from the one arm of the tube to the other. And if by any modification of the metallic electrodes (which remain unchanged by the passage of electricity) we could reduce the passive resistances to zero, so that the hydrogen could be carried reversibly from one mass to the other without finite variation of the electromotive force, the only possible value of the electromotive force would be represented by the expression $t\dfrac{d\eta}{de}$, as a very close approximation. It will be observed that, although gravity plays an essential part in a cell of this kind by maintaining the difference of pressure in the masses of hydrogen, the electromotive force cannot possibly

* *Philosophical Magazine*, vol. xlix, p. 311.

be ascribed to gravity, since the work done by gravity, when hydrogen passes from the denser to the rarer mass, is negative.

Again, it is entirely improbable that the electrical currents caused by differences in the concentration of solutions of salts, (as in a cell containing sulphate of zinc between zinc electrodes, or sulphate of copper between copper electrodes, the solution of the salt being of unequal strength at the two electrodes,) which have recently been investigated theoretically and experimentally by MM. Helmholtz and Moser,* are confined to cases in which the mixture of solutions of different degrees of concentration will produce heat. Yet in cases in which the mixture of more and less concentrated solutions is not attended with evolution or absorption of heat, the electromotive force must vanish in a cell of the kind considered, if it is determined simply by the diminution of energy in the cell. And when the mixture produces cold, the same rule would make any electromotive force impossible except in the direction which would tend to increase the difference of concentration. Such conclusions as would be quite irreconcilable with the theory of the phenomena given by Professor Helmholtz.

A more striking example of the necessity of taking account of the variations of entropy in the cell in *a priori* determinations of electromotive force is afforded by electrodes of zinc and mercury in a solution of sulphate of zinc. Since heat is absorbed when zinc is dissolved in mercury,† the energy of the cell is increased by a transfer of zinc to the mercury, when the temperature is maintained constant. Yet in this combination, the electromotive force acts in the direction of the current producing such a transfer.‡ The couple presents certain anomalies when a considerable quantity of zinc is united with the mercury. The electromotive force changes its direction, so that this case is usually cited as an illustration of the principle that the electromotive force is in the direction of the current which diminishes the energy of the cell, i.e., which produces or allows those changes which are accompanied by evolution of heat when they take place directly. But whatever may be the cause of the electromotive force which has been observed acting in the direction from the amalgam through the electrolyte to the zinc (a force which according to the determinations of M. Gaugain is only one twenty-fifth part of that which acts in the reverse direction when pure mercury takes the place of the amalgam), these anomalies can hardly affect the general conclusions with which alone we are here concerned. If the electrodes of a cell are pure zinc and an amalgam containing zinc not in excess of the amount which the mercury will dissolve at the temperature of the experiment without losing its fluidity, and if the only change (other than thermal) accompanying a current is a transfer of zinc from one electrode to the other,—conditions which may not have been satisfied in all the experiments recorded, but which it is allowable to suppose in a theoretical discussion,

* *Annalen der Physik und Chemie*, Neue Folge, Band iii, February, 1878.
† J. Regnauld, *Comptes Rendus*, t. ii, p. 778.
‡ Gaugain, *Comptes Rendus*, t. xlii, p. 430.

and which certainly will not be regarded as inconsistent with the fact that heat is absorbed when zinc is dissolved in mercury,—it is impossible that the electromotive force should be in the direction of a current transferring zinc from the amalgam to the electrode of pure zinc. For, since the zinc eliminated from the amalgam by the electrolytic process might be re-dissolved directly, such a direction of the electromotive force would involve the possibility of obtaining an indefinite amount of electromotive work, and therefore of mechanical work, without other expenditure than that of heat at the constant temperature of the cell.

None of the cases which we have been considering involve combinations by definite proportions, and, except in the case of the cell with electrodes of mercury and zinc, the electromotive forces are quite small. It may perhaps be thought that with respect to those cells in which combinations take place by definite proportions, the electromotive force may be calculated with substantial accuracy from the diminution of the energy, without regarding the variation of entropy. But the phenomena of chemical combination do not in general seem to indicate any possibility of obtaining from the combination of substances by any process whatever an amount of mechanical work which is equivalent to the heat produced by the direct union of the substances.

Electrochemical Thermodynamics.

(From the *Report of the British Association of Advanced Science*, pp. 388–9 (1887), 343–6 (1889).)

[*Since submitting proof sheets I have been favoured with the following most interesting letter from* Professor J. WILLARD GIBBS.—O.L.]

NEW HAVEN: *January* 8, 1887.

DEAR SIR,—Please accept my thanks for the proof copy of your Report on Electrolysis in its Physical and Chemical Bearings, which I received a few days ago with the invitation, as I understand it, to comment thereon.

I do not know that I have anything to say on the subjects more specifically discussed in this report, but I hope I shall not do violence to the spirit of your kind invitation or too much presume on your patience if I shall say a few words on that part of the general subject which you discussed with great clearness in your last report on pages 745, ff. (Aberdeen). To be more readily understood, I shall use your notation and terminology, and consider the most simple case possible.

Suppose that two radicles unite in a galvanic cell during the passage of a unit of electricity, and suppose that the same quantities of the radicles would give $\theta\epsilon$ units of heat in uniting directly, that is, without production of current; will the union of the radicles in the galvanic cell give $J\theta\epsilon$ units of electrical work? Certainly not, unless the radicles can produce the heat at an infinitely high temperature, which is not, so far as we know, the usual case. Suppose the highest temperature at which the heat can be produced is t'', so that at this temperature the union of the radicles with evolution of heat is a reversible process; and let t' be the temperature of the cell, both temperatures being measured on the absolute scale. Now $\theta\epsilon$ units of heat at the temperature t'' are equivalent to $\theta\epsilon\dfrac{t'}{t''}$ units of heat at the temperature t', together with $J\theta\epsilon\dfrac{t''-t'}{t''}$ units of mechanical or electrical work. (I use the term equivalent *strictly* to denote reciprocal convertibility, and not in the loose and often misleading sense in which we speak of heat and work as equivalent when there is only a one-sided convertibility.) Therefore the *rendement* of a perfect or reversible galvanic cell would be $J\theta\epsilon\dfrac{t''-t'}{t''}$ units of electrical work, with $\theta\epsilon\dfrac{t''}{t'}$ units of (reversible) heat, for each unit of electricity which passes.

You will observe that we have thus solved a very different problem from that which finds its answer in the Joule-Helmholtz-Thomson equation with term for reversible heat. That equation gives a relation between the E. M. F. and the reversible heat and certain other quantities, so that if we set up the cell and measure the reversible heat, we may determine the E. M. F. without direct measurement, or *vice versa*. But the considerations just adduced enable us to predict both the electro-motive force and the reversible heat without setting up the cell at all. Only in the case that the reversible heat is zero does this distinction vanish, and not then unless we have some way of knowing *à priori* that this is the case.

From this point of view it will appear, I think, that the production of reversible heat is by no means anything accidental, or superposed, or separable, but that it belongs to the very essence of the operation.

The thermochemical data on which such a prediction of E. M. F. and reversible heat is based must be something more than the heat of union of the radicles. They must give information on the more delicate question of the temperature at which that heat can be obtained. In the terminology of Clausius they must relate to entropy as well as to energy—a field of inquiry which has been far too much neglected.

Essentially the same view of the subject I have given in a form more general and more analytical, and, I fear, less easily intelligible, in the closing pages of a somewhat lengthy paper on the Equilibrium of Heterogeneous Substances ('Conn. Acad. Trans.,' Vol. III., 1878), of which I send you the Second Part, which contains the passage in question. My separate edition of the First Part has long been exhausted. The question whether the 'reversible heat' is a negligible quantity is discussed somewhat at length on pp. 510–519. On page 503 is shown the connection between the electromotive force of a cell and the difference in the value of (what I call) the *potential of one of the ions* at the electrodes. The definition of the *potential for a material substance*, in the sense in which I use the term, will be found on page 443 of the synopis from the 'Am. Jour. Sci.,' vol. xvi., which I enclose. I cannot say that the term has been adopted by physicists. It has, however, received the unqualified commendation of 'Professor Maxwell (although not with reference to this particular application—See his lecture on the Equilibrium of Heterogeneous Substances, in the science conferences at South Kensington, 1876); and I do not see how we can do very well without the idea in certain kinds of investigations.

Hoping that the importance of the subject will excuse the length of this letter, I remain

Yours faithfully,
J. Willard Gibbs.

Note by the Editor.—It is perhaps hardly wise to comment on the letter of so great an authority without further consideration, but it naturally occurs to one to ask provisionally whether he is not regarding a galvanic cell as too simply a heat engine? Surely if the union of certain elements can generate $\theta\epsilon$ units of heat when heat-production is all that is allowed, they can, under favourable circumstances, do $J\theta\epsilon$ units of (say) electrical work instead, quite independently of any considerations of entropy or of the temperature at which the heat might have been generated? In other words, is Professor Gibbs not assuming that in a cell the union of elements primarily produces heat, and secondarily propels a current, instead of (as may well be the case) primarily generating a current, and secondarily producing heat when that current is given nothing better to do? To this Professor Gibbs will doubtless reply: No, the highest temperature at which the heat could reversibly be produced, viz., the temperature of complete dissociation of the compound formed, is of the essence of the question, whatever be the mode of exciting the current. It is needless to point out the extreme interest and importance of such a view.   O. L.

Electro-Chemical Thermo-Dynamics. (Letter from Professor Willard Gibbs *to the Secretary of the Electrolysis Committee of the British Association.)*

New Haven: *November* 21, 1887.

Professor Oliver J. Lodge,

Dear Sir,—As the letter which I wrote you some time since concerning the *rendement* of a perfect or reversible galvanic cell seems to have occasioned some discussion, I should like to express my views a little more fully.

It is easy to put the matter in the canonical form of a Carnot's cycle. Let a unit of electricity pass through the cell producing certain changes. We may suppose the cell brought back to its original condition by some reversible chemical process, involving a certain expenditure (positive or negative) of work and heat, but involving no electrical current nor any permanent changes in other bodies except the supply of this work and heat.

Now the first law of thermo-dynamics requires that the algebraic sum of all the work and heat (measured in 'equivalent' units) supplied by external bodies during the passage of the electricity through the cell, and the subsequent processes by which the cell is restored to its original condition, shall be zero.

And the second law requires that the algebraic sum of all the heat received from external bodies, divided, each portion thereof, by the absolute temperature at which it is received, shall be zero.

Let us write W for the work and Q for the heat supplied by external bodies during the passage of the electricity, and [W], [Q] for the work and heat supplied in the subsequent processes.

Then
$$W + Q + [W] + [Q] = 0, \qquad (1)$$

and
$$\frac{Q}{t'} + \int \frac{d[Q]}{t} = 0, \qquad (2)$$

where t under the integral sign denotes the temperature at which the element of heat $d[Q]$ is supplied, and t' the temperature of the cell, which we may suppose constant.

Now the work W includes that required to carry a unit of electricity from the cathode having the potential V'' to the anode having the potential V'. (These potentials are to be measured in masses of the same kind of metal attached to the electrodes.) When there is any change of volume, a part of the work will be done by the atmosphere or other body enclosing the cell. Let this part be denoted by W_P. In some cases it may be necessary to add a term relating to gravity, but as such considerations are somewhat foreign to the essential nature of the problem which we are considering, we may set such cases aside. We have then
$$W = V' - V'' + W_P. \qquad (3)$$

Combining these equations we obtain
$$V'' - V' = W_P + [W] + [Q] - t' \int \frac{d[Q]}{t} \qquad (4)$$

It will be observed that this equation gives the electromotive force in terms of quantities which may be determined *without setting up the cell.*

Now [W] + [Q] represents the increase of the intrinsic energy of the substances in the cell during the processes to which the brackets relate, and $\int \frac{d[Q]}{t}$ represents their increase of entropy during the same processes. The same expressions, therefore, with the contrary signs, will represent the increase of energy and entropy in the cell during the passage of the current. We may therefore write
$$V'' - V' = -\Delta\epsilon + t' \Delta\eta + W_P \qquad (5)$$

where $\Delta\epsilon$ and $\Delta\eta$ denote respectively the increase of energy and entropy in the cell during the passage of a unit of electricity. This equation is identical in meaning, and nearly so in form, with equation (694) of the paper cited in my former letter, except that the latter contains the term relating to gravity. See 'Trans. Connect. Acad.'' III. (1878), p. 509. The matter is thus reduced to a question of energy and entropy. Thus, if we knew the energy and entropy of oxygen and hydrogen at the temperature and pressure at which they are disengaged in an electrolytic cell, and also the energy and entropy of the acidulated water from which they are set free (the latter, in strictness, as functions of the degree of concentration of the acid), we could at once determine the electromotive force for a reversible cell. This would be a limit below which the electromotive force required in an actual cell used electrolytically could not fall, and above which the electromotive force of any such cell used to produce a current (as in a Grove's gas battery) could not reach.

Returning to equation (4), we may observe that if t under the integral sign has a constant value, say t'', the equation will reduce to

$$V'' - V' = \frac{t'' - t'}{t''} [Q] + [W] + W_P. \tag{6}$$

Such would be the case if we should suppose that at the temperature t'' the chemical processes to which the brackets relate take place reversibly with evolution or absorption of heat, and that the heat required to bring the substances from the temperature of the cell to the temperature t'', and that obtained in bringing them back again to the temperature of the cell, may be neglected as counterbalancing each other. This is the point of view of my former letter. I do not know that it is necessary to discuss the question whether any such case has a real existence. It appears to me that in supposing such a case we do not exceed the liberty usually allowed in theoretical discussions. But if this should appear doubtful, I would observe that the equation (6) must hold in all cases if we give a slightly different definition to t'', viz., if t'' be defined as a temperature determined so that

$$\frac{[Q]}{t''} = \int \frac{d[Q]}{t}. \tag{7}$$

The temperature t'', thus defined, will have an important physical meaning. For by means of perfect thermo-dynamic engines we may change a supply of heat $[Q]$ at the constant temperature t'' into a supply distributed among the various temperatures represented by t in the manner implied in the integral, or *vice versa*. We may therefore, while vastly complicating the experimental operations involved, obtain a theoretical result which may be very simply stated and discussed. For we now see that after the passage of the current we may (theoretically) by reversible processes bring back the cell to its original state simply by the expenditure of the heat $[Q]$ supplied at the temperature t'', with perhaps a certain amount of work represented by $[W]$, and that the electromotive force of the cell is determined by these quantities in the manner indicated by equation (6), which may sometimes be further simplified by the vanishing of $[W]$ and W_P.

If the current causes a separation of radicles, which are afterwards united with evolution of heat, $[Q]$ being in this case negative, t'' represents the highest temperature at which this heat can be obtained. I do not mean the highest at which any part of the heat can be obtained—that would be quite indefinite—but the highest at which the whole can be obtained. I should add that if the effect of the union of the radicles is obtained partly in work—[W], and partly in heat—[Q], we may vary the proportion of work and heat; and t'' will then vary directly as [Q]. But if the effect is obtained entirely in heat, t'' will have a perfectly definite value.

It is easy to show that these results are in complete accordance with Helmholtz's differential equation. We have only to differentiate the value which we have found for the electromotive force. For this purpose equation (5) is most suitable. It will be convenient to write E for the electromotive force $V' - V''$, and for the differences $\Delta\epsilon$, $\Delta\eta$ to write the fuller forms $\epsilon'' - \epsilon'$, $\eta'' - \eta'$, where the single and double accents distinguish the values before and after the passage of the current. We may also set $p(v' - v'')$ for W_P, where p is the pressure (supposed uniform) to which the cell is subjected, and $v'' - v'$ is the increase of volume due to the passage of the current. If we also omit the accent on the t, which is no longer required, the equation will read

$$E = \epsilon'' - \epsilon' - t(\eta'' - \eta') + p(v'' - v'). \tag{8}$$

If we suppose the temperature to vary, the pressure remaining constant, we have

$$dE = d\epsilon'' - d\epsilon' - t\,d\eta'' + t\,d\eta' - (\eta'' - \eta')\,dt + p\,dv'' - p\,dv' \tag{9}$$

Now, the increase of energy $d\epsilon'$ is equal to the heat required to increase the temperature of the cell by dt diminished by the work done by the cell in expanding. Since $d\eta'$ is the heat imparted divided by the temperature, the heat imparted is $t\,d\eta'$, and the work is obviously $p\,dv'$. Hence

$$d\epsilon' = t\,d\eta' - p\,dv',$$

and in like manner

$$d\epsilon'' = t\,d\eta'' - p\,dv''.$$

If we substitute these values, the equation becomes

$$dE = (\eta' - \eta'')\,dt \tag{10}$$

We have already seen that $\eta' - \eta''$ represents the integral $\int \dfrac{d[Q]}{t}$ of equations (2) and (4), which by equation (2) is equal to the reversible heat evolved, $-Q$, divided by the temperature of the cell, which we now call t. Substitution of this value gives

$$\frac{dE}{dt} = -\frac{Q}{t}, \tag{11}$$

which is Helmholtz's equation.

These results of the second law of thermo-dynamics are of course not to be applied to any real cells, except so far as they approach the condition of reversible action. They give, however, in many cases limits on one side of which the actual values must lie. Thus, if we set $\leqq$ for $=$ in equations (2), (4), (5), (6), and $\geqq$ for $=$ in (8), the formula will there hold true without the limitation of reversibility. But we cannot get anything by differentiating an inequality, and it does not appear *à priori* which side of (10) is the greater when the condition of reversibility is not satisfied. The term $\dfrac{Q}{t}$ in (11) is certainly not greater than $\eta'' - \eta'$, for which it was substituted. But this does not determine which side of (11) is the greater in case of irreversibility. It is the same with Helmholtz's method of proof, which is quite different from that here given, but indicates nothing except so far as the condition of reversibility is fulfilled. (See 'Sitzungsberichte, Berl. Acad.,' 1882, pp. 24, 25.)

I fear that it is a poor requital for the kind wish which you expressed at Manchester, that I were present to explain and support my position, for me to impose so long a letter upon you. Trusting, however, in your forbearance, I remain yours faithfully,

J. WILLARD GIBBS.

CHAPTER 5

On the Theory of Light

In 1690 the Dutch physicist Christiaan Huygens (1629–95) proposed a longitudinal wave theory of light. Meanwhile, the English mathematician and physicist Sir Isaac Newton (1642–1727) had proposed a space-filling elastic medium capable of propagating vibrations. The wave theory was revived in 1801 as a transversal vibration by the English physician and physicist Thomas Young (1773–1829) and in 1815 by the French physicist Augustin Jean Fresnel (1788–1827). It was evident that the luminiferous medium, the so-called ether, would have to have the properties of an elastic solid rather than those of a fluid. This type of theory was developed in 1830 by the French mathematician Augustin Louis Cauchy (1789–1857). More successful models were devised in 1839 by the English mathematician George Green (1793–1841) and by the Irish physicist James MacCullough (1809–47). In 1873 J. C. Maxwell formulated the electromagnetic theory of light. Gibbs, who had been interested in optics at the beginning of his teaching career, found his interest reviewed. In 1882–3 he published three papers on the application of Maxwell's theory to the propagation of light in crystals. They illustrated his general avoidance of special hypotheses with respect to the structure of matter. Two of his basic assumptions are as true today as then, viz. (1) the motion in a fine-grained unit volume is the sum of the average regular motion and an irregular component whose average is zero, and (2) the frequency of the light vibrations is the same as that of the excited medium. His third assumption was a novel conception of Maxwell's electric displacement; the fourth assumption was that the irregular displacement was a linear function of the regular (first paper) and also of its space-rate of change (second paper). The first two papers deduced theoretically the phenomena of double refraction of certain crystals (Fresnel's laws), the normal dispersion of colors, and the circular and elliptical polarization shown naturally by some substances. The restriction to transparent media was removed in the third paper (given here); a general equation was devised for the propagation of monochromatic radiation. Owing to his different definition of electric displacement from that of Maxwell, Gibbs' equation differed from Maxwell's (except for transparent media). Although the theoretical predictions agreed with experimental results, the method of Gibbs was not generally pursued by others owing partly to Maxwell's prestige and partly to the development of electron theory by H. A. Lorentz—not to mention his own general reluctance not to speculate on the constitution of matter. Although Gibbs apparently never abandoned the idea of an ether, he was quite critical of the ultra-mechanistic speculations requisite for W. Thomson's (Kelvin) quasi-labile ether (1888). In 1886 Gibbs showed that the American physicist Albert Abraham Michelson's (1852–1931) measurement (1885) of the speed of light in carbon disulphide was strictly its group speed.

Notes on the Electromagnetic Theory of Light; On the General Equations of Monochromatic Light in Media of Every Degree of Transparency.

(From the *American Journal of Science*, xxv, pp. 107–18 (1883).)

1. The last April and June numbers of this Journal* contain an investigation of the velocity of plain waves of light, in which they are regarded as consisting of solenoidal electrical boxes in an indefinitely extended medium of uniform and very fine-grained structure. It was also supposed that the medium was perfectly transparent, although without discussion of the physical properties on which transparency depends, and that the electrical motions were not complicated by any distinctively magnetic phenomena.

In the present paper† the subject will be treated with more generality, so as to obtain the general equations of monochromatic light for media of every degree of transparency, whether sensibly homogeneous or otherwise, which

---

* See volume xxiii of this Journal, pages 206–275, and 460–476.

† This paper contains, with some additional developments, the substance of a communication to the National Academy of Sciences in November, 1882.

have a very find-grained molecular structure as measured by a wave-length of light. There will be no restriction with respect to magnetic influence, except that an oscillating magnetization of the medium will be excluded.*

In order to conform as much as possible to the ordinary view of electrical phenomena,† we shall not introduce at first the hypothesis of Maxwell that electrical fluxes are solenoidal.‡ Our results however, will be such as to require us to admit the substantial truth of this hypothesis, if we regard the processes involved in the transmission of light as electrical.

With regard to the undetermined questions of electrodynamic induction, we shall adopt provisionally that hypothesis which appears the most simple, yet proceed in such a manner that it will be evident exactly how our results must be altered, if we prefer any other hypothesis.

---

* Where a body capable of magnetization is subjected to the influence of light (as when light is reflected from the surface of iron) there are two simple hypotheses which present themselves with respect to the magnetic state of the body. One is that the magnetic forces due to the light are not of sufficient duration to show the molecular changes which constitute magnetization to take place to any notable extent. The other is that the magnetization has a constant ratio to the magnetic force without regard to its duration. We might easily make a more general hypothesis which would embrace both of those mentioned as extreme cases and which would be irreproachable from a theoretical stand-point; but it could complicate our equations to a degree which would not be compensated by their greater generality, since no phenomena depending on such magnetization have been observed, so far as the writer is aware, or are likely to be, except in a very limited class of cases.

For the purposes of this paper, therefore, it has seemed better to exclude media capable of magnetization, except so far as the first mentioned hypothesis may be applicable. But it does not appear that this requires us to exclude cases in which the medium is subject to the influence of a permanent magnetic force, such as produces the phenomenon of the magnetic rotation of the plane of polarization.

† It has, perhaps, retarded the acceptance of the electromagnetic theory of light that it was presented in connection with a theory of electrical action, which is probably more difficult to prove or disprove, and certainly presents more difficulties of comprehension, than the connection of optical and electrical phenomena, and which, as resting largely on *a priori* considerations, must naturally appear very differently to different minds. Moreover, the mathematical method by which the subject was treated, while it will remain a striking monument of its author's originality of thought, and profoundly modify the development of mathematical physics, must nevertheless, by its wide departure from ordinary methods, have tended to repel such as might not make it a matter of serious study.

‡ A flux is said to be *solenoidal* when it satisfies the conditions which characterize the motion of an incompressible fluid,—in other words, if u, v, w are the rectangular components of the flux, when

$$\frac{du}{dx} + \frac{dv}{dy} + \frac{dw}{dz} = 0,$$

and the normal component of the flux is the same on both sides of any surfaces of discontinuity which may exist.

Electrical quantities will be treated as measured in electromagnetic units.
2. We must distinguish, as before, between the *actual* electrical displacements, which are too complicated to follow in detail with analysis, and which in their minutiae elude experimental demonstration, and the displacements as *averaged* for spaces which are large enough to smooth out their minor irregularities, but not so large as to obliterate to any sensible extent those more regular features of the electrical motion, which form the subject of optical experiment. These spaces must therefore be large as measured by the least distances between molecules, but small as measured by a wave-length of light. We shall also have occasion to consider similar averages for other quantities, as electromotive force, the electrostatic potential, etc. It will be convenient to suppose that the space for which the average is taken is the same in all parts of the field,* say a sphere of uniform radius having its center at the point considered.

Whatever may be the quantities considered, such averages will be represented by the notation

$$[\quad]_{Ave}$$

If, then, ξ, η, ζ denote the components of the actual displacement at the point considered,

$$[\xi]_{Ave}, \quad [\eta]_{Ave}, \quad [\zeta]_{Ave}$$

will represent the average values of these components in the small sphere about that point. These average values we shall treat as functions of the coördinates of the center of the sphere and of the time, and may call them, for brevity, the *average values* of ξ, η, ζ. But however they may be designated, it is essential to remember that it is a space-average for a certain very small space, and never a time-average, that is intended.

The object of this paper will be accomplished when we have expressed (explicitly or implicitly), the relations which subsist between the values of $[\xi]_{Ave}$, $[\eta]_{Ave}$, $[\zeta]_{Ave}$, at different times and in different parts of the field,—in other words, when we have found the conditions which these quantities must satisfy as functions of the time and the coördinates.

3. Let us suppose that luminous vibrations of any one period† are somewhere excited, and that the disturbance is propagated through the medium. The motions which are excited in any part of the medium, and the forces by which they are kept up, will be expressed by harmonic functions of

---

* This is rather to fix our ideas, than on account of any mathematical necessity. For the space for which the average is taken may in general be considerably varied without sensibly affecting the value of the average.

† There is no real loss of generality in making the light monochromatic, since in every case it may be divided into parts, which are separately propagated, and each of which is monochromatic to any required degree of approximation.

the time, having the same period,* as may be proved by the single principle of the superposition of motions, quite independently of any theory of the constitution of the medium, or of the nature of the motions, as electrical or otherwise. This is equally true of the actual motions, and of the averages which we are to consider. We may therefore set

$$[\xi]_{\text{Ave}} = a_1 \cos \frac{2\pi}{p} t + a_2 \sin \frac{2\pi}{p} t, \biggr\} \tag{1}$$
$$\text{etc.,}$$

where t denotes the time, p the period, and a_1, a_2, functions of the coördinates. It follows that

$$[\ddot{\xi}]_{\text{Ave}} = -\frac{4\pi^2}{p^2} [\xi]_{\text{Ave}}, \biggr\} \tag{2}$$
$$\text{etc.}$$

4. Now, on the electrical theory, these motions are excited by electrical forces, which are of two kinds, distinguished as electrostatic and electrodynamic. The electrostatic force is determined by the electrostatic potential. If we write q for the actual value of the potential, and $[q]_{\text{Ave}}$ for its value as averaged in the manner specified above, the components of the actual electrostatic force will be

$$-\frac{dq}{dx}, \quad -\frac{dq}{dy}, \quad -\frac{dq}{dz};$$

and for the average values of these components in the small spaces described above we may write

$$-\frac{d[q]_{\text{Ave}}}{dx}, \quad -\frac{d[q]_{\text{Ave}}}{dy}, \quad -\frac{d[q]_{\text{Ave}}}{dz},$$

---

* It is of course possible that the expressions for the forces and displacements would have constant terms. But these will disappear, if the displacements are measured from the state of equilibrium about which the system vibrates, and we leave out of account in measuring the forces (and the electrostatic potential) that which would belong to the system in the state of equilibrium. To prevent misapprehension, it should be added that the term *electrical displacement* is *not* used in the restricted sense of *dielectric displacement* or *polarization*. The variation of the electrical displacement, as the term is used in this paper, constitutes what Maxwell calls the total motion of electricity or true current, and what he divides into two parts, which he distinguishes as the current of conduction and the variation of the electrical displacement. Such a division of the total motion of electricity is not necessary for the purposes of this paper, and the term displacement is used with reference to the total motion of electricity in a manner entirely analogous to that in which the term is ordinarily used in the theory of wave-motion.

for it will make no difference whether we take the average before or after differentiation.

5. The electrodynamic force is determined by the acceleration of electrical flux in all parts of the field, but physicists are not entirely agreed in regard to the laws by which it is determined. This difference of opinion is however of less importance, since it will not affect the result if electrical fluxes are always solenoidal. According to the most simple law, the components of the force are given by the volume-integrals

$$-\iiint \frac{\dot{\xi}}{r}\, dv, \qquad -\iiint \frac{\dot{\eta}}{r}\, dv, \qquad -\iiint \frac{\dot{\zeta}}{r}\, dv,$$

where dv represents an element of volume, and r the distance of this element from the point for which the value of the electromotive force is to be determined. In other words, the components of the force at any point are determined from the components of acceleration in all parts of the field by the same process by which (in the theories of gravitation, etc.,) the value of the potential at any point is determined from the density of matter in all parts of space, except that the sign is to be reversed. Adopting this law provisionally, at least, we may express it by saying that the components of electrodynamic force are equal to the potentials taken negatively of the components of acceleration of electrical flux. And we may write, for brevity,

$$-\text{Pot } \dot{\xi}, \qquad -\text{Pot } \dot{\eta}, \qquad -\text{Pot } \dot{\zeta},$$

for the components of force, using the symbol *Pot* to denote the operation by which the potential of a mass is derived from its density. For the average values of these components in the small spaces defined above, we may write

$$-\text{Pot } [\dot{\xi}]_{\text{Ave}}, \qquad -\text{Pot}[\dot{\eta}]_{\text{Ave}}, \qquad -\text{Pot}[\dot{\zeta}]_{\text{Ave}}$$

since it will make no difference whether we take the average before or after the operation of taking the potential.

6. If we write X, Y, Z for the components of the total electromotive force (electrostatic and electrodynamic), we have

$$[X]_{\text{Ave}} = -\text{Pot } [\dot{\xi}]_{\text{Ave}} - \frac{d[q]_{\text{Ave}}}{dx}, \Bigg\}$$
$$\text{etc.;}$$
(3)

or by (2)

$$[X]_{\text{Ave}} = \frac{4\pi^2}{p^2}\, \text{Pot}[\dot{\xi}]_{\text{Ave}} - \frac{d[q]_{\text{Ave}}}{dx}, \Bigg\}$$
$$\text{etc.}$$
(4)

It will be convenient to represent these relations by a vector notation. If we represent the displacement by U, and the electromotive force by E, the three equations of (3) will be represented by the single vector equation

$$[E]_{Ave} = -\text{Pot} \, [\ddot{U}]_{Ave} - \nabla[q]_{Ave}, \qquad (5)$$

and the three equations of (4) by the single vector equation

$$[E]_{Ave} = \frac{4\pi^2}{p^2} \, \text{Pot}[U]_{Ave} - \nabla[q]_{Ave}, \qquad (6)$$

where, in accordance with quaternionic usage, $\nabla[q]_{Ave}$ represents the vector which has for components the derivatives of $[q]_{Ave}$ with respect to rectangular coördinates. The symbol *Pot* in such a vector equation signifies that the operation which is denoted by this symbol in a scalar equation is to be performed upon each of the components of the vector.

7. We may here observe that if we are not satisfied with the law adopted for the determination of electrodynamic force, we have only to substitute for $-Pot$ in these vector equations, and in those which follow, the symbol for the operation, whatever it may be, by which we calculate the electrodynamic force from the acceleration.* For the operation must be of such a character, that if the acceleration consists of any number of parts, the force due to the whole acceleration will be the resultant of the forces due to the separate parts. It will evidently make no difference whether we take an average before or after such an operation.

8. Let us now examine the relation which subsists between the values of $[E]_{Ave}$ and $[U]_{Ave}$ for the same point, that is, between the average electromotive force and the average displacement in a small sphere with its center at the point considered. We have already seen that the forces and the displacements are harmonic functions of the time having a common period. A little consideration will show that if the average electromotive force in the sphere is given as a function of the time, the displacements in the sphere, both average and actual, must be entirely determined. Especially will this be evident, if we consider that since we have made the radius of the sphere very small in comparison with a wave-length, the average force must have sensibly the same value throughout the sphere, (that is, if we vary the position of the center of the sphere for which the average is taken by a distance not greater than the radius, the value of the average will not be sensibly affected,) and that the difference of the actual and average force at any point is entirely determined by the motions in the immediate vicinity of that point. If, then, certain oscillatory motions may be kept up in the sphere under the influence of

---

* The same would not be true of the corresponding scalar equations, (3) and (4). For one component of the force might depend upon all the components of acceleration. Such is in fact the case with the law of electromotive force proposed by Weber.

electrostatic and electrodynamic forces due to the motion in the whole field, and if we suppose the motions in and very near that sphere to be unchanged, but the motions in the remoter parts of the field to be altered, only not so as to affect the average resultant of electromotive force in the sphere, the actual resultant of electromotive force will also be unchanged throughout the sphere, and therefore the motions in the sphere will still be such as correspond to the forces.

Now the average displacement is a harmonic function of the time having a period which we suppose given. It is therefore entirely determined for the whole time the vibrations continue by the values of the six quantities

$$[\xi]_{\text{Ave}}, \quad [\eta]_{\text{Ave}}, \quad [\zeta]_{\text{Ave}}, \quad [\dot{\xi}]_{\text{Ave}}, \quad [\dot{\eta}]_{\text{Ave}}, \quad [\dot{\zeta}]_{\text{Ave}}$$

at any one instant. For the same reason the average electromotive force is entirely determined for the whole time by the values of the six quantities

$$[X]_{\text{Ave}}, \quad [Y]_{\text{Ave}}, \quad [Z]_{\text{Ave}}, \quad [\dot{X}]_{\text{Ave}}, \quad [\dot{Y}]_{\text{Ave}}, \quad [\dot{Z}]_{\text{Ave}}$$

for the same instant. The first six quantities will therefore be functions of the second, and the principle of the superposition of motions requires that they shall be homogeneous functions of the first degree. And the second six quantities will be homogeneous functions of the first degree of the first six. The coefficients by which these functions are expressed will depend upon the nature of the medium in the vicinity of the point considered. They will also depend upon the period of vibration, that is, upon the color of the light.*

We may therefore write in vector notation

$$[\mathsf{E}]_{\text{Ave}} = \Phi[\mathsf{U}]_{\text{Ave}} + \Psi[\dot{\mathsf{U}}]_{\text{Ave}} \tag{7}$$

where Φ and Ψ denote linear functions.†

The optical properties of media are determined by the form of these functions. But all forms of linear functions would not be consistent with the principle of the conservation of energy.

In media which are more or less opaque, and which therefore absorb energy, Ψ must be of such a form that the function always makes an acute

---

* The relations between the displacements in one of the small spaces considered and the average electromotive force is mathematically analogous to the relation between the displacements in a system of a high degree of complexity and certain forces exerted from without, which are harmonic functions of the time and under the influence of which the system vibrates. The ratio of the displacements to the forces will in general vary with the period, and may vary very rapidly.

An example in which these functions vary very rapidly with the period is afforded by the phenomena of selective absorption and abnormal dispersion.

† A vector is said to be a linear function of another, when the three components of the first are homogeneous functions of the first degree of the three components of the second.

angle (or none) with the independent variable. In perfectly transparent media Ψ must vanish, unless the function is at right angles to the independent variable. So far as is known, the last occurs only when the medium is subject to magnetic influence. In perfectly transparent media, the principle of the conservation of energy requires that Φ should be self-conjugate, i.e., that for three directions at right angles to one another, the function and independent variable should coincide in direction.

In all isotropic media not subject to magnetic influence, it is probable that Φ and Ψ reduce to numerical coefficients, as is certainly the case with Φ for transparent isotropic media.

9. Comparing the two values of $[E]_{Ave}$, we have

$$\frac{4\pi^2}{p^2}\,\text{Pot}[U]_{Ave} - \nabla[q]_{Ave} = \Phi[U]_{Ave} + \Psi[\dot{U}]_{Ave}. \tag{8}$$

This equation, in connection with that by which we express the solenoidal character of the displacements, if we regard them as necessarily solenoidal, or in connection with that which expresses the relation between the electrostatic potential and the displacements, if we reject the solenoidal hypothesis, may be regarded as the general equation of the vibrations of monochromatic light, considered as oscillating electrical fluxes. For the symbol *Pot*, however, we must substitute the symbol representing the operation by which electromotive force is calculated from acceleration of flux, with the negative sign, if we are not satisfied with the law provisionally adopted.

It is important to observe that the existence of molecular vibrations of ponderable matter, due to the passage of light through the medium, will not affect the reasoning by which this equation has been established, provided that the nature and intensity of these vibrations in any small part of the medium (as measured by a wave-length) are entirely determined by the electrical forces and motions in that part of the medium. But the equation would not hold in cases of molecular vibrations due to magnetic force. Such vibrations would constitute an oscillating magnetization of the medium, which has already been excluded from the discussion.

The supposition which has sometimes been made,* that electricity possesses a certain mass or inertia, would not at all affect the validity of the equation.

10. The equation may be reduced to a form in some respects more simple by the use of the so-called imaginary quantities. We shall write ι for $\sqrt{(-1)}$.

If we differentiate with respect to the time, and substitute $-\dfrac{4\pi^2}{p^2}\,[U]_{Ave}$ for $[\ddot{U}]_{Ave}$, we obtain

$$\frac{4\pi^2}{p^2}\,\text{Pot}[\dot{U}]_{Ave} - \nabla[\dot{q}]_{Ave} = \Phi[\dot{U}]_{Ave} - \frac{4\pi^2}{p^2}\,\Psi[U]_{Ave}.$$

---

* See Weber, *Abhandl. d. K. Sächs. Gesellsch. d. Wiss.*, vol. vi, pp. 593–597; Lorberg, *Crelle's Journal*, vol. lxi, p. 55.

7

If we multiply this equation by ι, either alone or in connection with any real factor, and add it to the preceding, we shall obtain an equation which will be equivalent to the two of which it is formed. Multiplying by $-\dfrac{p\iota}{2\pi}$ and adding, we have

$$\frac{4\pi^2}{p^2} \operatorname{Pot}\left([U]_{\mathrm{Ave}} - \iota \frac{p}{2\pi} [\dot{U}]_{\mathrm{Ave}}\right) - \nabla\left([q]_{\mathrm{Ave}} - \iota \frac{p}{2\pi} [\dot{q}]_{\mathrm{Ave}}\right)$$

$$= \left(\Phi + \iota \frac{2\pi}{p} \Psi\right)\left([U]_{\mathrm{Ave}} - \iota \frac{p}{2\pi} [\dot{U}]_{\mathrm{Ave}}\right).$$

If we set

$$\mathsf{W} = [U]_{\mathrm{Ave}} - \iota \frac{p}{2\pi} [\dot{U}]_{\mathrm{Ave}}, \tag{9}$$

$$\mathsf{Q} = [q]_{\mathrm{Ave}} - \iota \frac{p}{2\pi} [\dot{q}]_{\mathrm{Ave}}, \tag{10}$$

$$\Theta = \Phi + \iota \frac{2\pi}{p} \Psi, \tag{11}$$

our equation reduces to

$$\frac{4\pi^2}{p^2} \operatorname{Pot} \mathsf{W} - \nabla \mathsf{Q} = \Theta \mathsf{W}. \tag{12}$$

In this equation Θ denotes a complex linear vector function, *i.e.*, a vector function of which the X-, Y-, and Z-components are expressed in terms of the X-, Y-, and Z-components of the independent variable by means of coefficients of the form $a + \iota b$. W is a bi-vector of which the real part represents the averaged displacement $[U]_{\mathrm{Ave}}$, and the coefficient of ι the rate of increase of the same multiplied by a constant factor. This bi-vector therefore represents the average state of a small part of the field both with respect to position and velocity. We may also say that the coefficient of ι in W represents the value of the averaged displacement $[U]_{\mathrm{Ave}}$ at a time one-quarter of a vibration earlier than the time principally considered.

11. It may serve to fix our ideas to see how W is expressed as a function of the time. We may evidently set

$$[U]_{\mathrm{Ave}} = \mathsf{A}_1 \cos \frac{2\pi}{p} t + \mathsf{A}_2 \sin \frac{2\pi}{p} t$$

where A_1 and A_2 are vectors representing the amplitudes of the two parts into which the vibration is resolved. Then

$$\frac{p}{2\pi} [\dot{U}]_{\mathrm{Ave}} = -\mathsf{A}_1 \sin \frac{2\pi}{p} t + \mathsf{A}_2 \cos \frac{2\pi}{p} t,$$

and

$$[U]_{\text{Ave}} - \iota \frac{p}{2\pi} [\dot{U}]_{\text{Ave}} = (A_1 - \iota A_2)\left(\cos \frac{2\pi}{p} t + \iota \sin \frac{2\pi}{p} t\right);$$

that is, if we set $A = A_1 - \iota A_2$,

$$W = Ae^{2\pi \iota t/p}. \tag{13}$$

In like manner we may obtain

$$Q = ge^{2\pi \iota t/p}, \tag{14}$$

where g is a bi-scalar, or complex quantity of ordinary algebra. Substituting these values in (12), and cancelling the common factor containing the time, we have

$$\frac{4\pi^2}{p^2} \text{Pot } A - \nabla g = \Theta A. \tag{15}$$

Our equation is thus reduced to one between A and g, and may easily be reduced to one in A alone.* Now A represents six numerical quantities, (viz.: the three components of A_1, and the three of A_2), which may be called the six components of amplitude. The equation, therefore, substantially represents the relations between the six components of amplitude in different parts of the field.† The equation is, however, not really different from (12), since A and g are only particular values of W and Q.

12. From the general equation given above (8, 12, or 15), in connection with the solenoidal hypothesis, we may easily derive the laws of the propagation of plane waves in the interior of a sensibly homogeneous medium, and the laws of reflection and refraction at surfaces between such media. This has been done by Maxwell,‡ Lorentz,§ and others,¶ with fundamental equations more or less similar.

* The terms ∇Q, ∇q are allowed to remain in these equations, because the best manner of eliminating them will depend somewhat upon our admission or rejection of the solenoidal hypothesis.

† The representation of the six components of amplitude by a single letter should not be regarded as an analytical artifice. It only leaves undivided in our equation that which is undivided in the nature of things. The separation of the six components of amplitude is artificial, in that it introduces arbitrary elements into the discussion, viz. the directions of the axes of the coordinates, and the zero of time.

‡ *Phil. Trans.*, vol. clv (1865), p. 459, or *Treatise on Electricity and Magnetism*, Chap. XX.

§ *Schlömilch's Zeitschrift*, vol. xxii, pp. 1–30 and 205–219; xxiii, pp. 197–210.

¶ See Fitzgerald, *Phil. Trans.*, vol. clxxi, p. 691; J. J. Thomson, *Phil. Mag.*, V, vol. ix, p. 284; Rayleigh, *Phil. Mag.*, V, vol. xii, p. 81.

That the electromagnetic theory of light gives the conditions relative to the boundary of different media, which are required by the phenomena of reflection and refraction, was first shown by Helmholtz. See *Crelle's Journal*, vol. lxxii (1870), p. 57.

The method, however, by which the fundamental equation has been established in this paper seems free from certain objections which have been brought against the ordinary form of the theory. As ordinarily treated, the phenomena are made to depend entirely on the inductive capacity and the conductivity of the medium, in a manner which may be expressed by the equation

$$[U]_{Ave} = \left(\frac{K}{4\pi} - \frac{p^2C}{4\pi^2}\frac{d}{dt}\right)\left(\frac{4\pi^2}{p^2}\text{Pot}[U]_{Ave} - \nabla[q]_{Ave}\right), \qquad (16)$$

which will be equivalent to (12), if

$$W = \left(\frac{K}{4\pi} - \iota\frac{pC}{2\pi}\right)\left(\frac{4\pi^2}{p^2}\text{Pot } W - \nabla Q\right), \qquad (17)$$

where K and C denote in the most general case the linear vector functions, but in isotropic bodies the numerical coefficients, which represent inductive capacity and conductivity. By a simple transformation [see (9) and (10)], this equation becomes

$$\Theta^{-1} = \frac{K}{4\pi} - \iota\frac{pC}{2\pi}, \qquad (18)$$

where Θ^{-1} represents the function inverse to Θ.

Now, while experiment appears to verify the existence of such a law as is expressed by equation (12), it does not show that Θ has the precise form indicated by equation (16). In other words, experiment does not satisfactorily verify the relations expressed by (16) and (17), if K and C are understood to be the operators (or, in isotropic bodies, the numbers) which represent induction capacity and conductivity in the ordinary sense of the terms.

The discrepancy is most easily shown in the most simple case, when the medium is isotropic and perfectly transparent, and Θ reduces to a numerical quantity. The square of the velocity of plane waves is then equal to $\dfrac{\Theta}{4\pi}$, and equation (18) would make it independent of the period: that is, would give no dispersion of colors. The case is essentially the same in transparent bodies which are not isotropic.*

The case is worse with metals, which are characterized electrically by great conductivity, and optically by great opacity. In their papers cited above, Lorentz and Rayleigh have observed that the experiments of Jamin on the reflection of light from metallic surfaces would often require, as ordinarily interpreted on the electro-magnetic theory, a negative value for the inductive capacity of the metal. This would imply that the electrical equilibrium in the metal is unstable. The objection, therefore, is essentially the same as that which

* See note to the first paper of Lorentz, cited above, Schlömilch, vol. xxii, p. 23.

Lord Rayleigh had previously made to Cauchy's theory of metallic reflection, viz.: that the apparent mechanical explanation of the phenomena is illusory, since the numerical values given by experiment as interpreted on Cauchy's theory would involve an unstable equilibrium of the ether in the metal.*

13. All this points to the same conclusion—that the ordinary view of the phenomena is inadequate. The object of this paper will be accomplished, if it has been made clear, how a point of view more in accordance with what we know of the molecular constitution of bodies will give that part of the ordinary theory which is verified by experiment, without including that part which is in opposition to observed facts.†

While the writer has aimed at a greater degree of rigor than is usual in the establishment of the fundamental equation of monochromatic light, it is not claimed that this equation is absolutely exact. The contrary is evident from the fact that the equation does not embrace the phenomena which characterize such circularly polarising bodies as quartz. This, however, only implies the neglect of extremely small quantities—very small, for example, as compared with those which determine the dispersion of colors. In one of the papers already cited,‡ the case of a perfectly transparent body is treated with a higher degree of approximation, so as to embrace the phenomena in question.

* See *Phil. Mag.*, IV, vol. xliii (1872), p. 321.

† The consideration of the processes which we may suppose to take place in the smallest parts of a body through which light is transmitted, farther than is necessary to establish the general equation given above, is foreign to the design of this paper. Yet a word may be added with respect to the difficulties signalized in the ordinary form of the theory. The comparatively simple case of a perfectly transparent body has been examined more in detail in one of the papers already cited, where there is given an explanation of the dispersion of colors from the point of view of this paper. It is there shown that the effect of the non-homogeneity of the body in its smallest parts is to add a term to the expression for the kinetic energy of electrical waves, which for an isotropic body may be roughly described as similar to that which would be required if the electricity had a certain mass or inertia. (See especially §§7, 9 and 12, pages 266 ff. of volume xxiii of this Journal.) The same must be true of media of any degree of opacity. Now the difficulty with the optical properties of the metals is that the real part of θ (or θ^{-1}) is in some cases negative. This implies that at a moment of greatest displacement the electromotive force is in the direction opposite to the displacement instead of having the same direction, as in transparent isotropic bodies. Now a certain part of the electromotive force must be required to oppose the apparent inertia, and another part to oppose the electrical elasticity of the medium. These parts of the force must have opposite directions. In transparent bodies the latter part is by far the greater. But it need not surprise us that the former should be the greater in some metals.

It has been remarked by Lorentz that the difficulty with respect to metals would be in a measure relieved if we should suppose electricity to have the property of inertia. (See § 11 of his third paper, Schlömilch's Zeitschrift, vol. xxiii, p. 208.) But a supposition of this kind, taken literally, would involve a dispersion of colors in vacuo, and still be inadequate, as Lorentz remarks, to explain the phenomena observed in metals.

‡ See volume xxiii of this Journal, page 460.

CHAPTER 6

On Dynamics

In 1879 Gibbs formulated the customary variations of coordinates of a moving body with arbitrary variations in its acceleration by utilizing the method of J. L. Lagrange, who had applied the equilibrium principle of the French philosophical mathematician Jean Le Rond d'Alembert (1717?–83) to dynamics. In general, the conditions restricting the possible motions are given as equations of the coordinates and time. Gibbs generalized the motion to include cases where the conditions may be expressed only by inequalities. The laws of motion for a particle of mass m_0 are then given by

$$\sum_0 (X_0 - m_0\ddot{x}_0)\,\delta\ddot{x}_0 + (Y_0 - m_0\ddot{y}_0)\,\delta\ddot{y}_0 + (Z_0 - m_0\,\delta\ddot{z}_0)\,\delta\ddot{z}_0 \leq 0,$$

where x_0, y_0, z_0 are Cartesian coordinates of the particle, $\ddot{x}_0$, $\ddot{y}_0$, $\ddot{z}_0$ its acceleration components, and X_0, Y_0, Z_0 the corresponding components of the forces acting on it. Gibbs illustrated the usefulness of his method for a particle restricted to move above or on a surface so that x_i can only increase. The acceleration $\ddot{x}_0$ is determined by Gibbs' formula, whereas the classical formulation is not sufficient for its determination.

On the Fundamental Formulae of Dynamics

(From the *American Journal of Mathematics*, II, pp. 49–51 (1879).)

FORMATION OF A NEW INDETERMINATE FORMULA OF MOTION BY THE SUBSTITUTION OF THE VARIATIONS OF THE COMPONENTS OF ACCELERATION FOR THE VARIATIONS OF THE COORDINATES IN THE USUAL FORMULA.

The laws of motion are frequently expressed by an equation of the form

$$\sum [(X - m\ddot{x})\,\delta x + (Y - m\ddot{y})\,\delta y + (Z - m\ddot{z})\,\delta z] = 0, \tag{1}$$

in which

    m denotes the mass of a particle of the system considered,

    x, y, z its rectangular coordinates,

    $\ddot{x}, \ddot{y}, \ddot{z}$ the second differential coefficients of the coordinates with respect to the time,

    X, Y, Z the components of the forces acting on the particle,

    $\delta x, \delta y, \delta z$ any arbitrary variations of the coordinates which are simultaneously possible, and

    $\sum$ a summation with respect to all the particles of the system.

It is evident that we may substitute for δx, δy, δz any other expressions which are capable of the same and only of the same sets of simultaneous values.

Now if the nature of the system is such that certain functions A, B, etc. of the coordinates must be constant, or given functions of the time, we have

(2)
$$\begin{cases}
\sum\left(\dfrac{dA}{dx}\,\delta x + \dfrac{dA}{dy}\,\delta y + \dfrac{dA}{dz}\,\delta z\right) = 0, \\[2mm]
\sum\left(\dfrac{dB}{dx}\,\delta x + \dfrac{dB}{dy}\,\delta y + \dfrac{dB}{\delta z}\,\delta z\right) = 0, \\[2mm]
\text{etc.}
\end{cases}$$

These are the *equations of condition*, to which the variations in the general equation of motion (1) are subject. But if A is constant or a determined function of the time, the same must be true of $\dot{A}$ and $\ddot{A}$. Now

$$\dot{A} = \sum\left(\frac{dA}{dx}\,\dot{x} + \frac{dA}{dy}\,\dot{y} + \frac{dA}{dz}\,\dot{z}\right)$$

and

$$\ddot{A} = \sum\left(\frac{dA}{dx}\,\ddot{x} + \frac{dA}{dy}\,\ddot{y} + \frac{dA}{dz}\,\ddot{z}\right) + H,$$

where H represents terms containing only the second differential coefficients of A with respect to the coordinates, and the first differential coefficients of the coordinates with respect to the time. Therefore, if we conceive of a variation affecting the accelerations of the particles at the time considered, but not their positions or velocities, we have

(3)
$$\begin{cases}
\delta\dot{A} = \sum\left(\dfrac{dA}{dx}\,\delta\ddot{x} + \dfrac{dA}{dy}\,\delta\ddot{y} + \dfrac{dA}{dz}\,\delta\ddot{z}\right) = 0, \\[2mm]
\text{and, in like manner,} \\[2mm]
\delta B = \sum\left(\dfrac{dB}{dx}\,\delta\ddot{x} + \dfrac{dB}{dy}\,\delta\ddot{y} + \dfrac{dB}{dz}\,\delta\ddot{z}\right) = 0, \\[2mm]
\text{etc.}
\end{cases}$$

Comparing these equations with (2), we see that when the *accelerations* of the particles are regarded as subject to the variation denoted by δ, but not their positions or velocities, the possible values of $\delta\ddot{x}$, $\delta\ddot{y}$, $\delta\ddot{z}$ are subject to precisely the same restrictions as the values of δx, δy, δz, when the *positions* of the particles are regarded as variable. We may, therefore, write for the general equation of motion

$$(4) \qquad \sum[(X - m\ddot{x})\,\delta\ddot{x} + (Y - m\ddot{y})\,\delta\ddot{y} + (Z - m\ddot{z})\,\delta\ddot{z}] = 0,$$

regarding the positions and velocities of the particles as unaffected by the variation denoted by δ,—a condition which may be expressed by the equations

$$(5) \qquad \begin{cases} \delta x = 0, & \delta y = 0, & \delta z = 0, \\ \delta\dot{x} = 0, & \delta\dot{y} = 0, & \delta\dot{z} = 0. \end{cases}$$

We have so far supposed that the conditions which restrict the possible motions of the systems may be expressed by *equations* between the coordinates alone or the coordinates and the time. To extend the formula of motion to cases in which the conditions are expressed by the characters $\leqq$ or $\geqq$, we may write

$$(6) \qquad \sum[(X - m\ddot{x})\,\delta\ddot{x} + (Y - m\ddot{y})\,\delta\ddot{y} + (Z - m\ddot{z})\,\delta z] \leqq 0.$$

The conditions which determine the possible values of $\delta\ddot{x}$, $\delta\ddot{y}$, $\delta\ddot{z}$ will not, in such cases, be entirely similar to those which determine the possible values of δx, δy, δz, when the coordinates are regarded as variable. Nevertheless, the laws of motion are correctly expressed by the formula (6), while the formula

$$(7) \qquad \sum[(X - m\ddot{x})\,\delta x + (Y - m\ddot{y})\,\delta y + (Z - mz)\,\delta z] \leqq 0,$$

does not, as naturally interpreted, give so complete and accurate an expression of the laws of motion.

This may be illustrated by a simple example.

Let it be required to find the acceleration of a material point, which, at a given instant, is moving with given velocity on the frictionless surface of a body (which it cannot penetrate, but which it may leave), and is acted on by given forces. For simplicity, we may suppose that the normal to the surface, drawn outward from the moving point at the moment considered, is parallel to the axis of X and in the positive direction. The only restriction on the values of δx, δy, δz is that

$$\delta x \geqq 0.$$

Formula (7) will therefore give

$$\ddot{x} \geqq \frac{X}{m}, \qquad \ddot{y} = \frac{Y}{m}, \qquad = \frac{Z}{m}.$$

The condition that the point shall not penetrate the body gives another condition for the value of $\ddot{x}$. If the point remains upon the surface, $\ddot{x}$ must have a certain value N, determined by the form of the surface and the velocity of the point. If the value of $\ddot{x}$ is less than this, the point must penetrate the body. Therefore,

$$\ddot{x} \geqq N.$$

But this does not suffice to determine the acceleration of the point.

CHAPTER 7

On Mathematics

(a) MULTIPLE ALGEBRA

Multiple algebra denotes the algebra of quantities which require more than a single term for their definition; for example, complex numbers are a double algebra, vectors a triple algebra, quaternions a quadruple algebra, etc. Gibbs became interested in this subject owing to the use of quaternions by J. C. Maxwell in his 1873 *A Treatise on Electricity and Magnetism*. Quaternions had been formulated in 1844 by W. R. Hamilton, who had been inspired while crossing Brougham bridge on October 16, 1844, and had then devoted the rest of his life to it—including the writing of some 800 pages on the subject; Gibbs, however, rejected quaternions as being an unnecessary superstructure for the comparatively simple physical foundations. In his letter of acceptance of the Rumford Medal in 1881, he noted: "One of the principal objects of theoretical research in any department of knowledge is to find the point of view from which the subject appears in its greatest simplicity."[18] He preferred the general approach of H. G. Grassmann, with which he had become acquainted in 1877, namely, the "Ausdehnungslehre" (ed. 1844 and 1862). He found this n-fold algebra with its various products more general and more intimately related to the rest of mathematics. (It was in line with the homogeneous coordinates introduced in 1827 by the German mathematician August Ferdinand Möbius (1790–1868) and with the geometrical multiplication used by the French mathematical engineer Barré de Saint-Venant (1797–1886).) In this period, moreover, much attention was being focused upon B. Peirce's "Linear Associative Algebra" (1881) being developed by his son, C. S. Peirce. Impressed with the simplicity and unity of multiple algebra, Gibbs devoted his 1886 Vice-Presidential Address of the American Association for the Advancement of Science at Buffalo to this subject—his only public expression of his interest in strictly "pure" mathematics. He was interested in continuing work on it at the time of his death. It is given here in its entirety, partly because of its comprehensive thought along these lines and partly because of its suggestive *obiter dicta*, e.g. "In mathematics, a part often contains the whole", and his conclusion, "We begin by studying multiple algebras; we end, I think, by studying multiple algebra".

Multiple Algebra

(From the *Proceedings of the American Association for the Advancement of Science.* Address Vice-President, Section A (Mathematics and Astronomy), **35**, pp. 37–66 (1887).)

IT has been said that "the human mind has never invented a labor-saving machine equal to algebra."[1] If this be true, it is but natural and proper that an age like our own, characterized by the multiplication of labor-saving machinery, should be distinguished by an unexampled development of this most refined and most beautiful of machines. That such has been the case, none will question. The improvement has been in every part. Even to enumerate the principal lines of advance would be a task for any one; for me an impossibility. But if we should ask, in what direction the advance has been made, which is to characterize the development of algebra in our day, we may, I think, point to that broadening of its field and methods, which gives us *multiple algebra.*

Of the importance of this change in the conception of the office of algebra, it is hardly necessary to speak: that it is really characteristic of our time will be most evident if we go back some two- or threescore years, to the time when the seeds were sown which are now yielding so abundant a harvest. The failure of Möbius, Hamilton, Grassmann, Saint-Venant to make an immediate impression upon the course of mathematical thought in any way commensurate with the importance of their discoveries is the most conspicuous evidence that the times were not ripe for the methods which they sought to introduce. A satisfactory theory of the imaginary quantities of ordinary algebra, which is essentially a simple case of multiple algebra, with difficulty obtained recognition in the first third of this century. We must observe that this *double algebra*, as it has been called, was not sought for or invented; —it forced itself, unbidden, upon the attention of mathematicians, and with its rules already formed.

[1] *The Nation*, Vol. XXXIII, p. 237.

But the idea of double algebra, once received, although as it were unwillingly, must have suggested to many minds, more or less distinctly, the possibility of other multiple algebras, of higher orders, possessing interesting or useful properties.

The application of double algebra to the geometry of the plane suggested not unnaturally to Hamilton the idea of a triple algebra which should be capable of a similar application to the geometry of three dimensions. He was unable to find a satisfactory triple algebra, but discovered at length a quadruple algebra, *quaternions*, which answered his purpose, thus satisfying, as he says in one of his letters, an intellectual want which had haunted him at least fifteen years. So confident was he of the value of this algebra, that the same hour he obtained permission to lay his discovery before the Royal Irish Academy, which he did on November 13, 1843.[1] This system of multiple algebra is far better known than any other, except the ordinary double algebra of imaginary quantities,—far too well known to require any especial notice at my hands. All that here requires our attention is the close historical connection between the imaginaries of ordinary algebra and Hamilton's system, a fact emphasized by Hamilton himself and most writers on quaternions. It was quite otherwise with Möbius and Grassmann.

The point of departure of the *Barycentrischer Calcul* of Möbius, published in 1827,—a work of which Clebsch has said that it can never be admired enough,[2]—is the use of equations in which the terms consist of letters representing points with numerical coëfficients, to express barycentric relations between the points. Thus, that the point S is the centre of gravity of weights, a, b, c, d, placed at the points A, B, C, D, respectively, is expressed by the equation

$$(a + b + c + d)S = aA + bB + cC + dD.$$

An equation of the more general form

$$aA + bB + cC + \text{etc.}, = pP + qQ + rR + \text{etc.}$$

signifies that the weights a, b, c, etc., at the points A, B, C, etc., have the same sum and the same centre of gravity as the weights p, q, r, etc., at the points P, Q, R, etc., or, in other words, that the former are barycentrically equivalent to the latter. Such equations, of which each represents four ordinary equations, may evidently be multiplied or divided by scalars,[3] may be added or subtracted, and may have their terms arranged and transposed, exactly like the ordinary equations of algebra. It follows that the elimination of letters representing

---

[1] *Phil. Mag.* (3), Vol. XXV, p. 490; *North British Review*, Vol. XLV (1866), p. 57.

[2] See his eulogy on Plücken, p. 14, *Gött. Abhandl.*, vol. XVI.

[3] I use this term in Hamilton's sense, to denote the ordinary positive and negative quantities of algebra. It may, however, be observed that in most cases in which I shall have occasion to use it, the proposition would hold without exclusion of imaginary quantities,—that this exclusion is generally for simplicity and not from necessity.

points from equations of this kind is performed by the rules of ordinary algebra. This is evidently the beginning of a quadruple algebra, and is identical, as far as it goes, with Grassmann's marvellous geometrical algebra.

In the same work we find, also, for the first time, so far as I am aware, the distinction of positive and negative consistently carried out on the designation of segments of lines, of triangles and of tetrahedra, viz., that a change in place of two letters, in such expressions as AB, ABC, $ABCD$, is equivalent to prefixing the negative sign. It is impossible to overestimate the importance of this step, which gives to designations of this kind the generality and precision of algebra.

Moreover, if A, B, C are three points in the same straight line, and D any point outside of that line, the author observes that we have

$$AB + BC + CA = 0,$$

and, also, with D prefixed,

$$DAB + DBC + DCA = 0.$$

Again, if A, B, C, D are four points in the same plane, and E any point outside of that plane, we have

$$ABC - BCD + CDA - DAB = 0,$$

and also, with E prefixed,

$$EABC - EBCD + ECDA - EDAB = 0.$$

The similarity to multiplication in the derivation of these formulae cannot have escaped the author's notice. Yet he does not seem to have been able to generalize these processes. It was reserved for the genius of Grassmann to see that AB might be regarded as the product of A and B, DAB as the product of D and AB, and $EABC$ as the product of E and ABC. That Möbius could not make this step was evidently due to the fact that he had not the conception of the addition of other multiple quantities than such as may be represented by masses situated at points. Even the addition of vectors (*i. e.*, the fact that the composition of directed lines could be treated as an addition.) seems to have been unknown to him at this time, although he subsequently discovered it, and used it in his *Mechanik des Himmels*, which was published in 1843. This addition of vectors, or *geometrical addition*, seems to have occurred independently to many persons.

Seventeen years after the *Barycentrischer Calcul*, in 1844, the year in which Hamilton's first papers on quaternions appeared in print, Grassmann published his *Lineale Ausdehnungslehre*, in which he developed the idea and the properties of the *external* or *combinatorial product*, a conception which is perhaps to be regarded as the greatest monument of the author's genius. This volume was to have been followed by another, of the nature of which some intimation was given in the preface and in the work itself. We are especially told that the *internal product*,[1] which for vectors is identical except in sign with the scalar part of Hamilton's product (just as Grassmann's external product of two vectors is practically identical with the vector part of Hamilton's product), and the *open product*,[2] which in the language of to-day would be called a matrix, were to be treated in the second volume. But both the internal product of vectors and the open product are clearly defined, and their fundamental properties indicated, in this first volume.

This remarkable work remained unnoticed for more than twenty years, a fact which was doubtless due in part to the very abstract and philosophical manner in which the subject was presented. In consequence of this neglect, the author changed his plan, and instead of a supplementary volume, published in 1862 a single volume entitled *Ausdehnungslehre*, in which were treated, in an entirely different style, the same topics as in the first volume, as well as those which he had reserved for the second.

Deferring for the moment the discussions of these topics in order to follow the course of events, we find in the year following the first *Ausdehnungslehre* a remarkable memoir of Saint-Venant[3], in which are clearly described the addition both of vectors and of oriented areas, the differentiation of these with respect to a scalar quantity, and a multiplication of two vectors and of a vector and an oriented area. These multiplications, called by the author *geometrical*, are entirely identical with Grassmann's external multiplication of the same quantities.

It is a striking fact in the history of the subject, that the short period of less than two years was marked by the appearance of well-developed and valuable systems of multiple algebra by British, German, and French authors, working apparently entirely independently of one another. No system of multiple algebra had appeared before, so far as I know, except such as were confined to additive processes with multiplication by scalars, or related to the ordinary double algebra of imaginary quantities. But the appearance of a single one of these systems would have been sufficient to mark an epoch, perhaps the most important epoch in the history of the subject.

In 1853 and 1854, Cauchy published several memoirs on what he called *clefs algébriques*.[4] These were units subject generally to combinatorial multiplication. His principal application was to the theory of elimination. In this application, as in the law of multiplication, he had been anticipated by Grassmann.

We come next to Cayley's celebrated *Memoir on the Theory of Matrices*[5] in 1858, of which Sylvester has said that it seems to him to have ushered in the reign of Algebra the Second.[6] I quote this dictum of a master as showing his opinion of the importance of the subject and of the memoir. But the foundations of the theory of matrices, regarded as multiple quantities, seem to me to

[1] See the preface.   [2] See § 172.
[3] *C. R.* Vol. XXI, p. 620.   [4] *C. R.* Vols. XXXVI, ff.   [5] *Phil. Trans.* Vol. CXLVIII.
[6] *Amer. Journ. Math.* Vol. VI, p. 271.

have been already laid in the *Ausdehnungslehre* of 1844. To Grassmann's treatment of this subject we shall recur later.

After the *Ausdehnungslehre* of 1862, already mentioned, we come to Hankel's *Vorlesungen über die complexen Zahlen*, 1867. Under this title the author treats of the imaginary quantities of ordinary algebra, of what he calls *alternirende Zahlen*, and of quaternions. These alternate numbers, like Cauchy's *clefs*, are quantities subject to Grassmann's law of combinatorial multiplication. This treatise, published twenty-three years after the first *Ausdehnungslehre*, marks the first impression which we can discover of Grassmann's ideas upon the course of mathematical thought. The transcendent importance of these ideas was fully appreciated by the author, whose very able work seems to have had considerable influence in calling the attention of mathematicians to the subject.

In 1870, Professor Benjamin Peirce published his *Linear Associative Algebra*, subsequently developed and enriched by his son, Professor C. S. Peirce. The fact that the edition was lithographed seems to indicate that even at this late date a work of this kind could only be regarded as addressed to a limited number of readers. But the increasing interest in such subjects is shown by the republication of this memoir in 1881,[1] as by that of the first *Ausdehnungslehre* in 1878.

The article on quaternions which has just appeared in the *Encyclopaedia Brittanica* mentions twelve treatises, including second editions and translations, besides the original treatises of Hamilton. That all the twelve are later than 1861 and all but two later than 1872 shows the rapid increase of interest in this subject in the last years.

Finally, we arrive at the *Lectures on the Principles of Universal Algebra* by the distinguished foreigner whose sojourn among us has given such an impulse to mathematical study in this country. The publication of these lectures, commenced in 1884 in the *American Journal of Mathematics*, has not as yet been completed,—a want but imperfectly supplied by the author's somewhat desultory publication of many remarkable papers on the same subject (which might be more definitely expressed as the algebra of matrices) in various foreign journals.

It is not an accident that this century has seen the rise of multiple algebra. The course of the development of ideas in algebra and in geometry, although in the main independent of any aid from this source, has nevertheless to a very large extent been of a character which can only find its natural expression in multiple algebra.

Our Modern Higher Algebra is especially occupied with the theory of linear transformations. Now what are the first notions which we meet in this theory? We have a set of n variables, say x, y, z, and another set, say x', y', z', which are homogeneous linear functions of the first, and therefore expressible in terms of them by means of a block of n^2 coëfficients. Here the quantities occur

---

[1] *Amer. Journ. Math.*, Vol. IV.

by sets, and invite the notations of multiple algebra. It was in fact shown by Grassmann in his first *Ausdehnungslehre* and by Cauchy nine years later, that the notations of multiple algebra afford a natural key to the subject of elimination.

Now I do not merely mean that we may save a little time or space by writing perhaps ρ for x, y and z; ρ' for x', y' and z'; and Φ for a block of n^2 quantities. But I mean that the subject as usually treated under the title of determinants has a stunted and misdirected development on account of the limitations of single algebra. This will appear from a very simple illustration. After a little preliminary matter, the student comes generally to a chapter entitled "Multiplication of Determinants," in which he is taught that the product of the determinants of two matrices may be found by performing a somewhat lengthy operation on the two matrices, by which he obtains a third matrix, and then taking the determinant of this. But what significance, what value has this theorem? For aught that appears in the majority of treatises which I have seen, we have only a complicated and lengthy way of performing a simple operation. The real facts of the case may be stated as follows:

Suppose the set of n quantities ρ' to be derived from the set ρ by the matrix Φ, which we may express by

$$\rho' = \Phi \cdot \rho;$$

and suppose the set ρ'' to be derived from the set ρ' by the matrix Ψ, *i. e.*,

$$\rho'' = \Psi \cdot \rho',$$

and

$$\rho'' = \Psi \cdot \Phi \cdot \rho;$$

it is evident that ρ'' can be derived from ρ by the operation of a single matrix, say θ, *i. e.*,

$$\rho'' = \theta \cdot \rho,$$

so that

$$\theta = \Psi \cdot \Phi.$$

In the language of multiple algebra θ is called the product of Ψ and Φ. It is of course interesting to see how it is derived from the latter, and it is little more than a schoolboy's exercise to determine this. Now this matrix θ has the property that its determinant is equal to the products of the determinants of Ψ and Φ. And this property is all that is generally stated in the books, and the fundamental property, which is all that gives the subject its interest, that θ is itself the product of Ψ and Φ in the language of multiple algebra, *i. e.*, that operating by θ is equivalent to operating successively by Φ and Ψ, is generally omitted. The chapter on this subject, in most treatises which I have seen, reads very like the play of Hamlet with Hamlet's part left out.

And what is the cause of this omission? Certainly not ignorance of the property in question. The fact that it is occasionally given would be a sufficient bar to this answer. It is because the author fails to see that his real subject is matrices and not determinants. Of course, in a certain sense, the author has a right to choose his subject. But this does not mean that the choice is unimportant, or that it should be determined by chance or by caprice. The problem well put is half solved, as we all know. If one chooses the subject ill, it will develop itself in a cramped manner.

But the case is really much worse than I have stated it. Not only is the true significance of the formation of θ from Ψ and Φ not given, but the student is often not taught to form the matrix which is the product of Ψ and Φ, but one which is the product of one of these matrices and the conjugate of the other. Thus the proposition which is proved loses all its simplicity and significance, and must be recast before the instructor can explain its true bearings to the student. This fault has been denounced by Sylvester, and if anyone thinks I make too much of the standpoint from which the subject is viewed, I will refer him to the opening paragraphs of the "Lectures on Universal Algebra" in the sixth volume of the *American Journal of Mathematics*, where, with a wealth of illustration and an energy of diction which I cannot emulate, the most eloquent of mathematicians expresses his sense of the importance of the substitution of the idea of the matrix for that of the determinant. If then so important, why was the idea of the matrix let slip? Of course the writers on this subject had it to commence with. One cannot even define a determinant without the idea of a matrix. The simple fact is that in general the writers on this subject have especially developed those ideas, which are naturally expressed in simple algebra, and have postponed or slurred over or omitted altogether those ideas which find their natural expression in multiple algebra. But in this subject the latter happen to be the fundamental ideas, and those which ought to direct the whole course of thought.

I have taken a very simple illustration, perhaps the very first theorem which meets the student after those immediately connected with the introductory definitions, both because the simplest illustration is really the best, and because I am here most at home. But the principles of multiple algebra seem to me to shed a flood of light into every corner of the subjects usually treated under the title of determinants, the subject gaining as much in breadth from the new notions as in simplicity from the new notations; and in the more intricate subjects of invariants, covariants, etc., I believe that the principles of multiple algebra are ready to perform an equal service. Certainly they make many things seem very simple to me, which I should otherwise find difficult of comprehension.

Let us turn to geometry.

If we were asked to characterize in a single word our modern geometry, we would perhaps say that it is a geometry of position. Now position is essentially a multiple quantity, or if you prefer, is naturally represented in algebra by a multiple quantity. And the growth in this century of the so-called synthetic as opposed to analytical geometry seems due to the fact that by the ordinary analysis geometers could not easily express, except in a cumbersome and unnatural manner, the sort of relations in which they were particularly interested. With the introduction of the notations of multiple algebra, this difficulty falls away, and with it the opposition between synthetic and analytical geometry.

It is, however, interesting and very instructive to observe how the ingenuity of mathematicians has often triumphed over the limitations of ordinary algebra. A conspicuous example and one of the simplest is seen in the *Mécanique Analytique*, where the author, by the use of what are sometimes called indeterminate equations, is able to write in one equation the equivalent of an indefinite number. Thus the equation

$$X\,dx + Y\,dy + Z\,dz = 0,$$

by the indeterminateness of the values of dx, dy, dz, is made equivalent to the three equations

$$X = 0, \qquad Y = 0, \qquad Z = 0.$$

It is instructive to compare this with

$$Xi + Yj + Zk = 0,$$

which is the form that Hamilton or Grassmann would have used. The use of this analytical artifice, if such it can be called, runs all through the work and is fairly characteristic of it.

Again, the introduction of the potential in the theory of gravity, or electricity, or magnetism, gives us a scalar quantity instead of a vector as the subject of study; and in mechanics generally the use of the force-function substitutes a simple quantity for a complex This method is in reality not different from that just mentioned, since Lagrange's indeterminate equation expresses, at least in its origin, the variation of the force-function. It is indeed the real beauty of Lagrange's method that it is not so much an analytical artifice, as the natural development of the subject.

In modern analytical geometry we find methods in use which are exceedingly ingenious, and give forms curiously like those of multiple algebra, but which, at least if logically carried out very far, are excessively artificial, and that for the expression of the simplest things. The simplest conceptions of the geometry of three dimensions are points and planes, and the simplest relation between these is that a point lies in a plane. Let us see how these notions have been handled by means of ordinary algebra, and by multiple algebra. It will illustrate the characteristic difference of the methods, perhaps as well as the reading of an elaborate treatise.

In multiple algebra a point is designated by a single letter, just as it is in what is called synthetic geometry, and as it generally is by the ordinary analyst, when he is not writing equations. But in his equations, instead of a single letter the analyst introduces several letters (coördinates) to represent the point.

A plane may be represented in multiple algebra as in synthetic geometry by a single letter; in the ordinary algebra it is sometimes represented by three coördinates, for which it is most convenient to take the reciprocals of the segments cut off by the plane on three axes. But the modern analyst has a more ingenious method of representing the plane. He observes that the equation of the plane may be written

$$\xi x + \eta y + \zeta z = 1, \tag{1}$$

where ξ, η, ζ are the reciprocals of the segments, and x, y, z are the coördinates of any point in the plane. Now if we set

$$p = \xi x + \eta y + \zeta z, \tag{2}$$

this letter will represent an expression which represents the plane. In fact, we may say that p implicitly contains ξ, η, and ζ, which are the coördinates of the plane. We may therefore speak of the plane p, and for many purposes can introduce the letter p into our equations instead of ξ, η, ζ. For example, the equation

$$p''' = \frac{p' + p''}{2} \tag{3}$$

is equivalent to the three equations

$$\xi''' = \frac{\xi' + \xi''}{2}, \quad \eta''' = \frac{\eta' + \eta''}{2}, \quad \zeta''' = \frac{\zeta' + \zeta''}{2}. \tag{4}$$

It is to be noticed that on account of the indeterminateness of the x, y, and z, this method, regarded as an analytical artifice, is identical with that of Lagrange, also that in multiple algebra we should have an equation of precisely the same form as (3) to express the same relation between the planes, but that the equation would be explained to the student in a totally different manner. This we shall see more particularly hereafter.

It is curious that we have thus a simpler notation for a plane than for a point. This however may be reversed. If we commence with the notion of the coördinates of a plane, ξ, η, ζ, the equation of a point (*i. e.*, the equation between ξ, η, ζ which will hold for every plane passing through the point) will be

$$x\xi + y\eta + z\zeta = 1, \tag{5}$$

where x, y, z are the coördinates of the point. Now if we set

$$q = x\xi + y\eta + z\zeta, \tag{6}$$

we may regard the single letter q as representing the point, and use it, in many cases, instead of the coördinates x, y, z, which indeed it implicitly contains.

Thus we may write

$$q''' = \frac{q' + q''}{2} \tag{7}$$

for the three equations

$$x''' = \frac{x' + x''}{2}, \quad y''' = \frac{y' + y''}{2}, \quad z''' = \frac{z' + z''}{2}. \tag{8}$$

Here, by an analytical artifice, we come to equations identical in form and meaning to those used by Hamilton, Grassmann, and even by Möbius in 1827. But the explanations of the formulae would differ widely. The methods of the founders of multiple algebra are characterized by a bold simplicity, that of the modern geometry by a somewhat bewildering ingenuity. That p and q represent the same expression (in one case x, y, z, and in the other ξ, η, ζ being indeterminate) is a circumstance which may easily become perplexing. I am not quite certain that it would be convenient to use both of these abridged notations at the same time. In fact, if the geometer using these methods were asked to express by an equation in p and q that the point q lies in the plane p, he might find himself somewhat entangled in the meshes of his own ingenuity, and need some new artifice to extricate himself. I do not mean that his genius might not possibly be equal to the occasion, but I do mean very seriously that it is a vicious method which requires any ingenuity or any artifice to express so simple a relation.

If we use the methods of multiple algebra which are most comparable to those just described, a point is naturally represented by a vector (ρ) drawn to it from the origin, a plane by a vector (σ) drawn from the origin perpendicularly toward the plane and in length equal to the reciprocal of the distance of the plane from the origin. The equation

$$\sigma''' = \frac{\sigma' + \sigma''}{2} \tag{9}$$

will have precisely the same meaning as equation (3), and

$$\rho''' = \frac{\rho' + \rho''}{2} \tag{10}$$

will have precisely the same meaning as equation (7), viz., that the point ρ''' is in the middle between ρ' and ρ''. That the point ρ lies in the plane σ is expressed by equating to unity the product of ρ and σ called by Grassmann internal, or by Hamilton called the scalar part of the product taken negatively. By whatever name called, the quantity in question is the product of the lengths of the vectors and the cosine of the included angle. It is of course immaterial what particular sign we use to express this product, as whether we write

$$\rho \cdot \sigma = 1, \quad \text{or} \quad S\rho\sigma = -1. \tag{11}$$

I should myself prefer the simplest possible sign for so simple a relation. It may be observed that ρ and σ may be expressed as the geometrical sum of their components parallel to a set of perpendicular axes, viz.,

$$\rho = xi + yj + zk, \qquad \sigma = \xi i + \eta j + \zeta k. \tag{12}$$

By substitution of these values, equation (11) becomes by the laws of this kind of multiplication

$$x\xi + y\eta + z\zeta = 1. \tag{13}$$

My object in going over these elementary matters is to call attention to the very roundabout way in which the ordinary analysis makes out to represent a point or a plane by a single letter, as distinguished from the directness and simplicity of the notations of multiple algebra, and also to the fact that the representations of points and planes by single letters in the ordinary analysis are not, when obtained, as amenable to analytical treatment as are the notations of multiple algebra.

I have compared that form of the ordinary analysis which relates to Cartesian axes with a vector analysis. But the case is essentially the same, if we compare the form of ordinary analysis which relates to a fundamental tetrahedron with Grassmann's geometrical analysis, founded on the point as the elementary quantity.

In the method of ordinary analysis, a point is represented by four coördinates, of which each represents the distance of the point from a plane of the tetrahedron divided by the distance of the opposite vertex from the same plane. The equation of a plane may be put in the form

$$\xi x + \eta y + \zeta z + \omega w = 0, \tag{14}$$

where ξ, η, ζ, ω are the distances of the plane from the four points, and x, y, z, w are the coördinates of any point in the plane. Here we may set

$$p = \xi x + \eta y + \zeta z + \omega w, \tag{15}$$

and say that p represents the plane. To some extent we can introduce this letter into equations instead of ξ, η, ζ, ω. Thus the equation

$$lp' + mp'' + np''' = 0 \tag{16}$$

(which denotes that the planes p', p'', p''', meet in a common line, making angles of which the sines are proportional to l, m, and n) is equivalent to the four equations

$$l\xi' + m\xi'' + n\xi''' = 0, \qquad l\eta' + m\eta'' + n\eta''' = 0, \text{ etc.} \tag{17}$$

Again, we may regard ξ, η, ζ, ω as the coördinates of a plane. The equation of a point will then be

$$x\xi + y\eta + z\zeta + w\omega = 0. \tag{18}$$

If we set

$$q = x\xi + y\eta + z\zeta + w\omega,\tag{19}$$

we may say that q represents the point. The equation

$$q''' = \frac{q' + q''}{2},\tag{20}$$

which indicates that the point q''' bisects the line between q' and q'', is equivalent to the four equations

$$\xi' = \frac{\xi'' + \xi'''}{2}, \qquad \eta' = \frac{\eta'' + \eta''''}{2}, \text{ etc.}\tag{21}$$

To express that the point q lies in the plane p does not seem easy, without going back to the use of coördinates.

The form of multiple algebra which is to be compared to this is the geometrical algebra of Möbius and Grassmann, in which points without reference to any origin are represented by single letters, say by Italic capitals, and planes may also be represented by single letters, say by Greek capitals. An equation like

$$Q''' = \frac{Q' + Q''}{2},\tag{22}$$

has exactly the same meaning as equation (20) of ordinary algebra. So

$$l\Pi' + m\Pi'' + n\Pi''' = 0\tag{23}$$

has precisely the same meaning as equation (16) of ordinary algebra. That the point Q lies in the plane Π is expressed by equating to zero the product of Q and Π which is called by Grassmann external and which might be defined as the distance of the point from the plane. We may write this

$$Q \times \Pi = 0.\tag{24}$$

To show that so simple an expression is really amenable to analytical treatment, I observe that Q may be expressed in terms of any four points (not in the same plane) on the barycentric principle explained above, viz.,

$$Q = xA + yB + zC + wD,\tag{25}$$

and Π may be expressed in terms of combinatorial products of A, B, C, and D, viz.,

$$\Pi = \xi B \times C \times D + \eta C \times A \times D + \zeta D \times A \times B + \omega A \times C \times B,\tag{26}$$

and by these substitutions, by the laws of the combinatorial product to be mentioned hereafter, equation (24) is transformed into

$$w\omega + x\xi + y\eta + z\zeta = 0, \tag{27}$$

which is identical with the formula of ordinary analysis.[1]

I have gone at length into this very simple point, in order to illustrate the fact which I think is a general one, that the modern geometry is not only tending to results which are appropriately expressed in multiple algebra, but that it is actually striving to clothe itself in forms which are remarkably similar to the notations of multiple algebra, only less simple and general, and far less amenable to analytical treatment, and therefore, that a certain logical necessity calls for throwing off the yoke under which analytical geometry has so long labored. And lest this should seem to be the utterance of an uninformed enthusiasm, or the echoing of the possibly exaggerated claims of the devotees of a particular branch of mathematical study, I will quote a sentence from Clebsch and from Clifford, relating to the past and to the future of multiple algebra. The former in his eulogy on Plücker,[2] in 1871, speaking of recent advances in geometry, says that "in a certain sense the coördinates of a straight line, and in general a great part of the fundamental conceptions of the newer algebra, are contained in the *Ausdehnungslehre* of 1844," and Clifford[3] in the last year of his life, speaking of the *Ausdehnungslehre*, with which he had but recently become acquainted, expresses "his profound admiration of that extraordinary work, and his conviction that its principles will exercise a vast influence upon the future of mathematical science."

Another subject in which we find a tendency toward the forms and methods of multiple algebra, is the calculus of operations. Our ordinary analysis introduces operators; and the successive operations A and B may be equivalent to the operation C. To express this in an equation we may write

$$BA(x) = C(x),$$

where x is any quantity or function. We may also have occasion to write

$$A(x) + B(x) = D(x), \quad \text{or} \quad (A + B)(x) = D(x).$$

But it is almost impossible to resist the tendency to express these relations in the form

$$BA = C,$$
$$A + B = D,$$

in which the operators appear in a sense as quantities, *i.e.*, as subjects of functional operation. Now since these operators are often of such nature that

[1] The letters ξ, η, ζ, ω, here denote the distances of the plane Π from the points A, B, C, D, divided by six times the volume of the tetrahedron A, B, C, D. The letters x, y, z, w, denote the tetrahedral coördinates as above.

[2] *Gött. Abhandl.* Vol. 16, p. 28.   [3] *Amer. Journ. Math.*, Vol. 1, p. 350.

they cannot be perfectly specified by a single numerical quantity, when we treat them as quantities they must be regarded as multiple quantities. In this way certain formulæ which essentially belong to multiple algebra get a precarious footing where they are only allowed because they are regarded as abridged notations for equations in ordinary algebra. Yet the logical development of such notations would lead a good way in multiple algebra, and doubtless many investigators have entered the field from this side.

One might also notice, to show how the ordinary algebra is becoming saturated with the notions and notations which seem destined to turn it into a multiple algebra, the notation so common in the higher algebra

$$(a, b, c)(x, y, z)$$

for

$$ax + by + cz.$$

This is evidently the same as Grassmann's internal product of the multiple quantities (a, b, c) and (x, y, z), or, in the language of quaternions, the scalar part, taken negatively, of the product of the vectors of which a, b, c and x, y, z are the components. A similar correspondence with Grassmann's methods might, I think, be shown in such notations as, for example,

$$(a, b, c, d,)(x, y)^3.$$

The free admission of such notations is doubtless due to the fact that they are regarded simply as abridged notations.

The author of the celebrated "Memoir on the Theory of Matrices," goes much farther than this in his use of the forms of multiple algebra. Thus he writes explicitly one equation to stand for several, without the use of any of the analytical artifices which have been mentioned. This work has indeed, as we have seen, been characterized as marking the commencement of multiple algebra,—a view to which we can only take exception as not doing justice to earlier writers.

But the significance of this memoir with regard to the point which I am now considering is that it shows that the chasm so marked in the second quarter of this century is destined to be closed up. Notions and notations for which a Cayley is sponsor will not be excluded from good society among mathematicians. And if we admit as suitable the notations used in this memoir (where it is noticeable that the author rather avoids multiple algebra, and only uses it very sparingly), we shall logically be brought to use a great deal more. For example, if it is a good thing to write in our equations a single letter to represent a matrix of n^2 numerical quantities, why not use a single letter to represent the n quantities operated upon, as Grassmann and Hamilton have done? Logical consistency seems to demand it. And if we may use the sign () to denote an operation by which two sets of quantities are combined to form a third set, as is the case in this memoir, why not use other signs to denote other functional operations of which the result is a multiple quantity? If it be conceded that this is the proper method to follow where simplicity of conception, or brevity of expression, or ease of transformation is served thereby, our algebra will become in large part a multiple algebra.

We have considered the subject a good while from the outside; we have glanced at the principal events in the history of multiple algebra; we have seen how the course of modern thought seems to demand its aid, how it is actually leaning toward it, and beginning to adopt its methods. It may be worth while to direct our attention more critically to multiple algebra itself, and inquire into its essential character and its most important principles.

I do not know that anything useful or interesting, which relates to multiple quantity, and can be symbolically expressed, falls outside of the domain of multiple algebra. But if it is asked, what notions are to be regarded as fundamental, we must answer, here as elsewhere, those which are most simple and fruitful. Unquestionably, no relations are more so, than those which are known by the names of addition and multiplication.

Perhaps I should here notice the essentially different manner in which the multiplication of multiple quantities has been viewed by different writers. Some, as Hamilton, or De Morgan, or Peirce, speak of the product of two multiple quantities, as if only one product could exist, at least in the same algebra. Others, as Grassmann, speak of various kinds of products for the same multiple quantities. Thus Hamilton seems for many years to have agitated the question, what he should regard as the product of each pair of a set of triplets, or in the geometrical application of the subject, what he should regard as the product of each pair of a system of perpendicular directed lines.[1] Grassmann asks, What products, *i.e.*, what distributive functions of the multiple quantities are most important?

It may be that in some cases the fact that only one kind of product is known in ordinary algebra has led those to whom the problem presented itself in the form of finding a new algebra to adopt this characteristic derived from the old. Perhaps the reason lies deeper in a distinction like that in arithmetic between concrete and abstract numbers or quantities. The multiple quantities corresponding to concrete quantities such as ten apples or three miles, are evidently such combinations as ten apples + seven oranges, three miles northward + five miles eastward, or six miles in a direction fifty degrees east of north. Such are the fundamental multiple quantities from Grassmann's point of view. But if we ask what it is in multiple algebra which corresponds to an abstract number like twelve, which is essentially an operator, which changes one mile into twelve miles, and $1,000 into $12,000, the most general answer would evidently be, an operator which will work such changes as, for example, that of ten apples + seven oranges into fifty apples + 100 oranges, or that of one vector into another.

Now an operator has, of course, one characteristic relation, viz., its relation to the operand. This needs no especial definition, since it is contained in the

---

[1] *Phil. Mag.*, (3), xxv, p. 490; *North British Review*, xlv (1866), p. 57.

definition of the operator. If the operation is distributive, it may not inappropriately be called multiplication, and the result is *par excellence* the product of the operator and operand. The sum of operators *quâ* operators, is an operator which gives for the product the sum of the products given by the operators to be added. The product of two operators is an operator which is equivalent to the successive operations of the factors. This multiplication is necessarily associative, and its definition is not really different from that of the operators themselves. And here I may observe that Professor C. S. Peirce has shown that his father's associative algebras may be regarded as operational and matricular.[1]

Now, the calculus of distributive operators is a subject of great extent and importance, but Grassmann's view is the more comprehensive, since it embraces the other with something besides. For every quantitative operator may be regarded as a quantity, *i.e.*, as the subject of mathematical operation, but every quantity cannot be regarded as an operator; precisely as in grammar every verb may be taken as substantive, as in the infinitive, while every substantive does not give us a verb.

Grassmann's view seems also the most practical and convenient. For we often use many functions of the same pair of multiple quantities, which are distributive with respect to both, and we need some simple designation to indicate a property of such fundamental importance in the algebra of such functions, and no advantage appears in singling out a particular function to be alone called the product. Even in quaternions, where Hamilton speaks of only one product of two vectors (regarding it as a special case of the product of quaternions, *i.e.*, of operators), he nevertheless comes to use the scalar part of this product and the vector part separately. Now the distributive law is satisfied by each of these, which, therefore, may conveniently be called products. In this sense we have three kinds of products of vectors in Hamilton's analysis.

Let us then adopt the more general view of multiplication, and call any function of two or more multiple quantities, which is distributive with respect to all, a product, with only this limitation, that when one of the factors is simply an ordinary algebraic quantity, its effect is to be taken in the ordinary sense.

It is to be observed that this definition of multiplication implies that we have an addition both of the kind of quantity to which the product belongs, and of the kinds to which the factors belong. Of course, these must be subject to the general formal laws of addition. I do not know that it is necessary for the purposes of a general discussion to stop to define these operations more particularly, either on their own account or to complete the definition of multiplication. Algebra, as a formal science, may rest on a purely formal foundation. To take our illustration again from mechanics, we may say that

---

[1] *Amer. Journ. Math.*, Vol. IV, p. 221.

if a man is inventing a particular machine,—a sewing machine,—a reaper,—
nothing is more important than that he should have a precise idea of the
operation which his machine is to perform, yet when he is treating the general
principles of mechanics he may discuss the lever, or the form of the teeth of
wheels which will transmit uniform motion, without inquiring the purpose to
which the apparatus is to be applied; and in like manner that if we were
forming a particular algebra,—a geometrical algebra,—a mechanical algebra,—an algebra for the theory of elimination and substitution,—an algebra
for the study of quantics,—we should commence by asking, What are the
multiple quantities, or sets of quantities, which we have to consider? What
are the additive relations between them? What are the multiplicative relations
between them? etc., forming a perfectly defined and complete idea of these
relations as we go along; but in the development of a general algebra no such
definiteness of conception is requisite. Given only the purely formal law of the
distributive character of multiplication,—this is sufficient for the foundation
of a science. Nor will such a science be merely a pastime for an ingenious
mind. It will serve a thousand purposes in the formation of particular algebras.
Perhaps we shall find that in the most important cases, the particular algebra
is little more than an application or interpretation of the general.

Grassmann observes that any kind of multiplication of n-fold quantities is
characterized by the relations which hold between the products of n independent units. In certain kinds of multiplication these characteristic relations
will hold true of the products of any of the quantities.

Thus if the value of a product is independent of the order of the factors
when these belong to the system of units, it will always be independent of the
order of the factors. The kind of multiplication characterized by this relation
and no other between the products is called by Grassmann *algebraic*, because
its rules coincide with those of ordinary algebra. It is to be observed, however,
that it gives rise to multiple quantities of higher orders. If n independent units
are required to express the original quantities, $n(n + 1)/2$ units will be required for the products of two factors, $n[(n + 1)(n + 2)/(2 \cdot 3)]$ for the
products of three factors, etc.

Again, if the value of a product of factors belonging to a system of units is
multiplied by -1 when two factors change places, the same will be true of the
product of any factors obtained by addition of the units. The kind of multiplication characterized by this relation and no other is called by Grassmann
external or *combinatorial*. For our present purpose we may denote it by the
sign $\times$. It gives rise to multiple quantities of higher orders, $n(n - 1)/2$ units
being required to express the products of two factors, $n[(n - 1)(n - 2)/
(2 \cdot 3)]$ units for products of three factors, etc. All products of more than n
factors are zero. The products of n factors may be expressed by a single unit,
viz., the product of the n original units taken in a specified order, which is
generally set equal to 1. The products of $n - 1$ factors are expressed in terms
of n units, those of $n - 2$ factors in terms of $n(n - 1)/2$ units, etc. This kind
of multiplication is associative, like the algebraic.

Grassmann observes, with respect to binary products, that these two kinds of multiplication are the only kinds characterized by laws which are the same for any factors as for particular units, except indeed that characterized by no special laws, and that for which all products are zero.[1] The last we may evidently reject as pugatory. That for which there are no special laws, *i. e.*, in which no equations subsist between the products of a system of independent units, is also rejected by Grassmann, as not appearing to afford important applications. I shall, however, have occasion to speak of it, and shall call it the indeterminate product. In this kind of multiplication, n^2 units are required to express the products of two factors, and n^3 units for products of three factors, etc. It evidently may be regarded as associative.

Another very important kind of multiplication is that called by Grassmann *internal*. In the form in which I shall give it, which is less general than Grassmann's, it is in one respect the most simple of all, since its only result is a numerical quantity. It is essentially binary and characterized by laws of the form

$$i \cdot i = 1, \quad j \cdot j = 1, \quad k \cdot k = 1, \text{ etc.,}$$
$$i \cdot j = 0, \quad j \cdot i = 0, \quad \text{etc.,}$$

where i, j, k, etc., represent a system of independent units. I use the dot as significant of this kind of multiplication.

Grassmann derives this kind of multiplication from the combinatorial by the following process. He defines the complement (Ergänzung) of a unit as the combinatorial product of all the other units, taken with such a sign that the combinatorial product of the unit and its complement shall be positive. The combinatorial product of a unit and its complement is therefore unity, and that of a unit and the complement of any other unit is zero. The internal product of two units is the combinatorial product of the first and the complement of the second.

It is important to observe that any scalar product of two factors of the same kind of multiple quantities, which is positive when the factors are identical, may be regarded as an internal product, *i.e.*, we may always find such a system of units, that the characteristic equations of the product will reduce to the above form. The nature of the subject may afford a definition of the product independent of any reference to a system of units. Such a definition will then have obvious advantages. An important case of this kind occurs in geometry in that product of two vectors which is obtained by multiplying the products of their lengths by the cosine of the angle which they include. This is an internal product in Grassmann's sense.

Let us now return to the indeterminate product, which I am inclined to regard as the most important of all, since we may derive from it the algebraic and the combinatorial. For this end, we will prefix $\sum$ to an indeterminate

[1] Crelle's *Journ. f. Math.*, Vol. XLIX, p. 138.

product to denote the sum of all the terms obtained by taking the factors in every possible order. Then,

$$\sum \alpha \,|\beta|\, \gamma,$$

for instance, where the vertical line is used to denote the indeterminate product,[1] is a distributive function of α, β and γ. It is evidently not affected by changing the order of the letters. It is, therefore, an algebraic product in the sense in which the term has been defined.

So, again, if we prefix $\Sigma \pm$ to an indeterminate product to denote the sum of all terms obtained by giving the factors every possible order, those terms being taken negatively which are obtained by an odd number of simple permutations,

$$\sum \pm\alpha \,|\beta|\, \gamma,$$

for instance, will be a distributive function of α, β, γ, which is multiplied by -1 when two of these letters change places. It will therefore be a combinatorial product.

It is a characteristic and very important property of an indeterminate product that every product of all its factors with any other quantities is also a product of the indeterminate product and the other quantities. We need not stop for a formal proof of this proposition, which indeed is an immediate consequence of the definitions of the terms.

These considerations bring us naturally to what Grassmann calls *regressive multiplication*, which I will first illustrate by a very simple example. If n, the degree of multiplicity of our original quantities, is 4, the combinatorial product of $\alpha \times \beta \times \gamma$ and $\delta \times \varepsilon$, viz.,

$$\alpha \times \beta \times \gamma \times \delta \times \varepsilon,$$

is necessarily zero, since the number of factors exceeds four. But if for $\delta \times \varepsilon$ we set its equivalent

$$\delta \,|\, \varepsilon - \varepsilon \,|\, \delta,$$

we may multiply the first factor in each of these indeterminate products combinatorially by $\alpha \times \beta \times \gamma$, and prefix the result, which is a numerical quantity, as coëfficient to the second factor. This will give

$$(\alpha \times \beta \times \gamma \times \delta)\varepsilon - (\alpha \times \beta \times \gamma \times \varepsilon)\,\delta.$$

Now, the first term of this expression is a product of $\alpha \times \beta \times \gamma$, δ and ε, and therefore, by the principle just stated, a product of $\alpha \times \beta \times \gamma$ and $\delta \,|\, \varepsilon$. The second term is a similar product of $\alpha \times \beta \times \gamma$ and $\varepsilon \,|\, \delta$. Therefore the whole expression is a product of $\alpha \times \beta \times \gamma$ and $\delta \,|\, \varepsilon - \varepsilon \,|\, \delta$, that is, of $\alpha \times \beta \times \gamma$ and $\delta \times \varepsilon$. This is, except in sign, what Grassmann calls the *regressive product* of $\alpha \times \beta \times \gamma$ and $\delta \times \varepsilon$.

---

[1] This notation must not be confounded with Grassmann's use of the vertical line.

To generalize this process, we first observe than an expression of the form

$$\sum \pm \alpha \times \beta \mid \gamma \times \delta,$$

in which each term is an indeterminate product of two combinatorial products, and in which $\sum \pm$ denotes the sum of all terms obtained by putting every different pair of the letters before the dividing line, the negative sign being used for any terms which may be obtained by an odd number of simple permutations of the letters,—in other words, the expression

$$\alpha \times \beta \mid \gamma \times \delta - \alpha \times \gamma \mid \beta \times \delta - \alpha \times \delta \mid \gamma \times \beta + \beta \times \gamma \mid \alpha \times \delta$$
$$- \beta \times \delta \mid \alpha \times \gamma + \gamma \times \delta \mid \alpha \times \beta,$$

is a distributive function of α, β, γ, and δ, which is multiplied by -1 when two of these letters change places, and may, therefore, be regarded as equivalent to the combinatorial product $\alpha \times \beta \times \gamma \times \delta$. Now, if $n = 5$, the combinatorial product of

$$\rho \times \sigma \times \tau \quad \text{and} \quad \alpha \times \beta \times \gamma \times \delta$$

is zero. But if we multiply the first member of each of the above indeterminate products by $\rho \times \sigma \times \tau$, and prefix the result as coëfficient to the second member, we obtain

$$(\rho \times \sigma \times \tau \times \alpha \times \beta)\gamma \times \delta - (\rho \times \sigma \times \tau \times \alpha \times \gamma)\beta \times \delta + \text{etc.},$$

which is what Grassmann calls the regressive product of $\rho \times \sigma \times \tau$ and $\alpha \times \beta \times \gamma \times \delta$. It is easy to see that the principle may be extended so as to give a regressive product in any case in which the total number of factors of two combinatorial products is greater than n. Also, that we might form a regressive product by treating the first of the given combinatorials as we have treated the second. It may easily be shown that this would give the same result, except in some cases with a difference of sign. To avoid this inconvenience, we may make the rule, that whenever in the substitution of a sum of indeterminate products for a combinatorial, both factors of the indeterminate products are of odd degree, we change the sign of the whole expression. With this understanding, the results which we obtain will be identical with Grassmann's regressive product. The property of the name consists in the fact that the product is of less degree than either of the factors. For the contrary reason, the ordinary external or combinatorial multiplication is sometimes called by Grassmann *progressive*.

Regressive multiplication is associative and exhibits a very remarkable analogy with the progressive. This analogy I have not time here to develop, but will only remark that in this analogy lies in its most general form that celebrated *principle of duality*, which appears in various forms in geometry and certain branches of analysis.

To fix our ideas, I may observe that in geometry the progressive multiplication of points gives successively lines, planes and volumes; the regressive multiplication of planes gives successively lines, points and scalar quantities.

The indeterminate product affords a natural key to the subject of matrices. In fact, a sum of indeterminate products of the second degree represents n^2 scalars, which constitute an ordinary or quadratic matrix; a sum of indeterminate products of the third degree represents n^3 scalars, which constitute a cubic matrix, etc. I shall confine myself to the simplest and most important case, that of quadratic matrices.

An expression of the form

$$\alpha(\lambda \cdot \rho)$$

being a product of α, λ, and ρ, may be regarded as a product of $\alpha \mid \lambda$ and ρ, by a principle already stated. Now if Φ denotes a sum of indeterminate products, of second degree, say $\alpha \mid \lambda + \beta \mid \mu +$ etc., we may write

$$\Phi \cdot \rho$$

for
$$\alpha(\lambda \cdot \rho) + \beta(\mu \cdot \rho) + \text{etc.}$$

This is like ρ, a quantity of the first degree, and it is a homogeneous linear function of ρ. It is easy to see that the most general form of such a function may be expressed in this way. An equation like

$$\sigma = \Phi \cdot \rho$$

represents n equations in ordinary algebra, in which n variables are expressed as linear functions of n others by means of n^2 coëfficients.

The internal product of two indeterminate products may be defined by the equation

$$(\alpha \mid \beta) \cdot (\gamma \mid \delta) = (\beta \cdot \gamma)\alpha \mid \delta.$$

This defines the internal product of matrices, as

$$\Psi \cdot \Phi.$$

This product evidently gives a matrix, the operation of which is equivalent to the successive operations of Φ and Ψ; *i.e.*,

$$(\Psi \cdot \Phi) \cdot \rho = \Psi \cdot (\Phi \cdot \rho).$$

We may express this a little more generally by saying that internal multiplication is associative when performed on a series of matrices, or on such a series terminated by a quantity of the first degree.

Another kind of multiplication of binary indeterminate products is that in which the preceding factors are multiplied combinatorially, and also the following. It may be defined by the equation

$$(\alpha \mid \lambda) \underset{\times}{\overset{\times}{\times}} (\beta \mid \mu) \underset{\times}{\overset{\times}{\times}} (\gamma \mid \nu) = \alpha \times \beta \times \gamma \mid \lambda \times \mu \times \nu.$$

This defines a multiplication of matrices denoted by the same symbol, as

$$\Phi \overset{\times}{\underset{\times}{}} \Psi \overset{\times}{\underset{\times}{}} \Omega, \qquad \Phi \overset{\times}{\underset{\times}{}} \eta \overset{\times}{\underset{\times}{}} \Omega \overset{\times}{\underset{\times}{}} \Theta.$$

This multiplication, which is associative and commutative, is of great importance in the theory of determinants. In fact,

$$\frac{1}{\boxed{\underline{n}}} \, \Phi \overset{\times n}{\underset{\times}{}}$$

is the determinant of the matrix Φ. A lower power, as the mth, with the divisor $n(n-1)\cdots(n-m+1)$ would express as multiple quantity all the sub-determinants of order m.[1]

It is evident that by the combination of the operations of indeterminate, algebraic, and combinatorial multiplication, we obtain multiple quantities of a more complicated nature than by the use of only one of these kinds of multiplication. The indeterminate product of combinatorial products we have already mentioned. The combinatorial product of algebraic products, and the indeterminate product of algebraic products, are also of great importance, especially in the theory of quantics. These three multiplications, with the internal, especially in connection with the general property of the indeterminate product given above, and the derivation of the algebraic and combinatorial products from the indeterminate, which affords a generalization of that property, give rise to a great wealth of multiplicative relations between these multiple quantities. I say "*wealth* of multiplicative relations" designedly, for there is hardly any kind of relations between things which are the objects of mathematical study, which add so much to the resources of the student as those which we call multiplicative, except, perhaps the simpler class, which we call additive, and which are presupposed in the multiplicative. This is a truth quite independent of our using any of the notations of multiple algebra, although a suitable notation for such relations will of course increase their value.

Perhaps, before closing, I ought to say a few words on the applications of multiple algebra.

First of all, geometry, and the geometrical sciences, which treat of things having position in space, kinematics, mechanics, astronomy, physics,

---

[1] Quadratic matrices may also be represented by a sum of indeterminate product of a quantity of the first degree with a combinatorial product of $(n-1)$st degree, as for example, when $n = 4$, by a sum of products of the form

$$\alpha \mid \beta \times \gamma \times \delta.$$

The theory of such matrices is almost identical with that of those of the other form, except that the external multiplication takes the place of the internal, in the multiplication of the matrices with each other and with quantities of the first degree.

crystallography, seem to demand a method of this kind, for position in space is essentially a multiple quantity, and can only be represented by simple quantities in an arbitrary and cumbersome manner. For this reason, and because our spatial intuitions are more developed than those of any other class of mathematical relations, these subjects are especially adapted to introduce the student to the methods of multiple algebra. Here, Nature herself takes us by the hand, and leads us along by easy steps, as a mother teaches her child to walk. In the contemplation of such subjects, Möbius, Hamilton, and Grassmann formed their algebras, although the philosophical mind of the last was not satisfied until he had produced a system unfettered by any spatial relations. It is probably in connection with some of these subjects that the notions of multiple algebra are most widely disseminated.

Maxwell's *Treatise on Electricity and Magnetism* has done so much to familiarize students of physics with quaternion notations, that it seems impossible that this subject should ever again be entirely divorced from the methods of multiple algebra.

I wish that I could say as much of astronomy. It is, I think, to be regretted, that the oldest of the scientific applications of mathematics, the most dignified, the most conservative, should keep so far aloof from the youngest of mathematical methods; and standing as I do to-day, by some chance, among astronomers, although not of the guild, I cannot but endeavor to improve the opportunity by expressing my conviction of the advantages which astronomers might gain by employing some of the methods of multiple algebra. A very few of the fundamental notions of a vector analysis, the addition of vectors and what quaternionists would call the scalar part and the vector part of the product of two vectors (which may be defined without the notion of the quaternion),—these three notions with some four fundamental properties relating to them are sufficient to reduce enormously the labor of mastering such subjects as the elementary theory of orbits, the determination of an orbit from three observations, the differential equations which are used in determining the best orbit from an indefinite number of observations by the method of least squares, or those which give the perturbations when the elements are treated as variable. In all these subjects the analytical work is greatly simplified, and it is far easier to find the best form for numerical calculation than by the use of the ordinary analysis.

I may here remark that in its geometrical applications multiple algebra will naturally take one of two principal forms, according as vectors or points are taken as elementary quantities, *i.e.*, according as something having magnitude and direction, or something having magnitude and position at a point, is the fundamental conception. These forms of multiple algebra may be distinguished as *vector analysis* and *point analysis*. The former we may call a triple, the latter a quadruple algebra, if we determine the degree of the algebra from the degree of multiplicity of the fundamental conception. The former is included in the latter, since the subtraction of points gives us vectors, and in this way Grassmann's vector analysis is included in his point analysis. Hamilton's system, in which the vector is the fundamental idea, is nevertheless made a quadruple algebra by the addition of ordinary numerical quantities. For practical purposes, we may regard Hamilton's system as equivalent to Grassmann's algebra of vectors. Such practical equivalence is of course consistent with great differences of notation, and of the point of view from which the subject is regarded.

Perhaps I should add a word in regard to the nature of the problems which require a vector analysis, or the more general form of Grassmann's point analysis. The distinction of the problems is very marked, and corresponds precisely to the distinction familiar to all analysis between problems which are suitable for Cartesian coördinates, and those which are suitable for the use of tetrahedral, or, in plane geometry, triangular coördinates. Thus, in mechanics, kinematics, astronomy, physics, or crystallography, Grassmann's point analysis will rarely be wanted. One might teach these subjects for years by a vector analysis, and never perhaps feel the need of any of the notions or notations which are peculiar to the point analysis, precisely as in ordinary algebra one might use the Cartesian coördinates in teaching these subjects, without any occasion for the use of tetrahedral coördinates. I think of one exception, which, however, confirms the rule. The very important theory of forces acting on a rigid body is much better treated by point analysis than by vector analysis, exactly as in ordinary algebra it is much better treated by tetrahedral coördinates than by Cartesian,—I mean for the purpose of the elegant development of general propositions. A sufficient theory for the purposes of numerical calculations can easily enough be given by any method, and the most familiar to the student is for such practical purposes of course the best. On the other hand, the projective properties of bodies, the relations of collinearity, and similar subjects, seem to demand the point analysis for their adequate treatment.

If I have said that the algebra of vectors is contained in the algebra of points, it does not follow that in a certain sense the algebra of points is not deducible from the algebra of vectors. In mathematics, a part often contains the whole. If we represent points by vectors drawn from a common origin, and then develop those relations between such vectors representing points, which are independent of the position of the origin,—by this simple process we may obtain a large part, possibly all, of an algebra of points. In this way the vector analysis may be made to serve very conveniently for many of those subjects which I have mentioned as suitable for point analysis. The vector analysis, thus enlarged, is hardly to be distinguished from a point analysis, but the treatment of the subject in this way has somewhat of a makeshift character, as distinguished from the unity and simplicity of the subject when developed directly from the idea of something situated at a point.

Of those subjects which have no relations to space, the elementary theory of eliminations and substitutions, including the theory of matrices and determinants, seems to afford the most simple application of multiple algebra. I have already indicated what seems to me the appropriate foundation for the theory of matrices. The method is essentially that which Grassmann has sketched in his first *Ausdehnungslehre*, under the name of the *open product* and has developed at length in the second.

In the theory of quantics, Grassmann's algebraic product finds an application, the quantic appearing as a sum of algebraic products in Grassmann's sense of the term. As it has been stated that these products are subject to the same laws as the ordinary products of algebra, it may seem that we have here a distinction without an important difference. If the quantics were to be subject to no farther multiplications, except the algebraic in Grassmann's sense, such an objection would be valid. But quantics regarded as sums of algebraic products, in Grassmann's sense, are multiple quantities and subject to a great variety of other multiplications than the algebraic, by which they were formed. Of these, the most important are doubtless the combinatorial, the internal, and the indeterminate. The combinatorial and the internal may be applied, not only to the quantic as a whole or to the algebraic products of which it consists, but also to the individual factors in each term, in accordance with the general principle which has been stated with respect to the indeterminate product and which will apply also to the algebraic, since the algebraic may be regarded as a sum of indeterminate products.

In the differential and integral calculus it is often advantageous to regard as multiple quantities various sets of variables, especially the independent variables, or those which may be taken as such. It is often convenient to represent in the form of a single differential coëfficient, as

$$\frac{d\tau}{d\rho},$$

a block or matrix of ordinary differential coëfficients. In this expression, ρ may be a multiple quantity representing say n independent variables, and τ another representing perhaps the same number of dependent variables. Then $d\rho$ represents the n differentials of the former, and $d\tau$ the n differentials of the latter. The whole expression represents an operator which turns $d\rho$ into $d\tau$, so that we may write identically

$$d\tau = \frac{d\tau}{d\rho}\, d\rho.$$

Here we see a matrix of n^2 differential coëfficients represented by a quotient. This conception is due to Grassmann, as well as the representation of the matrix by a sum of products, which we have already considered. It is to be observed that these multiple differential coëfficients are subject to algebraic laws very similar to those which relate to ordinary differential coëfficients when there is a single independent variable, *e. g.*,

$$\frac{d\sigma}{d\tau}\frac{d\tau}{d\rho} = \frac{d\sigma}{d\rho},$$

$$\frac{d\rho}{d\tau}\frac{d\tau}{d\rho} = 1.$$

In the integral calculus, the transformation of multiple integrals by change of variables is made very simple and clear by the methods of multiple algebra.

In the geometrical applications of the calculus, there is a certain class of theorems, of which Green's and Poisson's are the most notable examples, which seem to have been first noticed in connection with certain physical theories, especially those of electricity and magnetism, and which have only recently begun to find their way into treatises on the calculus. These not only find simplicity of expression and demonstration in the infinitesimal calculus of multiple quantities, but also their natural position, which they hardly seem to find in the ordinary treatises.

But I do not so much desire to call your attention to the diversity of the applications of multiple algebra, as to the simplicity and unity of its principles. The student of multiple algebra suddenly finds himself freed from various restrictions to which he has been accustomed. To many, doubtless, this liberty seems like an invitation to license. Here is a boundless field in which caprice may riot. It is not strange if some look with distrust for the result of such an experiment. But the farther we advance, the more evident it becomes that this too is a realm subject to law. The more we study the subject, the more we find all that is most useful and beautiful attaching itself to a few central principles. We begin by studying *multiple algebras:* we end, I think, by studying MULTIPLE ALGEBRA.

(b) VECTOR ANALYSIS

In his address on "Multiple Algebra" (1886), Gibbs expressed his conviction that "Nature herself takes us by the hand and leads us along by easy steps;" hence his belief that "the problem well put is half solved". In line with the nineteenth-century emphasis upon intuitive synthetic geometry rather than physically unnatural and mathematically cumbersome analytic geometry, Gibbs preferred vectorial representation of physical quantities, associated with directions, to their somewhat arbitrary Cartesian components. Furthermore, in contrast to quaternions, the concept of vectors can be readily extended to n-dimensional space. Vector analysis, the algebra of vectors, is easily formulated and used. It is based upon four basic ideas: the vector sum, the scalar (direct) product (Grassmann's internal product), the vector (skew) product (Grassmann's external product), and the space differentiator (called by Hamilton Nabla—after the Hebrew harp). In Gibbs' notation for two vectors **a** and **b** crossing at an angle θ these operations are, respectively; $a + b, a \cdot b$ (the dot signifies cos θ), **a** × **b** (the cross represents sin θ—in the direction of an ordinary screw), ∇ gradient operator

$$\left(\mathbf{i} \frac{\partial}{\partial x} + \mathbf{j} \frac{\partial}{\partial y} + \mathbf{k} \frac{\partial}{\partial z} \right)$$

where **i**, **j**, **k** are unit vectors along the Cartesian axes. As was his custom, Gibbs began with these simple concepts and developed more recondite ones as requisite, e.g. the dyadic, which is practically the linear vector operator as quantity, together with its indeterminate product.

Gibbs never published his work on vector analysis, although he did have printed privately a pamphlet on "Elements of Vector Analysis" (chapters 1, 2 for a course added in 1881 and chapters 3, 4, 5 in 1884), primarily for his physics students, but widely distributed (he had used vectors in a course on electricity and magnetism in 1879). O. Heaviside, who introduced Clarendon type for vectors, expressed his indebtedness to the ideas in the pamphlet in his own electrical papers (1882–93). Gibbs was apparently undecided about the most convenient form of vector notation and delayed publishing this material in view of more urgent interests; he published work only when it was completely satisfactory to him. He did, however, approve the Yale Bicentennial (1901) publication of a textbook on his *Vector Analysis*[21] by E. B. Wilson. It should, however, be borne in mind that Gibbs did not regard uniformity of notation as of paramount importance; he was concerned more with the notions themselves. His introduction to dyadics—probably his most original contribution to vector analysis—is presented here.

*Elements of Vector Analysis**

CHAPTER III

CONCERNING LINEAR VECTOR FUNCTIONS.

105. *Def.*—A vector function of a vector is said to be *linear*, when the function of the sum of any two vectors is equal to the sum of the functions of the vectors. That is, if

$$\text{func.}[\rho + \rho'] = \text{func.}[\rho] + \text{func.}[\rho']$$

for all values of ρ and ρ', the function is linear. In such cases it is easily shown that

func.$[a\rho + b\rho' + c\rho'' + \text{etc.}]$

$$= a\,\text{func.}[\rho] + b\,\text{func.}[\rho'] + c\,\text{func.}[\rho''] + \text{etc.}$$

106. An expression of the form

$$\alpha\lambda \cdot \rho + \beta\mu \cdot \rho + \text{etc.}$$

evidently represents a linear function of ρ, and may be conveniently written in the form

$$\{\alpha\lambda + \beta\mu + \text{etc.}\} \cdot \rho.$$

The expression

$$\rho \cdot \alpha\lambda + \rho \cdot \beta\mu + \text{etc.},$$

or

$$\rho \cdot \{\alpha\lambda + \beta\mu + \text{etc.}\},$$

also represents a linear function of ρ, which is, in general, different from the preceding, and will be called its *conjugate*.

107. *Def.*—An expression of the form $\alpha\lambda$ or $\beta\mu$ will be called a *dyad*. An expression consisting of any number of dyads united by the signs $+$ or $-$ will be called a *dyadic binomial*, *trinomial*, etc., as the case may be, or more briefly, a *dyadic*. The latter term will be used so as to include the case of a single dyad. When we desire to express a dyadic by a single letter, the Greek capitals will be used, except such as are like the Roman, and also Δ and Σ. The letter I will also be used to represent a certain dyadic, to be mentioned hereafter.

Since any linear vector function may be expressed by means of a dyadic, (as we shall see more particularly hereafter, see No. 110,) the study of such

* (Not published) New Haven, pp. 40–51 (1881–4).

functions, which is evidently of primary importance in the theory of vectors, may be reduced to that of dyadics.

108. *Def.*—Any two dyadics Φ and Ψ are equal,

when $\quad\Phi \cdot \rho = \Psi \cdot \rho \quad$ for all values of ρ,

or, when $\quad \rho \cdot \Phi = \rho \cdot \Psi \quad$ for all values of ρ,

or, when $\sigma \cdot \Phi \cdot \rho = \sigma \cdot \Psi \cdot \rho$ for all values of σ and of ρ.

The third condition is easily shown to be equivalent both to the first and to the second. The three conditions are therefore equivalent.

It follows that $\Phi = \Psi$, if $\Phi \cdot \rho = \Psi \cdot \rho$, or $\rho \cdot \Phi = \rho \cdot \Psi$, for three non-complanar values of ρ.

109. *Def.*—We shall call the vector $\Phi \cdot \rho$ the (direct) product of Φ and ρ, the vector $\rho \cdot \Phi$ the (direct) product of ρ and Φ, and the scalar $\sigma \cdot \Phi \cdot \rho$ the (direct) product of σ, Φ, and ρ.

In the combination $\Phi \cdot \rho$, we shall say that Φ is used as a *prefactor*, in the combination $\rho \cdot \Phi$, as a *postfactor*.

110. If τ is any linear function of ρ, and for $\rho = i$, $\rho = j$, $\rho = k$, the values of τ are respectively α, β, and γ, we may set

$$\tau = \{\alpha i + \beta j + \gamma k\} \cdot \rho,$$

and also

$$\tau = \rho \cdot \{i\alpha + j\beta + k\gamma\}.$$

Therefore, any linear function may be expressed by a dyadic as prefactor and also by a dyadic as postfactor.

111. *Def.*—We shall say that a dyadic is multiplied by a scalar, when one of the vectors of each of its component dyads is multiplied by that scalar. It is evidently immaterial to which vector of any dyad the scalar factor is applied. The product of the dyadic Φ and the scalar a may be written either $a\Phi$ or Φa. The minus sign before a dyadic reverses the signs of all its terms.

112. The sign $+$ in a dyadic, or connecting dyadics, may be regarded as expressing addition, since the combination of dyads and dyadics with this sign is subject to the laws of association and commutation.

113. The combination of vectors in a dyad is evidently distributive. That is,

$$[\alpha + \beta + \text{etc.}][\lambda + \mu + \text{etc.}] = \alpha\lambda + \alpha\mu + \beta\lambda + \beta\mu + \text{etc.}$$

We may therefore regard the dyad as a kind of product of the two vectors of which it is formed. Since this kind of product is not commutative, we shall have occasion to distinguish the factors as *antecedent* and *consequent*.

114. Since any vector may be expressed as a sum of i, j, and k with scalar coefficients, every dyadic may be reduced to a sum of the nine dyads

$$ii, ij, ik, ji, jj, jk, ki, kj, kk,$$

with scalar coefficients. Two such sums cannot be equal according to the definitions of No. 108, unless their coefficients are equal each to each. Hence dyadics are equal only when their equality can be deduced from the principle that the operation of forming a dyad is a distributive one.

On this account, we may regard the dyad as the most general form of product of two vectors. We shall call it the indeterminate product. The complete determination of a single dyad involves six independent scalars, of a dyadic, nine.

115. It follows from the principles of the last paragraph that if

$$\sum \alpha\beta = \sum \kappa\lambda,$$

then

$$\sum \alpha \times \beta = \sum \kappa \times \lambda,$$

and

$$\sum \alpha \cdot \beta = \sum \kappa \cdot \lambda.$$

In other words, the vector and the scalar obtained from a dyadic by insertion of the sign of skew or direct multiplication in each dyad are both independent of the particular form in which the dyadic is expressed.

We shall write $\Phi_\times$ and Φ_S to indicate the vector and the scalar thus obtained.

$$\Phi_\times = (j \cdot \Phi \cdot k - k \cdot \Phi \cdot j)i + (k \cdot \Phi \cdot i - i \cdot \Phi \cdot k)j + (i \cdot \Phi \cdot j - j \cdot \Phi \cdot i)k,$$
$$\Phi_S = i \cdot \Phi \cdot i + j \cdot \Phi \cdot j + k \cdot \Phi \cdot k,$$

as is at once evident, if we suppose Φ to be expanded in terms of ii, ij, etc.

116. *Def.*—The (*direct*) *product* of two dyads (indicated by a dot) is the dyad formed of the first and last of the four factors, multiplied by the direct product of the second and third. That is,

$$\{\alpha\beta\} \cdot \{\gamma\delta\} = \alpha\beta \cdot \gamma\delta = \beta \cdot \gamma\alpha \, \delta.$$

The (direct) product of two dyadics is the sum of all the products formed by prefixing a term of the first dyadic to a term of the second. Since the direct product of one dyadic with another is a dyadic, it may be multiplied in the same way by a third, and so on indefinitely. This kind of multiplication is evidently associative, as well as distributive. The same is true of the direct product of a series of factors of which the first and the last are either dyadics or vectors, and the other factors are dyadics. Thus the values of the expressions

$$\alpha \cdot \Phi \cdot \Theta \cdot \Psi \cdot \beta, \qquad \alpha \cdot \Phi \cdot \Theta, \qquad \Phi \cdot \Theta \cdot \Psi \cdot \beta, \qquad \Phi \cdot \Theta \cdot \Psi$$

will not be affected by any insertion of parentheses. But this kind of multiplication is not commutative, except in the case of the direct product of two vectors.

117. *Def.*—The expressions $\Phi \times \rho$ and $\rho \times \Phi$ represent dyadics which we shall call the *skew* products of Φ and ρ. If

$$\Phi = \alpha\lambda + \beta\mu + \text{etc.},$$

these skew products are defined by the equations

$$\Phi \times \rho = \alpha\lambda \times \rho + \beta\mu \times \rho + \text{etc.},$$
$$\rho \times \Phi = \rho \times \alpha\lambda + \rho \times \beta\mu + \text{etc.}$$

It is evident that

$$\{\rho \times \Phi\} \cdot \Psi = \rho \times \{\Phi \cdot \Psi\}, \qquad \Psi \cdot \{\Phi \times \rho\} = \{\Psi \cdot \Phi\} \times \rho,$$
$$\{\rho \times \Phi\} \cdot \alpha = \rho \times [\Phi \cdot \alpha], \qquad \alpha \cdot \{\Phi \times \rho\} = [\alpha \cdot \Phi] \times \rho,$$
$$\{\rho \times \Phi\} \times \alpha = \rho \times \{\Phi \times \alpha\}.$$

We may therefore write without ambiguity

$$\rho \times \Phi \cdot \Psi, \qquad \Psi \cdot \Phi \times \rho, \qquad \rho \times \Phi \cdot \alpha, \qquad \alpha \cdot \Phi \times \rho, \qquad \rho \times \Phi \cdot \alpha.$$

This may be expressed a little more generally by saying that the associative principle enunciated in No. 116 may be extended to cases in which the initial or final vectors are connected with the other factors by the sign of skew multiplication.

Moreover,

$$\alpha \cdot \rho \times \Phi = [\alpha \times \rho] \cdot \Phi \quad \text{and} \quad \Phi \times \rho \cdot \alpha = \Phi \cdot [\rho \times \alpha].$$

These expressions evidently represent vectors. So

$$\Psi \cdot \{\rho \times \Phi\} = \{\Psi \times \rho\} \cdot \Phi.$$

These expressions represent dyadics. The braces cannot be omitted without ambiguity.

118. Since all the antecedents or all the consequents in any dyadic may be expressed in parts of any three non-complanar vectors, and since the sum of any number of dyads having the same antecedent or the same consequent may be expressed by a single dyad, it follows that any dyadic may be expressed as the sum of three dyads, and so, that either the antecedents or the consequents shall be any desired non-complanar vectors, but only in one way when either the antecedents or the consequents are thus given.

In particular, the dyadic

$$aii + bij + cik$$
$$+ a'ji + b'jj + c'jk$$
$$+ a''ki + b''kj + c''kk,$$

which may for brevity be written

$$\begin{Bmatrix} a & b & c \\ a' & b' & c' \\ a'' & b'' & c'' \end{Bmatrix},$$

is equal to

$$\alpha i + \beta j + \gamma k,$$

where

$$\alpha = ai + a'j + a''k,$$
$$\beta = bi + b'j + b''k,$$
$$\gamma = ci + c'j + c''k,$$

and to

$$i\lambda + j\mu + k\nu,$$

where

$$\lambda = ai + bj + ck$$
$$\mu = a'i + b'j + c'k$$
$$\nu = a''i + b''j + c''k.$$

119. By a similar process, the sum of three dyads may be reduced to the sum of two dyads, whenever either the antecedents or the consequents are complanar, and only in such cases. To prove the latter point, let us suppose that in the dyadic

$$\alpha\lambda + \beta\mu + \gamma\nu$$

neither the antecedents nor the consequents are complanar. The vector

$$\{\alpha\lambda + \beta\mu + \gamma\nu\} \cdot \rho$$

is a linear function of ρ which will be parallel to α when ρ is perpendicular to μ and ν, which will be parallel to β when ρ is perpendicular to ν and λ, and which will be parallel to γ when ρ is perpendicular to λ and μ. Hence, the function may be given any value whatever by giving the proper value to ρ. This would evidently not be the case with the sum of two dyads. Hence, by No. 108, this dyadic cannot be equal to the sum of two dyads.

120. In like manner, the sum of two dyads may be reduced to a single dyad, if either the antecedents or the consequents are parallel, and only in such cases.

A sum of three dyads cannot be reduced to a single dyad, unless either their antecedents or consequents are parallel, or both antecedents and consequents are (separately) complanar. In the first case the reduction can always be made, in the second, occasionally.

121. *Def.*—A dyadic which cannot be reduced to the sum of less than three dyads will be called *complete*.

A dyadic which can be reduced to the sum of two dyads will be called *planar*. When the plane of the antecedents coincides with that of the consequents, the dyadic will be called *uniplanar*. These planes are invariable for a given dyadic, although the dyadic may be so expressed that either the two antecedents or the two consequents may have any desired values (which are not parallel) within their planes.

A dyadic which can be reduced to a single dyad will be called *linear*. When the antecedent and consequent are parallel, it will be called *unilinear*.

A dyadic is said to have the value zero, when all its terms vanish.

122. If we set

$$\sigma = \Phi \cdot \rho, \qquad \tau = \rho \cdot \Phi,$$

and give ρ all possible values, σ and τ will receive all possible values, if Φ is complete. The values of σ and τ will be confined each to a plane, if Φ is planar, which planes will coincide, if Φ is uniplanar. The values of σ and τ will be confined each to a line if Φ is linear, which lines will coincide, if Φ is unilinear.

123. The products of complete dyadics are complete, of complete and planar dyadics are planar, of complete and linear dyadics are linear.

The products of planar dyadics are planar, except that when the plane of the consequents of the first dyadic is perpendicular to the plane of the antecedents of the second dyadic, the product reduces to a linear dyadic.

The products of linear dyadics are linear, except that when the consequent of the first is perpendicular to the antecedent of the second, the product reduces to zero.

The products of planar and linear dyadics are linear, except when, the planar preceding, the plane of its consequents is perpendicular to the antecedent of the linear, or, the linear preceding, its consequent is perpendicular to the plane of the antecedents of the planar. In these cases the product is zero.

All these cases are readily proved, if we set

$$\sigma = \Phi \cdot \Psi \cdot \rho,$$

and consider the limits within which σ varies, when we give ρ all possible values.

The products $\Psi \times \rho$ and $\rho \times \Phi$ are evidently planar dyadics.

124. *Def.*—A dyadic Φ is said to be an *idemfactor*, when

$$\Phi \cdot \rho = \rho \text{ for all values of } \rho,$$

or when $\qquad \rho \cdot \Phi = \rho$ for all values of ρ.

If either of these conditions holds true, Φ must be reducible to the form

$$ii + jj + kk.$$

Therefore, both conditions will hold, if either do. All such dyadics are equal, by No. 108. They will be represented by the letter I.

The direct product of an idemfactor with another dyadic is equal to that dyadic. That is,

$$I \cdot \Phi = \Phi, \qquad \Phi \cdot I = \Phi,$$

where Φ is any dyadic.

A dyadic of the form

$$\alpha\alpha' + \beta\beta' + \gamma\gamma',$$

in which α', β', γ' are the reciprocals of α, β, γ, is an idemfactor. (See No. 38.)

A dyadic trinomial cannot be an idemfactor, unless its antecedents and consequents are reciprocals.

125. If one of the direct products of two dyadics is an idemfactor, the other is also. For, if $\Phi \cdot \Psi = I$,

$$\sigma \cdot \Phi \cdot \Psi = \sigma$$

for all values of σ, and Φ is complete;

$$\sigma \cdot \Phi \cdot \Psi \cdot \Phi = \sigma \cdot \Phi$$

for all values of σ, therefore for all values of $\sigma \cdot \Phi$, and therefore $\Psi \cdot \Phi = I$.

Def.—In this case, either dyadic is called the *reciprocal* of the other.

It is evident that an incomplete dyadic cannot have any (finite) reciprocal.

Reciprocals of the same dyadic are equal. For if Φ and Ψ are both reciprocals of Ω,

$$\Phi = \Phi \cdot \Omega \cdot \Psi = \Psi.$$

If two dyadics are reciprocals, the operators formed by using these dyadics as prefactors are inverse, also the operators formed by using them as postfactors.

126. The reciprocal of any complete dyadic

$$\alpha\lambda + \beta\mu + \gamma\nu$$

is $$\lambda'\alpha' + \mu'\beta' + \nu'\gamma',$$

where α', β', γ' are the reciprocals of α, β, γ, and λ', μ', ν' are the reciprocals of λ, μ, ν. (See No. 38.)

127. *Def.*—We shall write Φ^{-1} for the reciprocal of any (complete) dyadic Φ, also Φ^2 for $\Phi \cdot \Phi$, etc., and Φ^{-2}, for $\Phi^{-1} \cdot \Phi^{-1}$, etc. It is evident that Φ^{-n} is the reciprocal of Φ^n.

128. In the reduction of equations, if we have

$$\Phi \cdot \Psi = \Phi \cdot \Omega,$$

we may cancel the Φ (which is equivalent to multiplying by Φ^{-1}) if Φ is a complete dyadic, but not otherwise. The case is the same with such equations as

$$\Phi \cdot \sigma = \Phi \cdot \rho, \qquad \Psi \cdot \Phi = \Omega \cdot \Phi, \qquad \rho \cdot \Phi = \sigma \cdot \Phi.$$

To cancel an incomplete dyadic in such cases would be analogous to cancelling a zero factor in algebra.

129. *Def.*—If in any dyadic we transpose the factors in each term, the dyadic thus formed is said to be *conjugate* to the first. Thus

$$\alpha\lambda + \beta\mu + \gamma\nu \quad \text{and} \quad \lambda\alpha + \mu\beta + \nu\gamma$$

are conjugate to each other. A dyadic of which the value is not altered by such transposition is said to be *self-conjugate*. The conjugate of any dyadic Φ may be written Φ_C. It is evident that

$$\rho \cdot \Phi = \Phi_C \cdot \rho \quad \text{and} \quad \Phi \cdot \rho = \rho \cdot \Phi_C.$$

$\Phi_C \cdot \rho$ and $\Phi \cdot \rho$ are conjugate functions of ρ. (See No. 106). Since $\{\Phi_C\}^2 = \{\Phi^2\}_C$, we may write $\Phi_C{}^2$, etc., without ambiguity.

130. The reciprocal of the product of any number of dyadics is equal to the product of their reciprocals taken in inverse order. Thus

$$\{\Phi \cdot \Psi \cdot \Omega\}^{-1} = \Omega^{-1} \cdot \Psi^{-1} \cdot \Phi^{-1}.$$

The conjugate of the product of any number of dyadics is equal to the product of their conjugates taken in inverse order. Thus

$$\{\Phi \cdot \Psi \cdot \Omega\}_C = \Omega_C \cdot \Psi_C \cdot \Phi_C.$$

Hence, since

$$\Phi_C \cdot \{\Phi^{-1}\}_C = \{\Phi^{-1} \cdot \Phi\}_C = I,$$
$$\{\Phi^{-1}\}_C = \{\Phi_C\}^{-1},$$

and we may write $\Phi_C{}^{-1}$ without ambiguity.

131. It is sometimes convenient to be able to express by a dyadic taken in direct multiplication the same operation which would be effected by a given vector (α) in skew multiplication. The dyadic $I \times \alpha$ will answer this purpose. For, by No. 117,

$$\{I \times \alpha\} \cdot \rho = \alpha \times \rho, \qquad \rho \cdot \{I \times \alpha\} = \rho \times \alpha,$$
$$\{I \times \alpha\} \cdot \Phi = \alpha \times \Phi, \qquad \Phi \cdot \{I \times \alpha\} = \Phi \times \alpha.$$

The same is true of the dyadic $\alpha \times I$, which is indeed identical with $I \times \alpha$, as appears from the equation $I \cdot \{\alpha \times I\} = \{I \times \alpha\} \cdot I$.

If α is a unit vector,

$$\{I \times \alpha\}^2 = -\{I - \alpha\alpha\},$$
$$\{I \times \alpha\}^3 = -I \times \alpha,$$
$$\{I \times \alpha\}^4 = I - \alpha\alpha,$$
$$\{I \times \alpha\}^5 = I \times \alpha,$$

$$\text{etc.}$$

If i, j, k are a normal system of unit vectors,

$$I \times i = i \times I = kj - jk,$$
$$I \times j = j \times I = ik - ki,$$
$$I \times k = k \times I = ji - ij.$$

If α and β are any vectors,

$$[\alpha \times \beta] \times I = I \times [\alpha \times \beta] = \beta\alpha - \alpha\beta.$$

That is, the vector $\alpha \times \beta$ as a pre- or postfactor in skew multiplication is equivalent to the dyadic $\{\beta\alpha - \alpha\beta\}$ taken as pre- or postfactor in direct multiplication.

$$[\alpha \times \beta] \times \rho = \{\beta\alpha - \alpha\beta\} \cdot \rho,$$

$$\rho \times [\alpha \times \beta] = \rho \cdot \{\beta\alpha - \alpha\beta\}.$$

This is essentially the theorem of No. 27, expressed in a form more symmetrical, and more easily remembered.

132. The equation

$$\alpha\beta \times \gamma + \beta\gamma \times \alpha + \gamma\alpha \times \beta = \alpha \cdot \beta \times \gamma I$$

gives, on multiplication by any vector ρ, the identical equation

$$\rho \cdot \alpha\beta \times \gamma + \rho \cdot \beta\gamma \times \alpha + \rho \cdot \gamma\alpha \times \beta = \alpha \cdot \beta \times \gamma\rho.$$

(See No. 37.) The former equation is therefore identically true. (See No. 108.) It is a little more general than the equation

$$\alpha\alpha' + \beta\beta' + \gamma\gamma' = I,$$

which we have already considered (No. 124), since, in the form here given, it is not necessary that α, β, and γ should be non-complanar. We may also write

$$\beta \times \gamma\alpha + \gamma \times \alpha\beta + \alpha \times \beta\gamma = \alpha \cdot \beta \times \gamma I.$$

Multiplying this equation by ρ as prefactor, (or the first equation by ρ as postfactor,) we obtain

$$\rho \cdot \beta \times \gamma\alpha + \rho \cdot \gamma \times \alpha\beta + \rho \cdot \alpha \times \beta\gamma = \alpha \cdot \beta \times \gamma\rho.$$

(Compare No. 37.) For three complanar vectors we have

$$\alpha\beta \times \gamma + \beta\gamma \times \alpha + \gamma\alpha \times \beta = 0.$$

Multiplying this by ν, a unit normal to the plane of α, β, and γ, we have

$$\alpha\beta \times \gamma \cdot \nu + \beta\gamma \times \alpha \cdot \nu + \gamma\alpha \times \beta \cdot \nu = 0.$$

This equation expresses the well-known theorem that if the geometrical sum of three vectors is zero, the magnitude of each vector is proportional to the sine of the angle between the other two. It also indicates the numerical coefficients by which one of three complanar vectors may be expressed in parts of the other two.

133. *Def.*—If two dyadics Φ and Ψ are such that

$$\Phi \cdot \Psi = \Psi \cdot \Phi,$$

they are said to be *homologous*.

If any number of dyadics are homologous to one another, and any other dyadics are formed from them by the operations of taking multiples, sums,

differences, powers, reciprocals, or products, such dyadics will be homologous to each other and to the original dyadics. This requires demonstration
only in regard to reciprocals. Now if

$$\Phi \cdot \Psi = \Psi \cdot \Phi,$$

$$\Psi \cdot \Phi^{-1} = \Phi^{-1} \cdot \Phi \cdot \Psi \cdot \Phi^{-1} = \Phi^{-1} \cdot \Psi \cdot \Phi \cdot \Phi^{-1} = \Phi^{-1} \cdot \Psi.$$

That is, Φ^{-1} is homologous to Ψ, if Φ is.

134. If we call $\Psi \cdot \Phi^{-1}$ or $\Phi^{-1} \cdot \Psi$ the quotient of Ψ and Φ, we may say that
the rules of addition, subtraction, multiplication and division of homologous
dyadics are identical with those of arithmetic or ordinary algebra, except that
limitations analogous to those respecting zero in algebra must be observed
with respect to all incomplete dyadics.

It follows that the algebraic and higher analysis of homologous dyadics is
substantially identical with that of scalars.

135. It is always possible to express a dyadic in three terms, so that both
the antecedents and the consequents shall be perpendicular among themselves.

To show this for any dyadic Φ, let us set

$$\rho' = \Phi \cdot \rho,$$

ρ being a unit-vector, and consider the different values of ρ' for all possible
directions of ρ. Let the direction of the unit vector i be so determined that
when ρ coincides with i, the value of ρ' shall be at least as great as for any
other direction of ρ. And let the direction of the unit vector j be so determined
that when ρ coincides with j, the value of ρ' shall be at least as great as for any
other direction of ρ which is perpendicular to j. Let k have its usual position
with respect to i and j. It is evidently possible to express Φ in the form

$$\alpha i + \beta j + \gamma k.$$

We have therefore

$$\rho' = \{\alpha i + \beta j + \gamma k\} \cdot \rho,$$

and

$$d\rho' = \{\alpha i + \beta j + \gamma k\} \cdot d\rho.$$

Now the supposed property of the direction of i requires that when ρ coincides with i and $d\rho$ is perpendicular to i, $d\rho'$ shall be perpendicular to ρ',
which will then be parallel to α. But if $d\rho$ is parallel to j or k, it will be perpendicular to i, and $d\rho'$ will be parallel to β or γ, as the case may be. Therefore β and γ are perpendicular to α. In the same way it may be shown that the
condition relative to j requires that γ shall be perpendicular to β. We may
therefore set

$$\Phi = ai'i + bj'j + ck'k,$$

where i', j', k', like i, j, k, constitute a normal system of unit vectors (see
No. 11), and a, b, c are scalars which may be either positive or negative.

It makes an important difference whether the number of these scalars which are negative is even or odd. If two are negative, say a and b, we may make them positive by reversing the directions of i' and j'. The vectors i', j', k' will still constitute a normal system. But if we should reverse the directions of an odd number of these vectors, they would cease to constitute a normal system, and to be superposable upon the system i, j, k. We may, however, always set either

$$\Phi = ai'i + bj'j + ck'k,$$

or

$$\Phi = -\{ai'i + bj'j + ck'k\},$$

with positive values of a, b, and c. At the limit between these cases are the planar dyadics, in which one of the three terms vanishes, and the dyadic reduces to the form

$$ai'i + bj'j,$$

in which a and b may always be made positive by giving the proper directions to i' and j'.

If the numerical values of a, b, c are all unequal, there will be only one way in which the value of Φ may be thus expressed. If they are not all unequal, there will be an infinite number of ways in which Φ may be thus expressed, in all of which the three scalar coefficients will have the same values with exception of the changes of signs mentioned above. If the three values are numerically identical, we may give to either system of normal vectors an arbitrary position.

136. It follows that any self-conjugate dyadic may be expressed in the form

$$aii + bjj + ckk,$$

where i, j, k are a normal system of unit vectors, and a, b, c are positive or negative scalars.

137. Any dyadic may be divided into two parts, of which one shall be self-conjugate, and the other of the form $I \times \alpha$. These parts are found by taking half the sum and half the difference of the dyadic and its conjugate. It is evident that

$$\Phi = \tfrac{1}{2}\{\Phi + \Phi_C\} + \tfrac{1}{2}\{\Phi - \Phi_C\}.$$

Now $\tfrac{1}{2}\{\Phi + \Phi_C\}$ is self-conjugate, and

$$\tfrac{1}{2}\{\Phi - \Phi_C\} = I \times [-\tfrac{1}{2}\Phi_C].$$

(See No. 131.)

Gibbs was not an aggressive propagandist for himself or for his own ideas or even for science, but he found himself involved in a long and bitter controversy with several devotees of Hamilton's quaternions. T¹

English physicist Peter Guthrie Tait (1831–1902), who won the Edinburgh chair of natural philosophy over J. C. Maxwell (criticized for too much learning and originality), attacked Gibbs' vector analysis particularly acrimoniously. Two of the three published defences of Gibbs are given here primarily for their intrinsic worth with respect to his own apology for vector analysis, but secondarily for their revelation of the character of this meek man.

On the Role of Quaternions in the Algebra of Vectors

(From *Nature*, XLIII, pp. 511–13 (1891).)

THE following passage, which has recently come to my notice, in the preface to the third edition of Prof. Tait's "Quaternions," seems to call for some reply:

"Even Prof. Willard Gibbs must be ranked as one of the retarders of quaternion progress, in virtue of his pamphlet on 'Vector Analysis,' a sort of hermaphrodite monster, compounded of the notations of Hamilton and of Grassmann."

The merits or demerits of a pamphlet printed for private distribution a good many years ago do not constitute a subject of any great importance, but the assumptions implied in the sentence quoted are suggestive of certain reflections and inquiries which are of broader interest, and seem not untimely at a period when the methods and results of the various forms of multiple algebra are attracting so much attention. It seems to be assumed that a departure from quaternionic usage in the treatment of vectors is an enormity. If this assumption is true, it is an important truth; if not, it would be unfortunate if it should remain unchallenged, especially when supported by so high an authority. The criticism relates particularly to notations, but I believe that there is a deeper question of notions underlying that of notations. Indeed, if my offence had been solely in the matter of notation, it would have been less accurate to describe my production as a monstrosity, than to characterize its dress as uncouth.

Now what are the fundamental notions which are germane to a vector analysis? (A vector analysis is of course an algebra for vectors, or something which shall be to vectors what ordinary algebra is to ordinary quantities.) If we pass over those notions which are so simple that they go without saying, geometrical addition (denoted by $+$) is, perhaps, first to be mentioned. Then comes the product of the lengths of two vectors and the cosine of the angle which they include. This, taken negatively, is denoted in quaternions by $S\alpha\beta$, where α and β are the vectors. Equally important is a vector at right angles to α and β (on a specified side of their plane), and representing in length the product of their lengths and the sine of the angle which they include. This is denoted by Vαβ in quaternions. How these notions are represented in my pamphlet is a question of very subordinate consequence, which need not be considered at present. The importance of these notions, and the importance of a suitable notation for them, is not, I suppose, a matter on which there is any difference of opinion. Another function of α and β, called their product and written αβ, is used in quaternions. In the general case, this is neither a vector, like Vαβ, nor a scalar (or ordinary algebraic quantity), like Sαβ, but a quaternion—that is, it is part vector and part scalar. It may be defined by the equation—

$$\alpha\beta = V\alpha\beta + S\alpha\beta.$$

The question arises, whether the quaternionic product can claim a prominent and fundamental place in a system of vector analysis. It certainly does not hold any such place among the fundamental geometrical conceptions as the geometrical sum, the scalar product, or the vector product. The geometrical sum α + β represents the third side of a triangle as determined by the sides α and β. Vαβ represents in magnitude the area of the parallelogram determined by the sides α and β, and in direction the normal to the plane of the parallelogram. SγVαβ represents the volume of the parallelopiped determined by the edges α, β, and γ. These conceptions are the very foundations of geometry.

We may arrive at the same conclusion from a somewhat narrower but very practical point of view. It will hardly be denied that sines and cosines play the leading parts in trigonometry. Now the notations Vαβ and Sαβ represent the sine and the cosine of the angle included between α and β, combined in each case with certain other simple notions. But the sine and cosine combined with these auxiliary notions are incomparably more amenable to analytical transformation than the simple sine and cosine of trigonometry, exactly as numerical quantities combined (as in algebra) with the notion of positive or negative quality are incomparably more amenable to analytical transformation than the simple numerical quantities of arithmetic.

I do not know of anything which can be urged in favour of the quaternionic product of two vectors as a *fundamental* notion in vector analysis, which does not appear trivial or artificial in comparison with the above considerations. The same is true of the quaternionic quotient, and of the quaternion in general.

How much more deeply rooted in the nature of things are the functions Sαβ and Vαβ than any which depend on the definition of a quaternion, will appear in a strong light if we try to extend our formulae to space of four or more dimensions. It will not be claimed that the notions of quaternions will apply to such a space, except indeed in such a limited and artificial manner as to rob them of their value as a system of geometrical algebra. But vectors exist in such a space, and there must be a vector analysis for such a space. The notions of geometrical addition and the scalar product are evidently applicable to such a space. As we cannot define the direction of a vector in space of four or more dimensions by the condition of perpendicularity to two given vectors, the definition of $V\alpha\beta$, as given above, will not apply *totidem verbis* to space of four or more dimensions. But a little change in the definition, which would make no essential difference in three dimensions, would enable us to apply the idea at once to space of any number of dimensions.

These considerations are of a somewhat *a priori* nature. It may be more convincing to consider the use actually made of the quaternion as an instrument for the expression of spatial relations. The principal use seems to be the derivation of the functions expressed by $S\alpha\beta$ and $V\alpha\beta$. Each of these expressions is regarded by quaternionic writers as representing two distinct operations; first, the formation of the product $\alpha\beta$, which is the quaternion, and then the taking out of this quaternion the scalar or the vector part, as the case may be, this second process being represented by the selective symbol, S or V. This is, I suppose, the natural development of the subject in a treatise on quaternions, where the chosen subject seems to require that we should commence with the idea of a quaternion, or get there as soon as possible, and then develop everything from that particular point of view. In a system of vector analysis, in which the principle of development is not thus predetermined, it seems to me contrary to good method that the more simple and elementary notions should be defined by means of those which are less so.

The quaternion affords a convenient notation for rotations. The notation $q(\ )q^{-1}$, where q is a quaternion and the operand is to be written in the parenthesis, produces on all possible vectors just such changes as a (finite) rotation of a solid body. Rotations may also be represented, in a manner which seems to leave nothing to be desired, by linear vector functions. Doubtless each method has advantages in certain cases, or for certain purposes. But since nothing is more simple than the definition of a linear vector function, while the definition of a quaternion is far from simple, and since in any case linear vector functions must be treated in a system of vector analysis, capacity for representing rotations does not seem to me sufficient to entitle the quaternion to a place among the *fundamental* and *necessary* notions of a vector analysis.

Another use of the quaternionic idea is associated with the symbol ∇. The quantities written $S\nabla\omega$ and $V\nabla\omega$, where ω denotes a vector having values which vary in space, are of fundamental importance in physics. In quaternions these are derived from the quaternion $\nabla\omega$ by selecting respectively the scalar or the vector part. But the most simple and elementary definitions of $S\nabla\omega$ and $V\nabla\omega$ are quite independent of the conception of a quaternion, and the quaternion $\nabla\omega$ is scarcely used except in combination with the symbols S and V, expressed or implied. There are a few formulae in which there is a trifling gain in compactness in the use of the quaternion, but the gain is very trifling so far as I have observed, and generally, it seems to me, at the expense of perspicuity.

These considerations are sufficient, I think, to show that the position of the quaternionist is not the only one from which the subject of vector analysis may be viewed, and that a method which would be monstrous from one point of view, may be normal and inevitable from another.

Let us now pass to the subject of notations. I do not know wherein the notations of my pamphlet have any special resemblance to Grassmann's, although the point of view from which the pamphlet was written is certainly much nearer to his than to Hamilton's. But this is a matter of minor consequence. It is more important to ask, What are the requisites of a good notation for the purposes of vector analysis? There is no difference of opinion about the representation of geometrical addition. When we come to functions having an analogy to multiplication, the product of the lengths of two vectors and the cosine of the angle which they include, from any point of view except that of the quaternionist, seems more simple than the same quantity taken negatively. Therefore we want a notation for what is expressed by $-S\alpha\beta$, rather than $S\alpha\beta$, in quaternions. Shall the symbol denoting this function be a letter or some other sign? and shall it precede the vectors or be placed between them? A little reflection will show, I think, that while we must often have recourse to letters to supplement the number of signs available for the expression of all kinds of operations, it is better that the symbols expressing the most fundamental and frequently recurring operations should not be letters, and that a sign between the vectors, and, as it were, uniting them, is better than a sign before them in a case having a formal analogy with multiplication. The case may be compared with that of addition, for which $\alpha + \beta$ is evidently more convenient than $\Sigma (\alpha, \beta)$ or $\Sigma \alpha\beta$ would be. Similar considerations will apply to the function written in quaternions $V\alpha\beta$. It would seem that we obtain the *ne plus ultra* of simplicity and convenience, if we express the two functions by uniting the vectors in each case with a sign suggestive of multiplication. The particular forms of the signs which we adopt is a matter of minor consequence. In order to keep within the resources of an ordinary printing office, I have used a dot and a cross, which are already associated with multiplication, but are not needed for ordinary multiplication, which is best denoted by the simple juxtaposition of the factors. I have no especial predilection for these particular signs. The use of the dot is indeed liable to the objection that it interferes with its use as a separatrix, or instead of a parenthesis.

If, then, I have written $\alpha \cdot \beta$ and $\alpha \times \beta$ for what is expressed in quaternions by $-S\alpha\beta$ and $V\alpha\beta$, and in like manner $\nabla \cdot \omega$ and $\nabla \times \omega$ for $-S \nabla\omega$ and $V \nabla\omega$ in quaternions, it is because the natural development of a vector analysis seemed to lead logically to some such notations. But I think that I can show that these notations have some substantial advantages over the quaternions in point of convenience.

Any linear vector function of a variable vector ρ may be expressed in the form—

$$\alpha\lambda \cdot \rho + \beta\mu \cdot \rho + \gamma\nu \cdot \rho = (\alpha\lambda + \beta\mu + \gamma\nu) \cdot \rho = \Phi \cdot \rho,$$

where
$$\Phi = \alpha\lambda + \beta\mu + \gamma\nu;$$
or in quaternions
$$-\alpha S\lambda\rho - \beta S\mu\rho - \gamma S\nu\rho = -(\alpha S\lambda + \beta S\mu + \gamma S\nu)\rho = -\phi\rho,$$
where
$$\phi = \alpha S\lambda + \beta S\mu + \gamma S\nu.$$

If we take the scalar product of the vector $\Phi \cdot \rho$, and another vector σ, we obtain the scalar quantity
$$\sigma \cdot \Phi \cdot \rho = \sigma \cdot (\alpha\lambda + \beta\mu + \gamma\nu) \cdot \rho,$$
or in quaternions
$$S\sigma\phi\rho = S\sigma(\alpha S\lambda + \beta S\mu + \gamma S\nu)\rho.$$

This is a function of σ and of ρ, and it is exactly the same kind of function of σ that it is of ρ, a symmetry which is not so clearly exhibited in the quaternionic notation as in the other. Moreover, we can write $\sigma \cdot \Phi$ for $\sigma \cdot (\alpha\lambda + \beta\mu + \gamma\nu)$. This represents a vector which is a function of σ, viz. the function conjugate to $\Phi \cdot \sigma$; and $\sigma \cdot \Phi \cdot \rho$ may be regarded as the product of this vector and ρ. This is not so clearly indicated in the quaternionic notation, where it would be straining things a little to call $S\sigma\phi$ a vector.

The combinations $\alpha\lambda$, $\beta\mu$, &c., used above, are distributive with regard to each of the two vectors, and may be regarded as a kind of product. If we wish to express everything in terms of i, j, and k, Φ will appear as a sum of ii, ij, $ik, ji, jj, jk, ki, kj, kk$, each with a numerical coefficient. These nine coefficients may be arranged in a square, and constitute a matrix; and the study of the properties of expressions like Φ is identical with the study of ternary matrices. This expression of the matrix as a sum of products (which may be extended to matrices of any order) affords a point of departure from which the properties of matrices may be deduced with the utmost facility. The ordinary matricular product is expressed by a dot, as $\Phi \cdot \Psi$. Other important kinds of multiplication may be defined by the equations—
$$(\alpha\lambda) \overset{\times}{\times} (\beta\mu) = (\alpha \times \beta)(\lambda \times \mu), \qquad (\alpha\lambda):(\beta\mu) = (\alpha \cdot \beta)(\lambda \cdot \mu).$$

With these definitions $\frac{1}{6}\Phi \overset{\times}{\times} \Phi : \Phi$ will be the determinant of Φ, and $\Phi \overset{\times}{\times} \Phi$ will be the conjugate of the reciprocal of Φ multiplied by twice the determinant. If Φ represents the manner in which vectors are affected by a strain, $\frac{1}{2}\Phi \times \Phi$ will represent the manner in which surfaces are affected, and $\frac{1}{6}\Phi \overset{\times}{\times} \Phi : \Phi$ the manner in which volumes are affected. Considerations of this kind do not attach themselves so naturally to the notation $\phi = \alpha S\lambda + \beta S\mu + \gamma S\nu$, nor does the subject admit so free a development with this notation, principally because the symbol S refers to a special use of the matrix, and is very much in the way when we want to apply the matrix to other uses, or to subject it to various operations.   J. WILLARD GIBBS.

New Haven, Connecticut.

Quaternions and the Algebra of Vectors

(From *Nature*, XLVII, pp. 463–4 (1893).)

In a recent number of this Journal (p. 151) Mr. McAulay puts certain questions to Mr. Heaviside and to me, relating to a subject of such importance as to justify an answer somewhat at length. I cannot of course speak for Mr. Heaviside, although I suppose that his views are not very different from mine on the most essential points, but even if he shall have already replied before this letter can appear, I shall be glad to add whatever of force may belong to independent testimony.

Mr. McAulay asks: "What is the *first* duty of the physical vector analyst *quá* physical vector analyst?" The answer is not doubtful. It is to present the subject in such a form as to be most easily acquired, and most useful when acquired.

In regard to the slow progress of such methods toward recognition and use by physicists and others, which Mr. McAulay deplores, it does not seem possible to impute it to any want of uniformity of notation. I doubt whether there is any modern branch of mathematics which has been presented for so long a time with a greater uniformity of notation than quaternions.

What, then, is the cause of the fact which Mr. McAulay and all of us deplore? It is not far to seek. We need only a glance at the volumes in which Hamilton set forth his method. No wonder that physicists and others failed to perceive the possibilities of simplicity, perspicuity, and brevity which were contained in a system presented to them in ponderous volumes of 800 pages. Perhaps Hamilton may have intended these volumes as a sort of *thesaurus*, and we should look to his shorter papers for a compact account of his method. But if we turn to his earlier papers on Quaternions in the *Philosophical Magazine*, in which principally he introduced the subject to the notice of his contemporaries, we find them entitled "On Quaternions; or on a New System of Imaginaries in Algebra," and in them we find a great deal about imaginaries, and very little of a vector analysis. To show how slowly the system of vector analysis developed itself in the quaternionic *nidus*, we need only say that the symbols S, V, and ∇ do not appear until two or three years after the discovery of quaternions. In short, it seems to have been only a secondary object with Hamilton to express the geometrical relations of vectors,—secondary in time, and also secondary in this, that it was never allowed to give shape to his work.

But this relates to the past. In regard to the present *status*, I beg leave to quote what Mr. McAulay has said on another occasion (see *Phil. Mag.* June, 1892):—"Quaternions differ in an important respect from other branches of mathematics that are studied by mathematicians after they have in the course of years of hard labour laid the foundation of all their future work. In nearly all cases these branches are very properly so called. They each grow out of a definite spot of the main tree of mathematics, and derive their sustenance from the sap of the trunk as a whole. But not so with quaternions. To let these grow in the brain of a mathematician, he must start from the seed as with the rest of his mathematics regarded as a whole. He cannot graft them on his already flourishing tree, for they will die there. They are independent plants that require separate sowing and the consequent careful tending."

Can we wonder that mathematicians, physicists, astronomers, and geometers feel some doubt as to the value or necessity of something so separate from all other branches of learning? Can that be a natural treatment of the subject which has no relations to any other method, and, as one might suppose from reading some treatises, has only occurred to a single man? Or, at best, is it not discouraging to be told that in order to use the quaternionic method, one must give up the progress which he has already made in the pursuit of his favourite science, and go back to the beginning and start anew on a parallel course?

I believe, however, that if what I have quoted is true of vector methods, it is because there is something fundamentally wrong in the presentation of the subject. Of course, in some sense and to some extent it is and must be true. Whatever is special, accidental, and individual, will die, as it should; but that which is universal and essential should remain as an organic part of the whole intellectual acquisition. If that which is essential dies with the accidental, it must be because the accidental has been given the prominence which belongs to the essential. For myself, I should preach no such doctrine to those whom I wish to convert to the true faith.

In Italy, they say, all roads lead to Rome. In mechanics, kinematics, astronomy, physics, all study leads to the consideration of certain relations and operations. These are the capital notions; these should have the leading parts in any analysis suited to the subject.

If I wished to attract the student of any of these sciences to an algebra for vectors, I should tell him that the fundamental notions of this algebra were exactly those with which he was daily conversant. I should tell him that a vector algebra is so far from being any one man's production that half a century ago several were already working toward an algebra which should be primarily geometrical and not arithmetical, and that there is a remarkable similarity in the results to which these efforts led (see Proc. A.A.A.S. for 1886, pp. 37, ff.). I should call his attention to the fact that Lagrange and Gauss used the notation $(\alpha\beta\gamma)$ to denote precisely the same as Hamilton by his $S(\alpha\beta\gamma)$, except that Lagrange limited the expression to unit vectors, and Gauss to vectors of which the length is the secant of the latitude, and I should show him that we have only to give up these limitations, and the expression (in connection with the notion of geometrical addition) is endowed with an immense wealth of transformations. I should call his attention to the fact that the notation $[r_1 r_2]$, universal in the theory of orbits, is identical with Hamilton's $V(\rho_1 \rho_2)$, except that Hamilton takes the area as a vector, *i.e.* includes the notion of the direction of the normal to the plane of the triangle, and that with this simple modification (and with the notion of geometrical addition of surfaces as well as of lines) this expression becomes closely connected with the first-mentioned, and is not only endowed with a similar capability for transformation, but enriches the first with new capabilities. In fact, I should tell him that the notions which we use in vector analysis are those which he who reads between the lines will meet on every page of the great masters of analysis, or of those who have probed deepest the secrets of nature, the only difference being that the vector analyst, having regard to the weakness of the human intellect, does as the early painters who wrote beneath their pictures "This is a tree," "This is a horse."

I cannot attach quite so much importance as Mr. McAulay to uniformity of notation. That very uniformity, if it existed among those who use a vector analysis, would rather obscure than reveal their connection with the general course of modern thought in mathematics and physics. There are two ways in which we may measure the progress of any reform. The one consists in counting those who have adopted the *shibboleth* of the reformers; the other measure is the degree in which the community is imbued with the essential principles of the reform. I should apply the broader measure to the present case, and do not find it quite so bad as Mr. McAulay does.

Yet the question of notations, although not the vital question, is certainly important, and I assure Mr. McAulay that reluctance to make unnecessary innovations in notation has been a very powerful motive in restraining me from publication. Indeed my pamphlet on "Vector Analysis," which has excited the animadversion of quaternionists, was never formally published, although rather widely distributed, so long as I had copies to distribute, among those who I thought might be interested in the subject. I may say, however, since I am called upon to defend my position, that I have found the notations of that pamphlet more flexible than those generally used. Mr. McAulay, at least, will understand what I mean by this, if I say that some of the relations which he has thought of sufficient importance to express by means of special devices (see Proc. R. S. E., for 1890–91), may be expressed at least as briefly in the notations which I have used, and without special devices. But I should not have been satisfied for the purposes of my pamphlet with any notation which should suggest even to the careless reader any connection with the notion of the quaternion. For I confess that one of my objects was to show that a system of vector analysis does not require any support from the notion of the quaternion, or, I may add, of the imaginary in algebra.

I should hardly dare to express myself with so much freedom, if I could not shelter myself behind an authority which will not be questioned.

I do not see that I have done anything very different from what the eminent mathematician upon whom Hamilton's mantle has fallen has been doing, it would seem, unconsciously. Contrast the system of quaternions, which he has described in his sketch of Hamilton's life and work in the *North British Review* for September, 1866, with the system which he urges upon the attention of physicists in the *Philosophical Magazine* in 1890. In 1866 we have a great deal about imaginaries, and nearly as much about the quaternion. In 1890 we have nothing about imaginaries, and little about the quaternion. Prof. Tait has spoken of the calculus of quaternions as throwing off in the course of years its early Cartesian trammels. I wonder that he does not see how well the progress in which he has led may be described as throwing off the yoke of the quaternion. A characteristic example is seen in the use of the symbol ∇. Hamilton applies this to a vector to form a quaternion, Tait to form a linear vector function. But while breathing a new life into the formulae of quaternions, Prof. Tait stands stoutly by the letter.

Now I appreciate and admire the generous loyalty toward one whom he regards as his master, which has always led Prof. Tait to minimise the originality of his own work in regard to quaternions, and write as if everything was contained in the ideas which flashed into the mind of Hamilton at the classic Brougham Bridge. But not to speak of other claims of historical justice, we owe duties to our scholars as well as to our teachers, and the world is too large, and the current of modern thought is too broad, to be confined by the *ipse dixit* even of a Hamilton.   J. WILLARD GIBBS.

In 1889 (ref. 2, **II**, pp. 118–54) Gibbs illustrated the utility of the vector method in the approximate determination of an elliptic orbit from three complete observations; it provided an immense saving in astronomical calculations. Dr. Hugo Buchholz applied the theory satisfactorily to the orbit of Swift's Comet, 1880 V. Gibbs had calculation improvements in mind, but had not developed them at the time of his death owing probably to the lack of interest exhibited by astronomers (in view of the emergent period of astrophysics).

It should be emphasized that Gibbs was basically a physicist who used mathematics as a means, not an end in itself. His former student and colleague, C. S. Hastings, quoted Gibbs as once saying, "If I have had any success in mathematical physics, it is, I think, because I have been able to dodge mathematical difficulties".[9] The interrelation, however, of mathematics and physics evident in this period was a major contribution to the correlation of man's knowledge.

(c) FOURIER SERIES

Consider a piecewise smooth function $f(x)$ and its approximate representation by the partial sums of a Fourier series (French mathematical physicist, Baron Jean Baptiste Joseph Fourier (1768–1830)). In any interval that does not contain a discontinuity of $f(x)$, the Fourier graphs approach the graph of $f(x)$. In the immediate vicinity, however, of a jump discontinuity, where the converging Fourier graphs exhibit oscillations, which become progressively narrower when they move closer to the discontinuity point as the number of terms in the partial sum increases. At the same time, the total oscillation of the approximating curve does not approach the $f(x)$ jump—the so-called *Gibbs phenomenon*. For example, Gibbs found that the series

$$\sum_{n=1}^{\infty} \frac{\sin nx}{n}$$

"overshot the mark" in the neighborhood of the discontinuity at $x = 0$.

Fourier's Series

(From *Nature*, LIX, p. 200 (1898).)

In reply to Mr. Love's remarks in Nature of October 13. I would say that in the series

$$y = \sin x + \tfrac{1}{2}\sin 2x + \cdots + \frac{1}{n-1}\sin (n-1)x + \frac{1}{n}\sin nx,$$

in which $\frac{1}{n}\sin nx$ is the last term considered, x must be taken smaller than π/n in order to find the values of y in the immediate vicinity of $x = 0$.

If it is inadmissible to stop at "any convenient nth term," it is quite as illogical to stop at the equally "convenient" value π/n.

Albert A. Michelson.

The University of Chicago Ryerson Physical Laboratory,
Chicago, December 1.

Let us write $f_n(x)$ for the sum of the first n terms of the series

$$\sin x - \tfrac{1}{2}\sin 2x + \tfrac{1}{3}\sin 3x - \tfrac{1}{4}\sin 4x + \&c.$$

I suppose that there is no question concerning the form of the curve defined by any equation of the form

$$y = 2f_n(x).$$

Let us call such a curve C_n. As n increases without limit, the curve approaches a limiting form, which may be thus described. Let a point move from the origin in a straight line at an angle of 45° with the axis of X to the point (π, π), thence vertically in a straight line to the point $(\pi, -\pi)$, thence obliquely in a straight line to the point $(3\pi, \pi)$, &c. The broken line thus described (continued indefinitely forwards and backwards) is the limiting form of the curve as the number of terms increases indefinitely. That is, if any small distance d be first specified, a number n' may be then specified, such that for every value of n greater than n', the distance of any point in C_n from the broken line, and of any point in the broken line from C_n, will be less than the specified distance d.

But this limiting line is not the same as that expressed by the equation

$$y = \lim_{n=\infty} 2f_n(x).$$

The vertical portions of the broken line described above are wanting in the locus expressed by this equation, except the points in which they intersect the axis of X. The process indicated in the last equation is virtually to consider the intersections of C_n with fixed vertical transversals, and seek the limiting positions when n is increased without limit. It is not surprising that this process does not give the vertical portions of the limiting curve. If we should consider the intersections of C_n with horizontal transversals, and seek the limits which they approach when n is increased indefinitely, we should obtain the vertical portions of the limiting curve as well as the oblique portions.

It should be observed that if we take the equation

$$y = 2f_n(x),$$

and proceed to the limit for $n = \infty$, we do not necessarily get $y = 0$ for $x = \pi$. We may get that ratio by first setting $x = \pi$, and then passing to the limit. We may also get $y = 1$, $x = \pi$, by first setting $y = 1$, and then passing to the limit. Now the limit represented by the equation of the broken line described above is not a special or partial limit relating solely to some special method of passing to the limit, but it is the complete limit embracing all sets of values of x and y which can be obtained by any process of passing to the limit.

J. WILLARD GIBBS.

New Haven, Conn., November 29.

CHAPTER 8

Statistical Mechanics

THE kinetic theory of gases may be said to have begun with a proof of Boyle's law in 1738 by the Swiss mathematical physicist Daniel Bernoulli (1700–82). The theoretical establishment of the ideal-gas law was the result of the work (1848, published 1851) of J. P. Joule on the basis of the ideas of the English physicist John Herapath (1798–1868) in 1821, publicized in 1856 by the German chemist Karl Krönig (1822–79). The next significant development was the introduction (1857) of the concept of mean free path between collisions of molecules by R. J. E. Clausius. It was J. C. Maxwell who insisted that all molecules cannot move with the same speed. On the assumption of independent random motions, in 1859 (published 1860) he derived the law of distribution of molecular speeds—similar to the Gaussian law of distribution of errors; he showed it to be independent of collisions. In 1868 L. Boltzmann extended the theory to molecules with potential energy, both internal (polyatomic) and external (e.g. gravitational)—the so-called Maxwell–Boltzmann law. Later (1872) he discovered a particular function of the component speeds which, statistically analogous to entropy, never decreases—the so-called H-theorem. Meanwhile, in 1871 he introduced a new approach, namely, the statistical analysis of a whole system of particles rather than that of the individual particles themselves. He considered a group of gaseous systems all having the same number of particles and energy—a so-called ergodic distribution. The primary problem of such a method is how to reconcile the irreversible entropy increase of nature with the reversible laws of mechanics. L. Boltzmann assumed that the entropy S is given in terms of a probability P by

$$S = k \ln P + C,$$

where C was later taken to be zero by M. K. E. L. Planck (k is the so-called Boltzmann constant).

Gibbs' first note on statistical mechanics appeared in 1884 (in 1894–5 he gave a course in statistical mechanics supplementary to the one in thermodynamics).

On the Fundamental Formula of Statistical Mechanics, with Applications to Astronomy and Thermodynamics

(From the *Proceedings of the American Association of Advanced Science*, **33**, pp. 57–58 (1885).)

[ABSTRACT]

SUPPOSE that we have a great number of systems which consist of material points and are identical in character, but different in configuration and velocities, and in which the forces are determined by the configuration alone. Let the number of systems in which the coördinates and velocities lie severally between the following limits, viz., between

$$x_1 \text{ and } x_1 + dx_1,$$
$$y_1 \text{ and } y_1 + dy_1,$$
$$z_1 \text{ and } z_1 + dz_1,$$
$$x_2 \text{ and } x_2 + dx_2,$$
$$\text{etc.,}$$
$$\dot{x}_1 \text{ and } \dot{x}_1 + d\dot{x}_1,$$
$$\dot{y}_1 \text{ and } \dot{y}_1 + d\dot{y}_1,$$
$$\dot{z}_1 \text{ and } \dot{z}_1 + d\dot{z}_1,$$
$$\dot{x}_2 \text{ and } \dot{x}_2 + d\dot{x}_2,$$
$$\text{etc.,}$$

be denoted by

$$L \, dx_1 \, dy_1 \, dz_1 \, dx_2 \text{ etc. } d\dot{x}_1 \, d\dot{y}_1 \, d\dot{z}_1 \, d\dot{x}_2 \text{ etc.}$$

The manner in which the quantity L varies with the time is given by the equation

$$\frac{dL}{dt} = -\sum \left[\frac{dL}{dx} \dot{x} + \frac{dL}{d\dot{x}} \ddot{x} \right],$$

where t, x_1, y_1, z_1, x_2, etc., $\dot{x}_1$, $\dot{y}_1$, $\dot{z}_1$, $\dot{x}_2$, etc., are the independent variables, and the summation relates to all the coördinates.

The object of the paper is to establish this proposition (which is not claimed as new, but which has hardly received the recognition which it deserves) and to show its applications to astronomy and thermodynamics.

His next publication (his last) is *The Elementary Principles in Statistical Mechanics Developed with Especial Reference to the Rational Foundation of Thermodynamics*, which he prepared for Yale's Bicentennial in 1901 and which is a complementary sequel to his earlier work on thermodynamics.

Gibbs limited his own investigations to the purely statistical method. He sought to deduce rationally the experiential laws of thermodynamics from mechanics and statistics—hence his own descriptive phrase "statistical mechanics" (perhaps the term "thermostatistics" of H. A. Kramers (1949) is more apt today). To do so, he felt compelled not to utilize specific hypotheses with respect to the constitution of matter. His purpose, as stated in the Preface, necessitated his not "attempting to explain the mysteries of nature"; by this same strategy, however, he was enabled to develop a method which outlasted the ephemeral character of atomic theories.

(a) FUNDAMENTAL IDEAS

Consider a conservative mechanical system with n degrees of freedom; let it be described by generalized coordinates q_i and generalized momenta p_i, where $i = 1, \ldots, n$. Let the energy be $\epsilon(q_i, p_i)$. Then the equations of motion can be expressed in their Hamiltonian (1834) canonical form as follows:

$$\left.\begin{aligned} \dot{q}_i &= \frac{\partial \epsilon}{\partial p_i} \\[2mm] \dot{p}_i &= \frac{-\partial \epsilon}{\partial q_i} \end{aligned}\right\} \quad i = 1, \ldots, n,$$

where the dot refers to the time derivative. If the initial phase is completely known, the dynamical behavior of the system is determined for all time.

The phase for a degree of freedom is given by its generalized coordinate and the corresponding momentum; it can be represented by a point on a graph with the coordinate q_i as the abscissa and the momentum p_i as the ordinate (the physical dimension of an element of area is that of physical "action"). A whole system, therefore, can be represented by a point in $2n$-dimensional phase space (P. Ehrenfest's Γ-space (gas), as contrasted with μ-space (molecule)), which moves with time, subject to the constancy of its energy.

Consider an *ensemble* of similar mechanical systems, each having a different phase; the ensemble of such points will occupy an *extension-in-phase* and will move in this phase space like a fluid. In this case one can apply a theorem (1838) due to J. Liouville, namely, that the flow of such a mechanical system is divergenceless (*cf.* the so-called equation of continuity for an incompressible flow). Gibbs called this result *conservation of extension-in-phase.*

Let us denote the *density in phase* by D and define the *coefficient of probability* of phase P by

$$P = \frac{D}{N},$$

and the *index of probability* η by

$$\eta = \ln P.$$

If the coefficient of probability is independent of the time, there is said to be statistical equilibrium. It can be shown that both P and η are constant for moving systems of the ensemble so that the principle of conservation of extension-in-phase may be called the principle of conservation of probability of phase; hence

$$P \equiv P(\epsilon).$$

Elementary Principles in Statistical Mechanics*

PREFACE

THE usual point of view in the study of mechanics is that where the attention is mainly directed to the changes which take place in the course of time in a

* Ref. 1, pp. vii–xii, 3–9, 16–19.

given system. The principal problem is the determination of the condition of the system with respect to configuration and velocities at any required time, when its condition in these respects has been given for some one time, and the fundamental equations are those which express the changes continually taking place in the system. Inquiries of this kind are often simplified by taking into consideration conditions of the system other than those through which it actually passes or is supposed to pass, but our attention is not usually carried beyond conditions differing infinitesimally from those which are regarded as actual.

For some purposes, however, it is desirable to take a broader view of the subject. We may imagine a great number of systems of the same nature, but differing in the configurations and velocities which they have at a given instant, and differing not merely infinitesimally, but it may be so as to embrace every conceivable combination of configuration and velocities. And here we may set the problem, not to follow a particular system through its succession of configurations, but to determine how the whole number of systems will be distributed among the various conceivable configurations and velocities at any required time, when the distribution has been given for some one time. The fundamental equation for this inquiry is that which gives the rate of change of the number of systems which fall within any infinitesimal limits of configuration and velocity.

Such inquiries have been called by Maxwell *statistical*. They belong to a branch of mechanics which owes its origin to the desire to explain the laws of thermodynamics on mechanical principles, and of which Clausius, Maxwell, and Boltzmann are to be regarded as the principal founders. The first inquiries in this field were indeed somewhat narrower in their scope than that which has been mentioned, being applied to the particles of a system, rather than to independent systems. Statistical inquiries were next directed to the phases (or conditions with respect to configuration and velocity) which succeed one another in a given system in the course of time. The explicit consideration of a great number of systems and their distribution in phase, and of the permanence or alteration of this distribution in the course of time is perhaps first found in Boltzmann's paper on the "Zusammenhang zwischen den Sätzen über das Verhalten mehratomiger Gasmoleküle mit Jacobi's Princip des letzten Multiplicators" (1871).

But although, as a matter of history, statistical mechanics owes its origin to investigations in thermodynamics, it seems eminently worthy of an independent development, both on account of the elegance and simplicity of its principles, and because it yields new results and places old truths in a new light in departments quite outside of thermodynamics. Moreover, the separate study of this branch of mechanics seems to afford the best foundation for the study of rational thermodynamics and molecular mechanics.

The laws of thermodynamics, as empirically determined, express the approximate and probable behavior of systems of a great number of particles, or, more precisely, they express the laws of mechanics for such systems as they appear to beings who have not the fineness of perception to enable them to appreciate quantities of the order of magnitude of those which relate to single particles, and who cannot repeat their experiments often enough to obtain any but the most probable results. The laws of statistical mechanics apply to conservative systems of any number of degrees of freedom, and are exact. This does not make them more difficult to establish than the approximate laws for systems of a great many degrees of freedom, or for limited classes of such systems. The reverse is rather the case, for our attention is not diverted from what is essential by the peculiarities of the system considered, and we are not obliged to satisfy ourselves that the effect of the quantities and circumstances neglected will be negligible in the result. The laws of thermodynamics may be easily obtained from the principles of statistical mechanics, of which they are the incomplete expression, but they make a somewhat blind guide in our search for those laws. This is perhaps the principal cause of the slow progress of rational thermodynamics, as contrasted with the rapid deduction of the consequences of its laws as empirically established. To this must be added that the rational foundation of thermodynamics lay in a branch of mechanics of which the fundamental notions and principles, and the characteristic operations, were alike unfamiliar to students of mechanics.

We may therefore confidently believe that nothing will more conduce to the clear apprehension of the relation of thermodynamics to rational mechanics, and to the interpretation of observed phenomena with reference to their evidence respecting the molecular constitution of bodies, than the study of the fundamental notions and principles of that department of mechanics to which thermodynamics is especially related.

Moreover, we avoid the gravest difficulties when, giving up the attempt to frame hypotheses concerning the constitution of material bodies, we pursue statistical inquiries as a branch of rational mechanics. In the present state of science, it seems hardly possible to frame a dynamic theory of molecular action which shall embrace the phenomena of thermodynamics, of radiation, and of the electrical manifestations which accompany the union of atoms. Yet any theory is obviously inadequate which does not take account of all these phenomena. Even if we confine our attention to the phenomena distinctively thermodynamic, we do not escape difficulties in as simple a matter as the number of degrees of freedom of a diatomic gas. It is well known that while theory would assign to the gas six degrees of freedom per molecule, in our experiments on specific heat we cannot account for more than five. Certainly, one is building on an insecure foundation, who rests his work on hypotheses concerning the constitution of matter.

Difficulties of this kind have deterred the author from attempting to explain the mysteries of nature, and have forced him to be contented with the more modest aim of deducing some of the more obvious propositions relating to the statistical branch of mechanics. Here, there can be no mistake in regard to the

9

agreement of the hypotheses with the facts of nature, for nothing is assumed in that respect. The only error into which one can fall, is the want of agreement between the premises and the conclusions, and this, with care, one may hope, in the main, to avoid.

The matter of the present volume consists in large measure of results which have been obtained by the investigators mentioned above, although the point of view and the arrangement may be different. These results, given to the public one by one in the order of their discovery, have necessarily, in their original presentation, not been arranged in the most logical manner.

In the first chapter we consider the general problem which has been mentioned, and find what may be called the fundamental equation of statistical mechanics. A particular case of this equation will give the condition of statistical equilibrium, *i.e.*, the condition which the distribution of the systems in phase must satisfy in order that the distribution shall be permanent. In the general case, the fundamental equation admits an integration, which gives a principle which may be variously expressed, according to the point of view from which it is regarded, as the conservation of density-in-phase, or of extension-in-phase, or of probability of phase.

In the second chapter, we apply this principle of conservation of probability of phase to the theory of errors in the calculated phases of a system, when the determination of the arbitrary constants of the integral equations are subject to error. In this application, we do not go beyond the usual approximations. In other words, we combine the principle of conservation of probability of phase, which is exact, with those approximate relations, which it is customary to assume in the "theory of errors."

In the third chapter we apply the principle of conservation of extension-in-phase to the integration of the differential equations of motion. This gives Jacobi's "last multiplier," as has been shown by Boltzmann.

In the fourth and following chapters we return to the consideration of statistical equilibrium, and confine our attention to conservative systems. We consider especially ensembles of systems in which the index (or logarithm) of probability of phase is a linear function of the energy. This distribution, on account of its unique importance in the theory of statistical equilibrium, I have ventured to call *canonical*, and the divisor of the energy, the *modulus* of distribution. The moduli of ensembles have properties analogous to temperature, in that equality of the moduli is a condition of equilibrium with respect to exchange of energy, when such exchange is made possible.

We find a differential equation relating to average values in the ensemble which is identical in form with the fundamental differential equation of thermodynamics, the average index of probability of phase, with change of sign, corresponding to entropy, and the modulus to temperature.

For the average square of the anomalies of the energy, we find an expression which vanishes in comparison with the square of the average energy, when the number of degrees of freedom is indefinitely increased. An ensemble of systems in which the number of degrees of freedom is of the same order of magnitude as the number of molecules in the bodies with which we experiment, if distributed canonically, would therefore appear to human observation as an ensemble of systems in which all have the same energy.

We meet with other quantities, in the development of the subject, which, when the number of degrees of freedom is very great, coincide sensibly with the modulus, and with the average index of probability, taken negatively, in a canonical ensemble, and which, therefore, may also be regarded as corresponding to temperature and entropy. The correspondence is however imperfect, when the number of degrees of freedom is not very great, and there is nothing to recommend these quantities except that in definition they may be regarded as more simple than those which have been mentioned. In Chapter XIV, this subject of thermodynamic analogies is discussed somewhat at length.

Finally, in Chapter XV, we consider the modification of the preceding results which is necessary when we consider systems composed of a number of entirely similar particles, or, it may be, of a number of particles of several kinds, all of each kind being entirely similar to each other, and when one of the variations to be considered is that of the numbers of the particles of the various kinds which are contained in a system. This supposition would naturally have been introduced earlier, if our object had been simply the expression of the laws of nature. It seemed desirable, however, to separate sharply the purely thermodynamic laws from those special modifications which belong rather to the theory of the properties of matter.

J. W. G.

New Haven, December, 1901.

Elementary Principles in Statistical Mechanics*

CHAPTER I.

GENERAL NOTIONS. THE PRINCIPLE OF CONSERVATION OF EXTENSION-IN-PHASE.

We shall use Hamilton's form of the equations of motion for a system of n degrees of freedom, writing $q_1, \ldots q_n$ for the (generalized) coördinates, $\dot{q}_1, \ldots \dot{q}_n$ for the (generalized) velocities, and

$$F_1 \, dq_1 + F_2 \, dq_2 \cdots + F_n \, dq_n \qquad (1)$$

for the moment of the forces. We shall call the quantities $F_1, \ldots F_n$ the (generalized) forces, and the quantities $p_1 \cdots p_n$, defined by the equations

$$p_1 = \frac{d\epsilon_p}{dq_1}, \qquad p_2 = \frac{d\epsilon_p}{d\dot{q}_2}, \quad \text{etc.,} \qquad (2)$$

* Ref. 1, pp. 3–19.

where ϵ_p denotes the kinetic energy of the system, the (generalized) momenta. The kinetic energy is here regarded as a function of the velocities and coördinates. We shall usually regard it as a function of the momenta and coördinates,* and on this account we denote it by ϵ_p. This will not prevent us from occasionally using formulae like (2), where it is sufficiently evident the kinetic energy is regarded as function of the $\dot{q}$'s and q's. But in expressions like $d\epsilon_p/dq_1$, where the denominator does not determine the question, the kinetic energy is always to be treated in the differentiation as function of the p's and q's.

We have then

$$\dot{q}_1 = \frac{d\epsilon_p}{dp_1}, \quad \dot{p}_1 = -\frac{d\epsilon_p}{dq_1} + F_1, \quad \text{etc.} \tag{3}$$

These equations will hold for any forces whatever. If the forces are conservative, in other words, if the expression (1) is an exact differential, we may set

$$F_1 = -\frac{d\epsilon_q}{dq_1}, \quad F_2 = -\frac{d\epsilon_q}{dq_2}, \quad \text{etc.,} \tag{4}$$

where ϵ_q is a function of the coördinates which we shall call the potential energy of the system. If we write ϵ for the total energy, we shall have

$$\epsilon = \epsilon_p + \epsilon_q, \tag{5}$$

and equations (3) may be written

$$\dot{q}_1 = \frac{d\epsilon}{dp_1}, \quad \dot{p}_1 = -\frac{d\epsilon}{dq_1}, \quad \text{etc.} \tag{6}$$

The potential energy (ϵ_q) may depend on other variables beside the coördinates $q_1 \cdots q_n$. We shall often suppose it to depend in part on coördinates of external bodies, which we shall denote by a_1, a_2, etc. We shall then have for the complete value of the differential of the potential energy†

$$d\epsilon_q = -F_1\, dq_1 \cdots - F_n\, dq_n - A_1\, da_1 - A_2\, da_2 - \text{etc.,} \tag{7}$$

where A_1, A_2, etc., represent forces (in the generalized sense) exerted by the

---

* The use of the momenta instead of the velocities as independent variables is the characteristic of Hamilton's method which gives his equations of motion their remarkable degree of simplicity. We shall find that the fundamental notions of statistical mechanics are most easily defined, and are expressed in the most simple form, when the momenta with the coördinates are used to describe the state of a system.

† It will be observed, that although we call ϵ_q the potential energy of the system which we are considering, it is really so defined as to include that energy which might be described as mutual to that system and external bodies.

system on external bodies. For the total energy (ϵ) we shall have

$$d\epsilon = \dot{q}_1 \, dp_1 \cdots + \dot{q}_n \, dp_n - \dot{p}_1 \, dq_1 \cdots$$
$$- \dot{p}_n \, dq_n - A_1 \, da_1 - A_2 \, da_2 - \text{etc.} \tag{8}$$

It will be observed that the kinetic energy (ϵ_p) in the most general case is a quadratic function of the p's (or $\dot{q}$'s) involving also the q's but not the a's; that the potential energy, when it exists, is function of the q's and a's; and that the total energy, when it exists, is function of the p's (or $\dot{q}$'s), the q's, and the a's. In expressions like $d\epsilon/dq_1$, the p's, and not the $\dot{q}$'s, are to be taken as independent variables, as has already been stated with respect to the kinetic energy.

Let us imagine a great number of independent systems, identical in nature, but differing in phase, that is, in their condition with respect to configuration and velocity. The forces are supposed to be determined for every system by the same law, being functions of the coördinates of the system $q_1, \ldots q_n$, either alone or with the coördinates a_1, a_2, etc. of certain external bodies. It is not necessary that they should be derivable from a force-function. The external coördinates a_1, a_2, etc. may vary with the time, but at any given time have fixed values. In this they differ from the internal coördinates $q_1, \ldots q_n$, which at the same time have different values in the different systems considered.

Let us especially consider the number of systems which at a given instant fall within specified limits of phase, viz., those for which

$$\left. \begin{array}{ll} p_1' < p_1 < p_1'', & q_1' < q_1 < q_1'' \\ p_2' < p_2 < p_2'', & q_2' < q_2 < q_2'', \\ \cdots\cdots\cdots & \cdots\cdots\cdots \\ p_n' < p_n < p_n'', & q_n' < q_n < q_n'', \end{array} \right\} \tag{9}$$

the accented letters denoting constants. We shall suppose the differences $p_1'' - p_1'$, $q_1'' - q_1'$, etc. to be infinitesimal, and that the systems are distributed in phase in some continuous manner,* so that the number having phases within the limits specified may be represented by

$$D(p_1'' - p_1') \cdots (p_n'' - p_n')(q_1'' - q_1') \cdots (q_n'' - q_n'), \tag{10}$$

or more briefly by

$$D \, dp_1 \cdots dp_n \, dq_1 \cdots dq_n, \tag{11}$$

where D is a function of the p's and q's and in general of t also, for as time goes on, and the individual systems change their phases, the distribution of

---

* In strictness, a finite number of systems cannot be described continuously in phase. But by increasing indefinitely the number of systems, we may approximate to a continuous law of distribution, such as is here described. To avoid tedious circumlocution, language like the above may be allowed, although wanting in precision of expression, when the sense in which it is to be taken appears sufficiently clear.

the ensemble in phase will in general vary. In special cases, the distribution in phase will remain unchanged. These are cases of *statistical equilibrium*.

If we regard all possible phases as forming a sort of extension of $2n$ dimensions, we may regard the product of differentials in (11) as expressing an element of this extension, and D as expressing the density of the systems in that element. We shall call the product

$$dp_1 \cdots dp_n \, dq_1 \cdots dq_n \tag{12}$$

an element of *extension-in-phase*, and D the *density-in-phase* of the systems.

It is evident that the changes which take place in the density of the systems in any given element of extension-in-phase will depend on the dynamical nature of the systems and their distribution in phase at the time considered.

In the case of conservative systems, with which we shall be principally concerned, their dynamical nature is completely determined by the function which expresses the energy (ϵ) in terms of the p's, q's, and a's (a function supposed identical for all the systems); in the more general case which we are considering, the dynamical nature of the systems is determined by the functions which express the kinetic energy (ϵ_p) in terms of the p's and q's, and the forces in terms of the q's and a's. The distribution in phase is expressed for the time considered by D as function of the p's and q's. To find the value of dD/dt for the specified element of extension-in-phase, we observe that the number of systems within the limits can only be varied by systems passing the limits, which may take place in $4n$ different ways, viz., by the p_1 of a system passing the limit $p_1{}'$, or the limit $p_1{}''$, or by the q_1 of a system passing the limit $q_1{}'$, or the limit $q_1{}''$, etc. Let us consider these cases separately.

In the first place, let us consider the number of systems which in the time dt pass into or out of the specified element by p_1 passing the limit $p_1{}'$. It will be convenient, and it is evidently allowable, to suppose dt so small that the quantities $\dot{p}_1 \, dt$, $\dot{q}_1 \, dt$, etc., which represent the increments of p_1, q_1, etc., in the time dt shall be infinitely small in comparison with the infinitesimal differences $p_1{}'' - p_1{}'$, $q_1{}'' - q_1{}'$, etc., which determine the magnitude of the element of extension-in-phase. The systems for which p_1 passes the limit $p_1{}'$ in the interval dt are those for which at the commencement of this interval the value of p_1 lies between $p_1{}'$ and $p_1{}' - \dot{p}_1 \, dt$, as is evident if we consider separately the cases in which $\dot{p}_1$ is positive and negative. Those systems for which p_1 lies between these limits, and the other p's and q's between the limits specified in (9), will therefore pass into or out of the element considered according as $\dot{p}$ is positive or negative, unless indeed they also pass some other limit specified in (9) during the same interval of time. But the number which pass any two of these limits will be represented by an expression containing the square of dt as a factor, and is evidently negligible, when dt is sufficiently small, compared with the number which we are seeking to evaluate, and which (with neglect of terms containing dt^2) may be found by substituting $\dot{p}_1 \, dt$ for $p_1{}'' - p_1{}'$ in (10) or for dp_1 in (11).

The expression

$$D\dot{p}_1\, dt\, dp_2 \cdots dp_n\, dq_1 \cdots dq_n \qquad (13)$$

will therefore represent, according as it is positive or negative, the increase or decrease of the number of systems within the given limits which is due to systems passing the limit p_1'. A similar expression, in which however D and $\dot{p}$ will have slightly different values (being determined for p_1'' instead of p_1'), will represent the decrease or increase of the number of systems due to the passing of the limit p_1''. The difference of the two expressions, or

$$\frac{d(D\dot{p}_1)}{dp_1}\, dp_1 \cdots dp_n\, dq_1 \cdots dq_n\, dt \qquad (14)$$

will represent algebraically the decrease of the number of systems within the limits due to systems passing the limits p_1' and p_1''.

The decrease in the number of systems within the limits due to systems passing the limits q_1' and q_1'' may be found in the same way. This will give

$$\left(\frac{d(D\dot{p}_1)}{dp_1} + \frac{d(D\dot{q}_1)}{dq_1}\right) dp_1 \cdots dp_n\, dq_1 \cdots dq_n\, dt \qquad (15)$$

for the decrease due to passing the four limits p_1', p_1'', q_1', q_1''. But since the equations of motion (3) give

$$\frac{d\dot{p}_1}{dp_1} + \frac{d\dot{q}_1}{dq_1} = 0, \qquad (16)$$

the expression reduces to

$$\left(\frac{dD}{dp_1}\dot{p}_1 + \frac{dD}{dq_1}\dot{q}_1\right) dp_1 \cdots dp_n\, dq_1 \cdots dq_n\, dt. \qquad (17)$$

If we prefix Σ to denote summation relative to the suffixes $1 \cdots n$, we get the total decrease in the number of systems within the limits in the time dt. That is,

$$\Sigma\left(\frac{dD}{dp_1}\dot{p}_1 + \frac{dD}{dq_1}\dot{q}_1\right) dp_1 \cdots dp_n\, dq_1 \cdots dq_n\, dt$$

$$= -dD\, dp_1 \cdots dp_n\, dq_1 \cdots dq_n, \qquad (18)$$

or $\qquad \left(\dfrac{dD}{dt}\right)_{p,q} = -\Sigma\left(\dfrac{dD}{dp_1}\dot{p}_1 + \dfrac{dD}{dq_1}\dot{q}_1\right), \qquad (19)$

where the suffix applied to the differential coefficient indicates that the p's and q's are to be regarded as constant in the differentiation. The condition of statistical equilibrium is therefore

$$\sum \left(\frac{dD}{dp_1} \dot{p}_1 + \frac{dD}{dq_1} \dot{q}_1 \right) = 0. \tag{20}$$

If at any instant this condition is fulfilled for all values of the p's and q's, $(dD/dt)_{p,q}$ vanishes, and therefore the condition will continue to hold, and the distribution in phase will be permanent, so long as the external coördinates remain constant. But the statistical equilibrium would in general be disturbed by a change in the values of the external coördinates, which would alter the values of the $\dot{p}$'s as determined by equations (3), and thus disturb the relation expressed in the last equation.

If we write equation (19) in the form

$$\left(\frac{dD}{dt} \right)_{p,q} dt + \sum \left(\frac{dD}{dp_1} \dot{p}_1 \, dt + \frac{dD}{dq_1} \dot{q}_1 \, dt \right) = 0, \tag{21}$$

it will be seen to express a theorem of remarkable simplicity. Since D is a function of t, $p_1, \ldots p_n$, $q_1, \ldots q_n$, its complete differential will consist of parts due to the variations of all these quantities. Now the first term of the equation represents the increment of D due to an increment of t (with constant values of the p's and q's), and the rest of the first member represents the increments of D due to increments of the p's and q's, expressed by $\dot{p}_1 \, dt, \dot{q}_1 \, dt$, etc. But these are precisely the increments which the p's and q's receive in the movement of a system in the time dt. The whole expression represents the total increment of D for the varying phase of a moving system. We have therefore the theorem:—

*In an ensemble of mechanical systems identical in nature and subject to forces determined by identical laws, but distributed in phase in any continuous manner, the density-in-phase is constant in time for the varying phases of a moving system; provided, that the forces of a system are functions of its coordinates, either alone or with the time.**

This may be called the principle of *conservation of density-in-phase*.

. . . .

It is the relative numbers of systems which fall within different limits, rather than the absolute numbers, with which we are most concerned. It is indeed only with regard to relative numbers that such discussions as the preceding will apply with literal precision, since the nature of our reasoning implies that the number of systems in the smallest element of space which we consider is very great. This is evidently inconsistent with a finite value of the

---

* The condition that the forces $F_1, \ldots F_n$ are functions of $q_1, \ldots q_n$ and a_1, a_2, etc., which last are functions of the time, is analytically equivalent to the condition that $F_1, \ldots F_n$ are functions of $q_1, \ldots q_n$ and the time. Explicit mention of the external coördinates, a_1, a_2, etc., has been made in the preceding pages, because our purpose will require us hereafter to consider these coördinates and the connected forces, A_1, A_2, etc., which represent the action of the systems on external bodies.

total number of systems, or of the density-in-phase. Now if the value of D is infinite, we cannot speak of any definite number of systems within any finite limits, since all such numbers are infinite. But the ratios of these infinite numbers may be perfectly definite. If we write N for the total number of systems, and set

$$P = \frac{D}{N}, \tag{38}$$

P may remain finite, when N and D become infinite. The integral

$$\int \cdots \int P \, dp_1 \cdots dq_n \tag{39}$$

taken within any given limits, will evidently express the ratio of the number of systems falling within those limits to the whole number of systems. This is the same thing as the *probability* that an unspecified system of the ensemble (*i.e.* one of which we only know that it belongs to the ensemble) will lie within the given limits. The product

$$P \, dp_1 \cdots dq_n \tag{40}$$

expresses the probability that an unspecified system of the ensemble will be found in the element of extension-in-phase $dp_1 \cdots dq_n$. We shall call P the *coefficient of probability* of the phase considered. Its natural logarithm we shall call the *index of probability* of the phase, and denote it by the letter η.

If we substitute NP and Ne^{η} for D in equation (19), we get

$$\left(\frac{dP}{dt}\right)_{p,q} = - \sum \left(\frac{dP}{dp_1} \dot{p}_1 + \frac{dP}{dq_1} d\dot{q}_1\right), \tag{41}$$

and

$$\left(\frac{d\eta}{dt}\right)_{p,q} = - \sum \left(\frac{d\eta}{dp_1} \dot{p}_1 + \frac{d\eta}{dq_1} d\dot{q}_1\right). \tag{42}$$

The condition of statistical equilibrium may be expressed by equating to zero the second member of either of these equations.

The same substitutions in (22) give

$$\left(\frac{dP}{dt}\right)_{a,\ldots h} = 0, \tag{43}$$

and

$$\left(\frac{d\eta}{dt}\right)_{a,\ldots h} = 0. \tag{44}$$

That is, the values of P and η, like those of D, are constant in time for moving systems of the ensemble. From this point of view, the principle which otherwise regarded has been called the principle of conservation of density-in-phase or conservation of extension-in-phase, may be called the principle of conservation of the coefficient (or index) of probability of a phase varying according to dynamical laws, or more briefly, the principle of *conservation of probability of phase*. It is subject to the limitation that the forces must be functions of the coördinates of the system either alone or with the time.

The application of this principle is not limited to cases in which there is a formal and explicit reference to an ensemble of systems. Yet the conception of such an ensemble may serve to give precision to notions of probability. It is in fact customary in the discussion of probabilities to describe anything which is imperfectly known as something taken at random from a great number of things which are completely described. But if we prefer to avoid any reference to an ensemble of systems, we may observe that the probability that the phase of a system falls within certain limits at a certain time, is equal to the probability that at some other time the phase will fall within the limits formed by phases corresponding to the first. For either occurrence necessitates the other. That is, if we write P' for the coefficient of probability of the phase $p_1', \ldots q_n'$ at the time t', and P'' for that of the phase $p_1'', \ldots q_n''$ at the time t'',

$$\int \cdots \int P' \, dq_1' \cdots dq_n' = \int \cdots \int P'' \, dp_1'' \cdots dq_n'', \qquad (45)$$

where the limits in the two cases are formed by corresponding phases. When the integrations cover infinitely small variations of the momenta and coördinates, we may regard P' and P'' as constant in the integrations and write

$$P' \int \cdots \int dp_1' \cdots dq_n'' = P' \int \cdots \int dp_1'' \cdots dq_n''.$$

Now the principle of the conservation of extension-in-phase, which has been proved (viz., in the second demonstration given above) independently of any reference to an ensemble of systems, requires that the values of the multiple integrals in this equation shall be equal. This gives

$$P'' = P'.$$

With reference to an important class of cases this principle may be enunciated as follows.

When the differential equations of motion are exactly known, but the constants of the integral equations imperfectly determined, the coefficient of probability of any phase at any time is equal to the coefficient of probability of the corresponding phase at any other time. By corresponding phases are meant those which are calculated for different times from the same values of the arbitrary constants of the integral equations.

Since the sum of the probabilities of all possible cases is necessarily unity, it is evident that we must have

$$\int_{\text{phases}}^{\text{all}} \cdots \int P \, dp_1 \cdots dq_n = 1, \tag{46}$$

where the integration extends over all phases. This is indeed only a different form of the equation

$$N = \int_{\text{phases}}^{\text{all}} \cdots \int D \, dp_1 \cdots dq_n,$$

which we may regard as defining N.

The values of the coefficient and index of probability of phase, like that of the density-in-phase, are independent of the system of coördinates which is employed to express the distribution in phase of a given ensemble.

In dimensions, the coefficient of probability is the reciprocal of an extension-in-phase, that is, the reciprocal of the nth power of the product of time and energy. The index of probability is therefore affected by an additive constant when we change our units of time and energy. If the unit of time is multiplied by c_t and the unit of energy is multiplied by c_ϵ, all indices of probability relating to systems of n degrees of freedom will be increased by the addition of

$$n \log c_t + n \log c_\epsilon. \tag{47}$$

(b) CANONICAL AND MICROCANONICAL ENSEMBLES

The simplest relation for $P(\epsilon)$ is

$$P = e^{\frac{\psi - \epsilon}{\Theta}},$$

where ψ and Θ are constants, Θ positive. Such a distribution is said to be a *canonical ensemble* and Θ its *module of distribution*. The value of ψ is determined by the condition that the integration of the coefficient of probability over all phase space must equal unity; the statistical mechanical function ψ turns out to be the analogue of Gibbs' thermodynamic ψ (the Helmholtzian "free energy"). Gibbs showed that the value of Θ is determined by the fact that $n/2\Theta$ equals the average kinetic energy of a system with n-coordinates in the ensemble; it has properties analogous to those of temperature in thermodynamics. Likewise the statistical average $\bar{\eta}$ corresponds to the negative of the thermodynamical function. Specifically, he showed

$$d\bar{\epsilon} = -\Theta \, d\bar{\eta} - \sum_i A_i a_i,$$

where A_i is the external force corresponding to parameter a_i and the horizontal bar indicates a statistical mean.

Consider an ensemble with uniform density-in-phase between energies ϵ and ϵ', but zero elsewhere. The limiting distribution, as ϵ' approaches ϵ, is called a *microcanonical ensemble* (or sometimes an ergodic or F-ensemble). A canonical ensemble can be regarded as compounded of a family of microcanonical ensembles so that its properties can be deduced from those of the simpler microcanonical ensemble. In this connection, Gibbs found it convenient to introduce two new functions of the energy, namely, $V(\epsilon)$ and $\phi(\epsilon)$, where V is the total extension-in-phase below a limit of energy, i.e.

$$V = \int \cdots \int dp, \ldots, dq_n,$$

and

$$\phi = \ln \frac{dV}{d\epsilon}.$$

Gibbs' statistical mechanics is formally identical with Boltzmann's theory of gases if the actual gas is replaced by a virtual assembly of copies of the gas; the definition of entropy is the same, provided the number of degrees of freedom is indefinitely increased (Boltzmann's result is valid only in the limit, whereas Gibbs' result is exact for any number of degrees of freedom). Gibbs' approach, in general, is simpler and more elegant.

Elementary Principles in Statistical Mechanics *

CHAPTER IV

ON THE DISTRIBUTION IN PHASE CALLED CANONICAL, IN WHICH THE INDEX OF PROBABILITY IS A LINEAR FUNCTION OF THE ENERGY.

LET us now give our attention to the statistical equilibrium of ensembles of conservation systems, especially to those cases and properties which promise to throw light on the phenomena of thermodynamics.

* Ref. 1, pp. 32–37, 42–45, 87–88, 115–21.

The condition of statistical equilibrium may be expressed in the form*

$$\sum\left(\frac{dP}{dp_1}\dot{p}_1 + \frac{dP}{dq_1}\dot{q}_1\right) = 0, \tag{88}$$

where P is the coefficient of probability, or the quotient of the density-in-phase by the whole number of systems. To satisfy this condition, it is necessary and sufficient that P should be a function of the p's and q's (the momenta and coördinates) which does not vary with the time in a moving system. In all cases which we are now considering, the energy, or any function of the energy, is such a function.

$$P = \text{func. } (\epsilon)$$

will therefore satisfy the equation, as indeed appears identically if we write it in the form

$$\sum\left(\frac{dP}{dq_1}\frac{d\epsilon}{dp_1} - \frac{dP}{dp_1}\frac{d\epsilon}{dq_1}\right) = 0.$$

There are, however, other conditions to which P is subject, which are not so much conditions of statistical equilibrium, as conditions implicitly involved in the definition of the coefficient of probability, whether the case is one of equilibrium or not. These are: that P should be single-valued, and neither negative nor imaginary for any phase, and that expressed by equation (46), viz.,

$$\int_{\text{phases}}^{\text{all}} \cdots \int P\, dp_1 \cdots dq_n = 1. \tag{89}$$

These considerations exclude

$$P = \epsilon \times \text{constant},$$

as well as

$$P = \text{constant},$$

as cases to be considered.

The distribution represented by

$$\eta = \log P = \frac{\psi - \epsilon}{\Theta}, \tag{90}$$

or

$$P = e^{\frac{\psi-\epsilon}{\Theta}}, \tag{91}$$

* See equations (20), (41), (42), also the paragraph following equation (20). The positions of any external bodies which can affect the systems are here supposed uniform for all the systems and constant in time.

where Θ and ψ are constants, and Θ positive, seems to represent the most simple case conceivable, since it has the property that when the system consists of parts with separate energies, the laws of the distribution in phase of the separate parts are of the same nature,—a property which enormously simplifies the discussion, and is the foundation of extremely important relations to thermodynamics. The case is not rendered less simple by the divisor Θ, (a quantity of the same dimensions as ϵ,) but the reverse, since it makes the distribution independent of the units employed. The negative sign of ϵ is required by (89), which determines also the value of ψ for any given Θ, viz.,

$$e^{-\frac{\psi}{\Theta}} = \int \cdots \int\limits_{\text{phases}}^{\text{all}} e^{-\frac{\epsilon}{\Theta}} \, dp_1 \cdots dq_n. \tag{92}$$

When an ensemble of systems is distributed in phase in the manner described, *i.e.*, when the index of probability is a linear function of the energy, we shall say that the ensemble is *canonically distributed*, and shall call the divisor of the energy (Θ) the *modulus* of distribution.

The fractional part of an ensemble canonically distributed which lies within any given limits of phase is therefore represented by the multiple integral

$$\int \cdots \int e^{\frac{\psi - \epsilon}{\Theta}} \, dp_1 \cdots dq_n \tag{93}$$

taken within those limits. We may express the same thing by saying that the multiple integral expresses the probability that an unspecified system of the ensemble (*i.e.*, one of which we only know that it belongs to the ensemble) falls within the given limits.

Since the value of a multiple integral of the form (23) (which we have called an extension-in-phase) bounded by any given phases is independent of the system of coördinates by which it is evaluated, the same must be true of the multiple integral in (92), as appears at once if we divide up this integral into parts so small that the exponential factor may be regarded as constant in each. The value of ψ is therefore independent of the system of coördinates employed.

It is evident that ψ might be defined as the energy for which the coefficient of probability of phase has the value unity. Since however this coefficient has the dimensions of the inverse nth power of the product of energy and time,* the energy represented by ψ is not independent of the units of energy and time. But when these units have been chosen, the definition of ψ will involve the same arbitrary constant as ϵ, so that, while in any given case the numerical values of ψ or ϵ will be entirely indefinite until the zero of energy has also been

* See Chapter I, p. 19.

fixed for the system considered, the difference $\psi - \epsilon$ will represent a perfectly definite amount of energy, which is entirely independent of the zero of energy which we may choose to adopt.

It is evident that the canonical distribution is entirely determined by the modulus (considered as a quantity of energy) and the nature of the system considered, since when equation (92) is satisfied the value of the multiple integral (93) is independent of the units and of the coördinates employed, and of the zero chosen for the energy of the system.

In treating of the canonical distribution, we shall always suppose the multiple integral in equation (92) to have a finite value, as otherwise the coefficient of probability vanishes, and the law of distribution becomes illusory. This will exclude certain cases, but not such apparently, as will affect the value of our results with respect to their bearing on thermodynamics. It will exclude, for instance, cases in which the system or parts of it can be distributed in unlimited space (or in a space which has limits, but is still infinite in volume), while the energy remains beneath a finite limit. It also excludes many cases in which the energy can decrease without limit, as when the system contains material points which attract one another inversely as the squares of their distances. Cases of material points attracting each other inversely as the distances would be excluded for some values of Θ, and not for others. The investigation of such points is best left to the particular cases. For the purposes of a general discussion, it is sufficient to call attention to the assumption implicitly involved in the formula (92).*

The modulus Θ has properties analogous to those of temperature in thermodynamics. Let the system A be defined as one of an ensemble of systems of m degrees of freedom distributed in phase with a probability-coefficient

$$e^{\frac{\psi_A - \epsilon_A}{\Theta}},$$

and the system B as one of an ensemble of systems of n degrees of freedom distributed in phase with a probability-coefficient

$$e^{\frac{\psi_B - \epsilon_B}{\Theta}},$$

which has the same modulus. Let $q_1, \ldots q_m, p_1, \ldots p_m$ be the coördinates and momenta of A, and $q_{m+1}, \ldots q_{m+n}, p_{m+1}, \ldots p_{m+n}$ those of B. Now we may

---

* It will be observed that similar limitations exist in thermodynamics. In order that a mass of gas can be in thermodynamic equilibrium, it is necessary that it be enclosed. There is no thermodynamic equilibrium of a (finite) mass of gas in an infinite space. Again, that two attracting particles should be able to do an infinite amount of work in passing from one configuration (which is regarded as possible) to another, is a notion which, although perfectly intelligible in a mathematical formula, is quite foreign to our ordinary conceptions of matter.

regard the systems A and B as together forming a system C, having $m + n$ degrees of freedom, and the coördinates and momenta $q_1, \ldots q_{m+n}$, $p_1, \ldots p_{m+n}$. The probability that the phase of the system C, as thus defined, will fall within the limits

$$dp_1, \ldots dp_{m+n}, dq_1, \ldots dq_{m+n}$$

is evidently the product of the probabilities that the systems A and B will each fall within the specified limits, viz.,

$$e^{\frac{\psi_A + \psi_B - \epsilon_A - \epsilon_B}{\Theta}} \quad dp_1 \cdots dp_{m+n} \, dq_1 \cdots dq_{m+n}. \tag{94}$$

We may therefore regard C as an undetermined system of an ensemble distributed with the probability-coefficient

$$e^{\frac{\psi_A + \psi_B - (\epsilon_A + \epsilon_B)}{\Theta}}, \tag{95}$$

an ensemble which might be defined as formed by combining each system of the first ensemble with each of the second. But since $\epsilon_A + \epsilon_B$ is the energy of the whole system, and ψ_A and ψ_B are constants, the probability-coefficient is of the general form which we are considering, and the ensemble to which it relates is in statistical equilibrium and is canonically distributed.

This result, however, so far as statistical equilibrium is concerned, is rather nugatory, since conceiving of separate systems as forming a single system does not create any interaction between them, and if the systems combined belong to ensembles in statistical equilibrium, to say that the ensemble formed by such combinations as we have supposed is in statistical equilibrium, is only to repeat the data in different words. Let us therefore suppose that in forming the system C we add certain forces acting between A and B, and having the force-function $-\epsilon_{AB}$. The energy of the system C is now $\epsilon_A + \epsilon_B + \epsilon_{AB}$, and an ensemble of such systems distributed with a density proportional to

$$e^{\frac{-(\epsilon_A + \epsilon_B + \epsilon_{AB})}{\Theta}} \tag{96}$$

would be in statistical equilibrium. Comparing this with the probability-coefficient of C given above (95), we see that if we suppose ϵ_{AB} (or rather the variable part of this term when we consider all possible configurations of the systems A and B) to be infinitely small, the actual distribution in phase of C will differ infinitely little from one of statistical equilibrium, which is equivalent to saying that its distribution in phase will vary infinitely little even in a time indefinitely prolonged.* The case would be entirely different if A and B

---

* It will be observed that the above condition relating to the forces which act between the different systems is entirely analogous to that which must hold in the corresponding case in thermodynamics. The most simple test of the equality of belonged to ensembles having different moduli, say Θ_A and Θ_B. The probability-coefficient of C would then be

$$e^{\frac{\psi_A - \epsilon_A}{\Theta_A} + \frac{\psi_B - \epsilon_B}{\Theta_B}}, \tag{97}$$

which is not approximately proportional to any expression of the form (96).

The properties of canonically distributed ensembles of systems with respect to the equilibrium of the new ensembles which may be formed by combining each system of one ensemble with each system of another, are therefore not peculiar to them in the sense that analogous properties do not belong to some other distributions under special limitations in regard to the systems and forces considered. Yet the canonical distribution evidently constitutes the most simple case of the kind, and that for which the relations described hold with the least restrictions.

Returning to the case of the canonical distribution, we shall find other analogies with thermodynamic systems, if we suppose, as in the preceding chapters,* that the potential energy (ϵ_q) depends not only upon the coördinates $q_1 \cdots q_n$ which determine the configuration of the system, but also upon certain coördinates a_1, a_2, etc. of bodies which we call *external*, meaning by this simply that they are not to be regarded as forming any part of the system, although their positions affect the forces which act on the system. The forces exerted by the system upon these external bodies will be represented by $-d\epsilon_q/da_1$, $-d\epsilon_q/da_2$, etc., while $-d\epsilon_q/dq_1, \ldots -d\epsilon_q/dq_n$ represent all the forces acting upon the bodies of the system, including those which depend upon the position of the external bodies, as well as those which depend only upon the configuration of the system itself. It will be understood that ϵ_p depends only upon $q_1, \ldots q_n, p_1, \ldots p_n$, in other words, that the kinetic energy of the bodies which we call external forms no part of the kinetic energy of the system. It follows that we may write

$$\frac{d\epsilon}{da_1} = \frac{d\epsilon_q}{da_1} = -A_1, \tag{104}$$

although a similar equation would not hold for differentiations relative to the internal coördinates.

---

temperature of two bodies is that they remain in equilibrium when brought into thermal contact. Direct thermal contact implies molecular forces acting between the bodies. Now the test will fail unless the energy of these forces can be neglected in comparison with the other energies of the bodies. Thus, in the case of energetic chemical action between the bodies, or when the number of particles affected by the forces acting between the bodies is not negligible in comparison with the whole number of particles (as when the bodies have the form of exceedingly thin sheets), the contact of bodies of the same temperature may produce considerable thermal disturbance, and thus fail to afford a reliable criterion of the equality of temperature.

* See especially Chapter I, p. 4.

10

We always suppose these external coördinates to have the same values for all systems of any ensemble. In the case of a canonical distribution, *i.e.*, when the index of probability of phase is a linear function of the energy, it is evident that the values of the external coördinates will affect the distribution, since they affect the energy. In the equation

$$e^{-\frac{\psi}{\Theta}} = \int \cdots \int^{\text{all}}_{\text{phases}} e^{-\frac{\epsilon}{\Theta}} dp_1 \cdots dq_n, \tag{105}$$

by which ψ may be determined, the external coördinates, a_1, a_2, etc., contained implicitly in ϵ, as well as Θ, are to be regarded as constant in the integrations indicated. The equation indicates that ψ is a function of these constants. If we imagine their values varied, and the ensemble distributed canonically according to their new values, we have by differentiation of the equation

$$e^{-\frac{\psi}{\Theta}}\left(-\frac{1}{\Theta}\,d\psi + \frac{\psi}{\Theta^2}\,d\Theta\right) = \frac{1}{\Theta^2}\,d\Theta \int \cdots \int^{\text{all}}_{\text{phases}} \epsilon e^{-\frac{\epsilon}{\Theta}} dp_1 \cdots dq_n$$

$$-\frac{1}{\Theta}\,da_1 \int \cdots \int^{\text{all}}_{\text{phases}} \frac{d\epsilon}{da_1} e^{-\frac{\epsilon}{\Theta}} dp_1 \cdots dq_n$$

$$-\frac{1}{\Theta}\,da_2 \int \cdots \int^{\text{all}}_{\text{phases}} \frac{d\epsilon}{da_2} e^{-\frac{\epsilon}{\Theta}} dp_1 \cdots dq_n - \text{etc.}, \tag{106}$$

or, multiplying by $\Theta e^{\frac{\psi}{\Theta}}$, and setting

$$-\frac{d\epsilon}{da_1} = A_1, \qquad -\frac{d\epsilon}{da_2} = A_2, \text{ etc.},$$

$$-d\psi + \frac{\psi}{\Theta}\,d\Theta = \frac{1}{\Theta}\,d\Theta \int \cdots \int^{\text{all}}_{\text{phases}} \epsilon e^{\frac{\psi-\epsilon}{\Theta}} dp_1 \cdots dq_n$$

$$+\,da_1 \int \cdots \int^{\text{all}}_{\text{phases}} A_1 e^{\frac{\psi-\epsilon}{\Theta}} dp_1 \cdots dq_n$$

$$+\,da_2 \int \cdots \int^{\text{all}}_{\text{phases}} A_2 e^{\frac{\psi-\epsilon}{\Theta}} dp_1 \cdots dq_n + \text{etc.} \tag{107}$$

Now the average value in the ensemble of any quantity (which we shall denote in general by a horizontal line above the proper symbol) is determined by the equation

$$\bar{u} = \int \cdots \int_{\substack{\text{all} \\ \text{phases}}} u e^{\frac{\psi - \epsilon}{\Theta}} dp_1 \cdots dq_n. \tag{108}$$

Comparing this with the preceding equation, we have

$$d\psi = \frac{\psi}{\Theta} d\Theta - \frac{\epsilon}{\Theta} d\Theta - \bar{A}_1 da_1 - \bar{A}_2 da_2 - \text{etc.} \tag{109}$$

Or, since

$$\frac{\psi - \epsilon}{\Theta} = \eta, \tag{110}$$

and

$$\frac{\psi - \bar{\epsilon}}{\Theta} = \bar{\eta}, \tag{111}$$

$$d\psi = \bar{\eta} \, d\Theta - \bar{A}_1 da_1 - \bar{A}_2 da_2 - \text{etc.} \tag{112}$$

Moreover, since (111) gives

$$d\psi = d\bar{\epsilon} = \Theta \, d\bar{\eta} + \bar{\eta} \, d\Theta, \tag{113}$$

we have also

$$d\bar{\epsilon} = -\Theta \, d\bar{\eta} - \bar{A}_1 da_1 - \bar{A}_2 da_2 - \text{etc.} \tag{114}$$

This equation, if we neglect the sign of averages, is identical in form with the thermodynamic equation

$$d\eta = \frac{d\epsilon + A_1 da_1 + A_2 da_2 + \text{etc.}}{T}, \tag{115}$$

or

$$d\epsilon = T \, d\eta - A_1 da_1 - A_2 da_2 - \text{etc.}, \tag{116}$$

which expresses the relation between the energy, temperature, and entropy of a body in thermodynamic equilibrium, and the forces which it exerts on external bodies,—a relation which is the mathematical expression of the second law of thermodynamics for reversible changes. The modulus in the statistical equation corresponds to temperature in the thermodynamic equation, and the average index of probability *with its sign reversed* corresponds to entropy. But in the thermodynamic equation the entropy (η) is a quantity which is only defined by the equation itself, and incompletely defined in that the equation only determines its differential, and the constant of integration is arbitrary. On the other hand, the $\bar{\eta}$ in the statistical equation has been completely defined as the average value in a canonical ensemble of systems of the logarithm of the coefficient of probability of phase.

We may also compare equation (112) with the thermodynamic equation

$$\psi = -\eta\, dT - A_1\, da_1 - A_2\, da_2 - \text{etc.,} \tag{117}$$

where ψ represents the function obtained by subtracting the product of the temperature and entropy from the energy.

How far, or in what sense, the similarity of these equations constitutes any demonstration of the thermodynamic equations, or accounts for the behavior of material systems, as described in the theorems of thermodynamics, is a question of which we shall postpone the consideration until we have further investigated the properties of an ensemble of systems distributed in phase according to the law which we are considering. The analogies which have been pointed out will at least supply the motive for this investigation, which will naturally commence with the determination of the average values in the ensemble of the most important quantities relating to the systems, and to the distribution of the ensemble with respect to the different values of these quantities.

CHAPTER VIII

ON CERTAIN IMPORTANT FUNCTIONS OF THE ENERGIES OF A SYSTEM.

In order to consider more particularly the distribution of a canonical ensemble in energy, and for other purposes, it will be convenient to use the following definitions and notations.

Let us denote by V the extension-in-phase below a certain limit of energy which we shall call ϵ. That is, let

$$V = \int \cdots \int dp_1 \cdots dq_n, \tag{265}$$

the integration being extended (with constant values of the external coördinates) over all phases for which the energy is less than the limit ϵ. We shall suppose that the value of this integral is not infinite, except for an infinite value of the limiting energy. This will not exclude any kind of system to which the canonical distribution is applicable. For if

$$\int \cdots \int e^{-\frac{\epsilon}{\Theta}} dp_1 \cdots dq_n$$

taken without limits has a finite value,* the less value represented by

$$e^{-\frac{\epsilon}{\Theta}} \int \cdots \int dp_1 \cdots dq_n$$

taken below a limiting value of ϵ, and with the ϵ before the integral sign representing that limiting value, will also be finite. Therefore the value of V,

---

* This is a necessary condition of the canonical distribution. See Chapter IV, p. 35.

which differs only by a constant factor, will also be finite, for finite ϵ. It is a function of ϵ and the external coördinates, a continuous increasing function of ϵ, which becomes infinite with ϵ, and vanishes for the smallest possible value of ϵ, or for $\epsilon = -\infty$, if the energy may be diminished without limit.

Let us also set

$$\phi = \log \frac{dV}{d\epsilon}. \tag{266}$$

The extension in phase between any two limits of energy, ϵ' and ϵ'', will be represented by the integral

$$\int_{\epsilon'}^{\epsilon''} e^{\phi} \, d\epsilon. \tag{267}$$

And in general, we may substitute $e^{\phi} \, d\epsilon$ for $dp_1 \cdots dq_n$ in a $2n$-fold integral, reducing it to a simple integral, whenever the limits can be expressed by the energy alone, and the other factor under the integral sign is a function of the energy alone, or with quantities which are constant in the integration.

In particular we observe that the probability that the energy of an unspecified system of a canonical ensemble lies between the limits ϵ' and ϵ'' will be represented by the integral*

$$\int_{\epsilon'}^{\epsilon''} e^{\frac{\psi - \epsilon}{\Theta} + \phi} d\epsilon, \tag{268}$$

and that the average value in the ensemble of any quantity which only varies with the energy is given by the equation†

$$\bar{u} = \int_{V=0}^{\epsilon=\infty} u \, e^{\frac{\psi - \epsilon}{\Theta} + \phi} d\epsilon, \tag{269}$$

where we may regard the constant ψ as determined by the equation‡

$$e^{-\frac{\psi}{\Theta}} = \int_{V=0}^{\epsilon=\infty} e^{-\frac{\epsilon}{\Theta} + \phi} d\epsilon. \tag{270}$$

In regard to the lower limit in these integrals, it will be observed that $V = 0$ is equivalent to the condition that the value of ϵ is the least possible.

CHAPTER X

ON A DISTRIBUTION IN PHASE CALLED MICROCANONICAL IN WHICH ALL THE SYSTEMS HAVE THE SAME ENERGY.

AN important case of statistical equilibrium is that in which all systems of the ensemble have the same energy. We may arrive at the notion of a distribution

* Compare equation (93).   † Compare equation (108).
‡ Compare equation (92).

which will satisfy the necessary conditions by the following process. We may suppose that an ensemble is distributed with a uniform density-in-phase between two limiting values of the energy, ϵ' and ϵ'', and with density zero outside of those limits. Such an ensemble is evidently in statistical equilibrium according to the criterion in Chapter IV, since the density-in-phase may be regarded as a function of the energy. By diminishing the difference of ϵ' and ϵ'', we may diminish the differences of energy in the ensemble. The limit of this process gives us a permanent distribution in which the energy is constant.

We should arrive at the same result, if we should make the density any function of the energy between the limits ϵ' and ϵ'', and zero outside of those limits. Thus, the limiting distribution obtained from the part of a canonical ensemble between two limits of energy, when the difference of the limiting energies is indefinitely diminished, is independent of the modulus, being determined entirely by the energy, and is identical with the limiting distribution obtained from a uniform density between limits of energy approaching the same value.

We shall call the limiting distribution at which we arrive by this process *microcanonical*.

We shall find however, in certain cases, that for certain values of the energy, viz., for those for which e^ϕ is infinite, this process fails to define a limiting distribution in any such distinct sense as for other values of the energy. The difficulty is not in the process, but in the nature of the case, being entirely analogous to that which we meet when we try to find a canonical distribution in cases when ψ becomes infinite. We have not regarded such cases as affording true examples of the canonical distribution, and we shall not regard the cases in which e^ϕ is infinite as affording true examples of the microcanonical distribution. We shall in fact find as we go on that in such cases our most important formulae become illusory.

The use of formulae relating to a canonical ensemble which contain $e^\phi\,d\epsilon$ instead of $dp_1 \cdots dq_n$, as in the preceding chapters, amounts to the consideration of the ensemble as divided into an infinity of microcanonical elements.

From a certain point of view, the microcanonical distribution may seem more simple than the canonical, and it has perhaps been more studied, and been regarded as more closely related to the fundamental notions of thermodynamics. To this last point we shall return in a subsequent chapter. It is sufficient here to remark that analytically the canonical distribution is much more manageable than the microcanonical.

We may sometimes avoid difficulties which the microcanonical distribution presents by regarding it as the result of the following process, which involves conceptions less simple but more amenable to analytical treatment. We may suppose an ensemble distributed with a density proportional to

$$e^{-\frac{(\epsilon-\epsilon')^2}{\omega^2}},$$

where ω and ϵ' are constants, and then diminish indefinitely the value of the constant ω. Here the density is nowhere zero until we come to the limit, but at the limit it is zero for all energies except ϵ'. We thus avoid the analytical complication of discontinuities in the value of the density, which require the use of integrals with inconvenient limits.

In a microcanonical ensemble of systems the energy (ϵ) is constant, but the kinetic energy (ϵ_p) and the potential energy (ϵ_q) vary in the different systems, subject of course to the condition

$$\epsilon_p + \epsilon_q = \epsilon = \text{constant.} \tag{373}$$

Our first inquiries will relate to the division of energy into these two parts, and to the average values of functions of ϵ_p and ϵ_q.

We shall use the notation $\bar{u}|_\epsilon$ to denote an average value in a microcanonical ensemble of energy ϵ. An average value in a canonical ensemble of modulus Θ, which has hitherto been denoted by $\bar{u}$, we shall in this chapter denote by $\bar{u}|_\Theta$, to distinguish more clearly the two kinds of averages.

The extension-in-phase within any limits which can be given in terms of ϵ_p and ϵ_q may be expressed in the notations of the preceding chapter by the double integral

$$\iint dV_p \, dV_q$$

taken within those limits. If an ensemble of systems is distributed within those limits with a uniform density-in-phase, the average value in the ensemble of any function (u) of the kinetic and potential energies will be expressed by the quotient of integrals

$$\frac{\iint u \, dV_p \, dV_q}{\iint dV_p \, dV_q}$$

Since $dV_p = e^{\phi_p} \, d\epsilon_p$, and $d\epsilon_p = d\epsilon$ when ϵ_q is constant, the expression may be written

$$\frac{\iint u e^{\phi_p} \, d\epsilon \, dV_q}{\iint e^{\phi_p} \, d\epsilon \, dV_q}$$

To get the average value of u in an ensemble distributed microcanonically with the energy ϵ, we must make the integrations cover the extension-in-phase between the energies ϵ and $\epsilon + d\epsilon$. This gives

$$\overline{u}|_\epsilon = \frac{d\epsilon \int_{V_q=0}^{\epsilon_q=\epsilon} ue^{\phi_p}\, dV_q}{d\epsilon \int_{V_q=0}^{\epsilon_q=\epsilon} e^{\phi_p}\, dV_q}$$

But by (299) the value of the integral in the denominator is e^ϕ. We have therefore

$$\overline{u}|_\epsilon = e^{-\phi} \int_{V_q=0}^{\epsilon_q=\epsilon} ue^{\phi_p}\, dV_q, \tag{374}$$

where e^{ϕ_p} and V_q are connected by equation (373), and u, if given as function of ϵ_p, or of ϵ_p and ϵ_q, becomes in virtue of the same equation a function of ϵ_q alone.

We shall assume that e^ϕ has a finite value. If $n > 1$, it is evident from equation (305) that e^ϕ is an increasing function of ϵ, and therefore cannot be infinite for one value of ϵ without being infinite for all greater values of ϵ, which would make $-\psi$ infinite.* When $n > 1$, therefore, if we assume that e^ϕ is finite, we only exclude such cases as we found necessary to exclude in the study of the canonical distribution. But when $n = 1$, cases may occur in which the canonical distribution is perfectly applicable, but in which the formulae for the microcanonical distribution become illusory, for particular values of ϵ, on account of the infinite value of e^ϕ. Such failing cases of the microcanonical distribution *for particular values of the energy* will not prevent us from regarding the canonical ensemble as consisting of an infinity of microcanonical ensembles.†

From the last equation, with (298), we get

$$\overline{e^{-\phi_p} V_p}|_\epsilon = e^{-\phi} \int_{V_q=0}^{\epsilon_q=\epsilon} V_p\, dV_q = e^{-\phi}V. \tag{375}$$

---

* See equation (322).

† An example of the failing case of the microcanonical distribution is afforded by a material point, under the influence of gravity, and constrained to remain in a vertical circle. The failing case occurs when the energy is just sufficient to carry the material point to the highest point of the circle.

It will be observed that the difficulty is inherent in the nature of the case, and is quite independent of the mathematical formulae. The nature of the difficulty is at once apparent if we try to distribute a finite number of material points with this particular value of the energy as nearly as possible in statistical equilibrium, or if we ask: What is the probability that a point taken at random from an ensemble in statistical equilibrium with this value of the energy will be found in any specified part of the circle?

But by equations (288) and (289)

$$e^{-\phi_p} V_p = \frac{2}{n} \epsilon_p .$$ (376)

Therefore

$$e^{-\phi} V = \overline{e^{-\phi_p} V_p}\big|_\epsilon = \frac{2}{n} \overline{\epsilon_p}\big|_\epsilon.$$ (377)

Again, with the aid of equation (301), we get

$$\overline{\frac{d\phi_p}{d\epsilon_p}}\bigg|_\epsilon = e^{-\phi} \int_{V_q=0}^{\epsilon_q=\epsilon} \frac{d\phi_p}{d\epsilon_p} e^{\phi_p} dV_q = \frac{d\phi}{d\epsilon},$$ (378)

if $n > 2$. Therefore, by (289),

$$\frac{d\phi}{d\epsilon} = \overline{\frac{d\phi_p}{d\epsilon_p}}\bigg|_\epsilon = \left(\frac{n}{2} - 1\right) \overline{\epsilon_p^{-1}}\big|_\epsilon, \quad \text{if} \quad n > 2.$$ (379)

These results are interesting on account of the relations of the functions $e^{-\phi} V$ and $\dfrac{d\phi}{d\epsilon}$ to the notion of temperature in thermodynamics,—a subject to which we shall return hereafter. They are particular cases of a general relation easily deduced from equations (306), (374), (288) and (289). We have

$$\frac{d^h V}{d\epsilon^h} = \int_{V_q=0}^{\epsilon_q=\epsilon} \frac{d^h V_p}{d\epsilon_p^h} dV_q, \quad \text{if} \quad h < \tfrac{1}{2}n + 1.$$

The equation may be written

$$e^{-\phi} \frac{d^h V}{d\epsilon^h} = e^{-\phi} \int_{V_q=0}^{\epsilon_q=\epsilon} e^{-\phi_p} \frac{d^h V_p}{d\epsilon_p^h} e^{\phi_p} dV_q.$$

We have therefore

$$e^{-\phi} \frac{d^h V}{d\epsilon^h} = \overline{e^{-\phi_p} \frac{d^h V_p}{d\epsilon_p^h}}\bigg|_\epsilon = \frac{\Gamma(\tfrac{1}{2}n)}{\Gamma(\tfrac{1}{2}n - h + 1)} \overline{\epsilon_p^{1-h}}\big|_\epsilon,$$ (380)

if $h < \tfrac{1}{2}n + 1$. For example, when n is even, we may make $h = \tfrac{1}{2}n$, which gives, with (307),

$$(2\pi)^{\frac{n}{2}} e^{-\phi} (V_q)_{\epsilon_q=\epsilon} = \Gamma(\tfrac{1}{2}n) \overline{\epsilon_p^{1-\frac{n}{2}}}\big|_\epsilon.$$ (381)

Since any canonical ensemble of systems may be regarded as composed of microcanonical ensembles, if any quantities u and v have the same average values in every microcanonical ensemble, they will have the same values in every canonical ensemble. To bring equation (380) formally under this rule, we may observe that the first member being a function of ϵ is a constant value in a microcanonical ensemble, and therefore identical with its average value.

We get thus the general equation

$$\overline{e^{-\phi}\frac{d^h V}{d\epsilon^h}}\bigg|_\Theta = \overline{e^{-\phi_p}\frac{d^h V_p}{d\epsilon_p{}^h}}\bigg|_\Theta = \frac{\Gamma(\tfrac{1}{2}n)}{\Gamma(\tfrac{1}{2}n - h + 1)}\;\overline{\epsilon_p^{1-h}}\big|_\Theta = \Theta^{1-h}, \qquad (382)$$

if $h < \tfrac{1}{2}n + 1$.* The equations

$$\Theta = \overline{e^{-\phi}V}\big|_\Theta = \overline{e^{-\phi_p}V_p}\big|_\Theta = \frac{2}{n}\,\overline{\epsilon_p}\big|_\Theta, \qquad (383)$$

$$\frac{1}{\Theta} = \overline{\frac{d\phi}{d\epsilon}}\bigg|_\Theta = \overline{\frac{d\phi_p}{d\epsilon_p}}\bigg|_\Theta = \left(\frac{n}{2} - 1\right)\overline{\epsilon_p^{-1}}\big|_\Theta, \qquad (384)$$

may be regarded as particular cases of the general equation. The last equation is subject to the condition that $n > 2$.

The last two equations give for a canonical ensemble, if $n > 2$,

$$\left(1 - \frac{2}{n}\right)\overline{\epsilon_p}\big|_\Theta\,\overline{\epsilon_p^{-1}}\big|_\Theta = 1. \qquad (385)$$

The corresponding equations for a microcanonical ensemble give, if $n > 2$,

$$\left(1 - \frac{2}{n}\right)\overline{\epsilon_p}\big|_\epsilon\,\overline{\epsilon_p^{-1}}\big|_\epsilon = \frac{d\phi}{d\log V}, \qquad (386)$$

which shows that $d\phi\,d\log V$ approaches the value unity when n is very great.

(c) THERMODYNAMIC ANALOGUES

Gibbs compared in a comprehensive manner the relative merits of different statistical mechanical analogues of thermodynamic quantities. In particular, he sought equivalent mechanical definitions of temperature T and entropy η such that the basic thermodynamic equation is satisfied, i.e.

$$d\epsilon = T\,d\eta - \sum_i A_i\,da_i,$$

where $A_i\,da_i$ is the work done by the system on external bodies for the parameter a_i and its generalized force A_i. Gibbs showed that canonical ensembles satisfy the various requirements, but considered the micro-canonical ensemble as a more natural concept inasmuch as the energy and the quantity analogous to entropy do not appear here as averages. The logarithm of the phase volume, moreover, is simpler than the mean

* See equation (292).

index of probability. He compared two microcanonical ensembles ϵ which have

$$\frac{d\epsilon}{d(\ln V)} \quad \text{and} \quad \frac{d\epsilon}{d\phi}$$

as temperature analogues (Θ for canonical ensemble), both of which are imperfect. The entropy analogues ($\bar{\eta}$ for canonical ensemble) are $\ln V$ and ϕ, respectively. In general, the comparative advantages of the canonical ensemble and of these two microcanonical ensembles depend upon whether the energy or the temperature is regarded as the independent variable. In the case of energy the microcanonical ensembles are preferable, and of those two the $\ln V$ system, inasmuch as it deals with mean values and not with the less natural probable values of the ϕ system (despite the simpler definition of ϕ). Canonical ensembles, however, are preferable when temperature is considered the independent variable.

Recently (1957) Gibbs insights of statistical mechanics have been applied to biological problems[22] such as cell biology and complex chemical systems. The cybernetic and information theory approaches in contemporary biology have their roots in Gibbs' work.

*Elementary Principles in Statistical Mechanics**

CHAPTER XIV

DISCUSSION OF THERMODYNAMIC ANALOGUES.

IF we wish to find in rational mechanics an *a priori* foundation for the principles of thermodynamics, we must seek mechanical definitions of temperature and entropy. The quantities thus defined must satisfy (under conditions and with limitations which again must be specified in the language of mechanics) the differential equation

$$d\epsilon = T\,d\eta - A_1\,da_1 - A_2\,da_2 - \text{etc.,} \tag{482}$$

where ϵ, T, and η denote the energy, temperature, and entropy of the system considered, and $A_1\,da_1$, etc., the mechanical work (in the narrower sense in which the term is used in thermodynamics, *i.e.*, with exclusion of thermal action) done upon external bodies.

* Ref. 1, pp. 165–70.

This implies that we are able to distinguish in mechanical terms the thermal action of one system on another from that which we call mechanical in the narrower sense, if not indeed in every case in which the two may be combined, at least so as to specify cases of thermal action and cases of mechanical action.

Such a differential equation moreover implies a finite equation between ϵ, η, and a_1, a_2, etc., which may be regarded as fundamental in regard to those properties of the system which we call thermodynamic, or which may be called so from analogy. This fundamental thermodynamic equation is determined by the fundamental mechanical equation which expresses the energy of the system as function of its momenta and coördinates with those external coördinates (a_1, a_2, etc.) which appear in the differential expression of the work done on external bodies. We have to show the mathematical operations by which the fundamental thermodynamic equation, which in general is an equation of few variables, is derived from the fundamental mechanical equation, which in the case of the bodies of nature is one of an enormous number of variables.

We have also to enunciate in mechanical terms, and to prove, what we call the tendency of heat to pass from a system of higher temperature to one of lower, and to show that this tendency vanishes with respect to systems of the same temperature.

At least, we have to show by *a priori* reasoning that for such systems as the material bodies which nature presents to us, these relations hold with such approximation that they are sensibly true for human faculties of observation. This indeed is all that is really necessary to establish the science of thermodynamics on an *a priori* basis. Yet we will naturally desire to find the exact expression of those principles of which the laws of thermodynamics are the approximate expression. A very little study of the statistical properties of conservative systems of a finite number of degrees of freedom is sufficient to make it appear, more or less distinctly, that the general laws of thermodynamics are the limit toward which the exact laws of such systems approximate, when their number of degrees of freedom is indefinitely increased. And the problem of finding the exact relations, as distinguished from the approximate, for systems of a great number of degrees of freedom, is practically the same as that of finding the relations which hold for any number of degrees of freedom, as distinguished from those which have been established on an empirical basis for systems of a great number of degrees of freedom.

The enunciation and proof of these exact laws, for systems of any finite number of degrees of freedom, has been a principal object of the preceding discussion. But it should be distinctly stated that, if the results obtained when the numbers of degrees of freedom are enormous coincide sensibly with the general laws of thermodynamics, however interesting and significant this coincidence may be, we are still far from having explained the phenomena of nature with respect to these laws. For, as compared with the case of nature, the systems which we have considered are of an ideal simplicity. Although our only assumption is that we are considering conservative systems of a finite number of degrees of freedom, it would seem that this is assuming far too much, so far as the bodies of nature are concerned. The phenomena of radiant heat, which certainly should not be neglected in any complete system of thermodynamics, and the electrical phenomena associated with the combination of atoms, seem to show that the hypothesis of systems of a finite number of degrees of freedom is inadequate for the explanation of the properties of bodies.

Nor do the results of such assumptions in every detail appear to agree with experience. We should expect, for example, that a diatomic gas, so far as it could be treated independently of the phenomena of radiation, or of any sort of electrical manifestations, would have six degrees of freedom for each molecule. But the behavior of such a gas seems to indicate not more than five.

But although these difficulties, long recognized by physicists,* seem to prevent, in the present state of science, any satisfactory explanation of the phenomena of thermodynamics as presented to us in nature, the ideal case of systems of a finite number of degrees of freedom remains as a subject which is certainly not devoid of a theoretical interest, and which may serve to point the way to the solution of the far more difficult problems presented to us by nature. And if the study of the statistical properties of such systems gives us an exact expression of laws which in the limiting case take the form of the received laws of thermodynamics, its interest is so much the greater.

Now we have defined what we have called the *modulus* (Θ) of an ensemble of systems canonically distributed in phase, and what we have called the index of probability (η) of any phase in such an ensemble. It has been shown that between the modulus (Θ), the external coördinates (a_1, etc.), and the average values in the ensemble of the energy (ϵ), the index of probability (η), and the external forces (A_1, etc.) exerted by the systems, the following differential equation will hold:

$$d\bar{\epsilon} = -\Theta \, d\bar{\eta} - \bar{A}_1 \, da_1 - \bar{A}_2 \, da_2 - \text{etc.} \tag{483}$$

This equation, if we neglect the sign of averages, is identical in form with the thermodynamic equation (482), the modulus (Θ) corresponding to temperature, and the index of probability of phase with its sign reversed corresponding to entropy.†

We have also shown that the average square of the anomalies of ϵ, that is, of the deviations of the individual values from the average, is in general of the same order of magnitude as the reciprocal of the number of degrees of freedom, and therefore to human observation the individual values are indistinguishable from the average values when the number of degrees of freedom is very great.‡ In this case also the anomalies of η are practically

---

* See Boltzmann, Sitzb. der Wiener Akad., Bd. LXIII., S. 418, (1871).
† See Chapter IV, pages 44 ,45.   ‡ See Chapter VII, pages 73–75.

insensible. The same is true of the anomalies of the external forces (A_1, etc.), so far as these are the result of the anomalies of energy, so that when these forces are sensibly determined by the energy and the external coördinates, and the number of degrees of freedom is very great, the anomalies of these forces are insensible.

The mathematical operations by which the finite equation between $\bar{\epsilon}$, $\bar{\eta}$, and a_1, etc., is deduced from that which gives the energy (ϵ) of a system in terms of the momenta ($p_1 \cdots p_n$) and coördinates both internal ($q_1 \cdots q_n$) and external (a_1, etc.), are indicated by the equation

$$
e^{-\frac{\psi}{\Theta}} = \int_{\text{phases}}^{\text{all}} \cdots \int e^{-\frac{\epsilon}{\Theta}} \, dq_1 \cdots dq_n \, dp_1 \cdots dp_n, \tag{484}
$$

where $\psi = \Theta\bar{\eta} + \bar{\epsilon}.$

We have also shown that when systems of different ensembles are brought into conditions analogous to thermal contact, the average result is a passage of energy from the ensemble of the greater modulus to that of the less,[*] or in case of equal moduli, that we have a condition of statistical equilibrium in regard to the distribution of energy.[†]

Propositions have also been demonstrated analogous to those in thermo-dynamics relating to a Carnot's cycle,[‡] or to the tendency of entropy to increase,[§] especially when bodies of different temperature are brought into contact.[‖]

We have thus precisely defined quantities, and rigorously demonstrated propositions, which hold for any number of degrees of freedom, and which, when the number of degrees of freedom (n) is enormously great, would appear to human faculties as the quantities and propositions of empirical thermo-dynamics.

It is evident, however, that there may be more than one quantity defined for finite values of n, which approach the same limit, when n is increased indefinitely, and more than one proposition relating to finite values of n, which approach the same limiting form for $n = \infty$. There may be therefore, and there are, other quantities which may be thought to have some claim to be regarded as temperature and entropy with respect to systems of a finite number of degrees of freedom.

The definitions and propositions which we have been considering relate essentially to what we have called a canonical ensemble of systems. This may appear a less natural and simple conception than what we have called a

---

* See Chapter XIII, page 160.   † See Chapter IV, pages 35–37.
‡ See Chapter XIII, pages 162, 163.   § See Chapter XII, pages 143–151.
‖ See Chapter XIII, page 159.

microcanonical ensemble of systems, in which all have the same energy, and which in many cases represents simply the *time-ensemble*, or ensemble of phases through which a single system passes in the course of time.

It may therefore seem desirable to find definitions and propositions relating to these microcanonical ensembles, which shall correspond to what in thermodynamics are based on experience. Now the differential equation

$$d\epsilon = e^{-\phi} V \, d \log V - \overline{A_1}\big|_\epsilon \, da_1 - \overline{A_2}\big|_\epsilon \, da_2 - \text{etc.}, \qquad (485)$$

which has been demonstrated in Chapter X, and which relates to a microcanonical ensemble, $\overline{A_1}\big|_\epsilon$ denoting the average value of A_1 in such an ensemble, corresponds precisely to the thermodynamic equation, except for the sign of average applied to the external forces. But as these forces are not entirely determined by the energy with the external coördinates, the use of average values is entirely germane to the subject, and affords the readiest means of getting perfectly determined quantities. These averages, which are taken for a microcanonical ensemble, may seem from some points of view a more simple and natural conception than those which relate to a canonical ensemble. Moreover, the energy, and the quantity corresponding to entropy, are free from the sign of average in this equation.

The quantity in the equation which corresponds to entropy is $\log V$, the quantity V being defined as the extension-in-phase within which the energy is less than a certain limiting value (ϵ). This is certainly a more simple conception than the average value in a canonical ensemble of the index of probability of phase. Log V has the property that when it is constant

$$d\epsilon = -\overline{A_1}\big|_\epsilon \, da_1 - \overline{A_2}\big|_\epsilon \, da_2 + \text{etc.}, \qquad (486)$$

which closely corresponds to the thermodynamic property of entropy, that when it is constant

$$d\epsilon = -A_1 \, da_1 - A_2 \, da_2 + \text{etc.} \qquad (487)$$

The quantity in the equation which corresponds to temperature is $\epsilon^{-\phi} V$, or $d\epsilon/d \log V$. In a canonical ensemble, the average value of this quantity is equal to the modulus, as has been shown by different methods in Chapters IX and X.

For a very large number of degrees of freedom both definitions of entropy for the two microcanonical ensembles agree with that for the canonical ensemble.

(d) GRAND AND PETIT ENSEMBLES

Gibbs concluded his *Statistical Mechanics* by generalizing it similarly to his thermodynamic generalization for heterogeneous equilibria. One considers now a mechanical system composed of different substances with masses (or numbers of molecules) as additional independent variables. A *grand ensemble* is one in which the systems differ not only in p, q phases, but are also variable in the numbers of particles of the different kinds of substances—as contrasted with the *petit ensemble* which involves only phase differences (constant numbers of particles)— the type considered up to this point.

In this case one has to generalize the notion of a phase. In general, of course, a new phase occurs whenever two different kinds of molecules in a system are interchanged. There is, however, an ambiguity when the molecules are of the same species; Gibbs defined a *specific phase* if each individual molecule can be identified, a *generic phase* if only the kind of molecule can be distinguished (for v similar molecules a generic phase would be equivalent to $v!$ specific phases). The index of probability H of a generic phase for a canonical distribution in a grand ensemble is given by

$$H = \frac{\Omega + \sum_i \mu_i v_i - \epsilon}{\Theta},$$

where v_i represents the number of different kinds of molecules in any system i and Ω is a constant. Put $\bar{\psi} \equiv \bar{\epsilon} + \Theta\bar{H}$, then

$$d\bar{\psi} = \bar{H}\,d\Theta + \sum_i \mu_i\,dv_i - \sum_j A_j\,da_j.$$

From the corresponding thermodynamic equation for ψ (Helmholtzian free energy) we have

$$d\psi = -\eta\,dT + \sum_i \mu_i\,dm_i - \sum_j A_j\,da_j.$$

Thus we see that the statistical mechanical $\bar{\psi}$ corresponds to the thermodynamic ψ, $-\bar{H}$ to entropy η, Θ to T, and $\bar{\epsilon}$ to ϵ.

Gibbs ended the book with an explanation about the lack of entropy increase in the mixing of portions of the same gas (Gibbs' paradox) in terms of the generic phase.

In the last ten years progress[22] has been made in developing non-equilibrium thermodynamics and statistical mechanics to biology. Gibbs' ensemble technique with entropy as the base can apparently be extended beyond its initial application to equilibrium mechanics; it has potential use in biological problems.

*Elementary Principles in Statistical Mechanics**

CHAPTER XV

SYSTEMS COMPOSED OF MOLECULES.

THE nature of material bodies is such that especial interest attaches to the dynamics of systems composed of a great number of entirely similar particles, or, it may be, of a great number of particles of several kinds, all of each kind being entirely similar to each other. We shall therefore proceed to consider systems composed of such particles, whether in great numbers or otherwise, and especially to consider the statistical equilibrium of ensembles of such systems. One of the variations to be considered in regard to such systems is a variation in the numbers of the particles of the various kinds which it contains, and the question of statistical equilibrium between two ensembles of such systems relates in part to the tendencies of the various kinds of particles to pass from the one to the other.

First of all, we must define precisely what is meant by statistical equilibrium of such an ensemble of systems. The essence of statistical equilibrium is the permanence of the number of systems which fall within any given limits with respect to phase. We have therefore to define how the term "phase" is to be understood in such cases. If two phases differ only in that certain entirely similar particles have changed places with one another, are they to be regarded as identical or different phases? If the particles are regarded as indistinguishable, it seems in accordance with the spirit of the statistical method to regard the phases as identical. In fact, it might be urged that in such an ensemble of systems as we are considering no identity is possible between the particles of different systems except that of qualities, and if ν particles of one system are described as entirely similar to one another and to ν of another system, nothing remains on which to base the identification of any particular particle of the first system with any particular particle of the second. And this would be true, if the ensemble of systems had a simultaneous objective existence. But it hardly applies to the creations of the imagination. In the cases which we have been considering, and in those which we shall consider, it is not only possible to conceive of the motion of an ensemble of similar systems simply as possible cases of the motion of a single system, but it is actually in large measure for the sake of representing more clearly the possible cases of the motion of a single system that we use the conception of an ensemble of systems. The perfect similarity of several particles of a system will not in the least interfere with the identification of a particular particle in one case with a particular

* Ref. 1, pp. 187–91, 206–7.

particle in another. The question is one to be decided in accordance with the requirements of practical convenience in the discussion of the problems with which we are engaged.

Our present purpose will often require us to use the terms *phase, density-in-phase, statistical equilibrium,* and other connected terms on the supposition that phases are *not* altered by the exchange of places between similar particles. Some of the most important questions with which we are concerned have reference to phases thus defined. We shall call them phases determined by generic definitions, or briefly, generic phases. But we shall also be obliged to discuss phases defined by the narrower definition (so that exchange of position between similar particles is regarded as changing the phase), which will be called phases determined by specific definitions, or briefly, specific phases. For the analytical description of a specific phase is more simple than that of a generic phase. And it is a more simple matter to make a multiple integral extend over all possible specific phases than to make one extend without repetition over all possible generic phases.

It is evident that if ν_1, $\nu_2 \cdots \nu_h$, are the numbers of the different kinds of molecules in any system, the number of specific phases embraced in one generic phase is represented by the continued product $\lfloor\nu_1 \; \lfloor\nu_2 \cdots \lfloor\nu_h$, and the coefficient of probability of a generic phase is the sum of the probability-coefficients of the specific phases which it represents. When these are equal among themselves, the probability-coefficient of the generic phase is equal to that of the specific phase multiplied by $\lfloor\nu_1 \; \lfloor\nu_2 \cdots \lfloor\nu_h$. It is also evident that statistical equilibrium may subsist with respect to generic phases without statistical equilibrium with respect to specific phases, but not *vice versa*.

Similar questions arise where one particle is capable of several equivalent positions. Does the change from one of these positions to another change the phase? It would be most natural and logical to make it affect the specific phase, but not the generic. The number of specific phases contained in a generic phase would then be $\lfloor\nu_1 \, \kappa_1^{\nu_1} \cdots \lfloor\nu_h \, \kappa_h^{\nu_h}$, where $\kappa_1, \ldots \kappa_h$ denote the numbers of equivalent positions belonging to the several kinds of particles. The case in which a κ is infinite would then require especial attention. It does not appear that the resulting complications in the formulae would be compensated by any real advantage. The reason of this is that in problems of real interest equivalent positions of a particle will always be equally probable. In this respect, equivalent positions of the same particle are entirely unlike the $\lfloor\nu$ different ways in which ν particles may be distributed in ν different positions. Let it therefore be understood that in spite of the physical equivalence of different positions of the same particle they are to be considered as constituting a difference of generic phase as well as of specific. The number of specific phases contained in a generic phase is therefore always given by the product $\lfloor\nu_1 \; \lfloor\nu_2 \cdots \lfloor\nu_h$.

Instead of considering, as in the preceding chapters, ensembles of systems differing only in phase, we shall now suppose that the systems constituting an ensemble are composed of particles of various kinds, and that they differ not only in phase but also in the numbers of these particles which they contain. The external coördinates of all the systems in the ensemble are supposed, as heretofore, to have the same value, and when they vary, to vary together. For distinction, we may call such an ensemble a *grand ensemble*, and one in which the systems differ only in phase a *petit ensemble*. A grand ensemble is therefore composed of a multitude of petit ensembles. The ensembles which we have hitherto discussed are petit ensembles.

Let $\nu_1, \ldots \nu_h$, etc., denote the numbers of the different kinds of particles in a system, ϵ its energy, and $q_1, \ldots q_n, p_1, \ldots p_n$ its coördinates and momenta. If the particles are of the nature of material points, the number of coördinates (n) of the system will be equal to $3\nu_1 \cdots + 3\nu_h$. But if the particles are less simple in their nature, if they are to be treated as rigid solids, the orientation of which must be regarded, or if they consist each of several atoms, so as to have more than three degrees of freedom, the number of coördinates of the system will be equal to the sum of ν_1, ν_2, etc., multiplied each by the number of degrees of freedom of the kind of particle to which it relates.

Let us consider an ensemble in which the number of systems having $\nu_1, \ldots \nu_h$ particles of the several kinds, and having values of their coördinates and momenta lying between the limits q_1 and $q_1 + dq_1$, p_1 and $p_1 + dp_1$, etc., is represented by the expression

$$Ne^{\frac{\Omega + \mu_1 \nu_1 \cdots + \mu_h \nu_h - \epsilon}{\Theta}} \frac{1}{\lfloor\nu_1 \cdots \lfloor\nu_h} dp_1 \cdots dq_n, \tag{498}$$

where N, Ω, Θ, $\mu_1, \ldots \mu_h$ are constants, N denoting the total number of systems in the ensemble. The expression

$$Ne^{\frac{\Omega + \mu_1 \nu_1 \cdots + \mu_h \nu_h - \epsilon}{\Theta}} \frac{1}{\lfloor\nu_1 \cdots \lfloor\nu_h} \tag{499}$$

evidently represents the density-in-phase of the ensemble within the limits described, that is, for a phase specifically defined. The expression

$$e^{\frac{\Omega + \mu_1 \nu_1 \cdots + \mu_h \nu_h - \epsilon}{\Theta}} \frac{1}{\lfloor\nu_1 \cdots \lfloor\nu_h} \tag{500}$$

is therefore the probability-coefficient for a phase specifically defined. This has evidently the same value for all the $\lfloor\nu_1 \cdots \lfloor\nu_h$ phases obtained by interchanging the phases of particles of the same kind. The probability-coefficient for a generic phase will be $\lfloor\nu_1 \cdots \lfloor\nu_h$ times as great, viz.,

$$e^{\frac{\Omega + \mu_1 \nu_1 \cdots + \mu_h \nu_h - \epsilon}{\Theta}}. \tag{501}$$

We shall say that such an ensemble as has been described is *canonically distributed*, and shall call the constant Θ its modulus. It is evidently what we have called a grand ensemble. The petit ensembles of which it is composed are canonically distributed, according to the definitions of Chapter IV, since the expression

$$\frac{e^{\frac{\Omega+\mu_1\nu_1\cdots+\mu_h\nu_h}{\Theta}}}{\lfloor\nu_1\cdots\lfloor\nu_h}\tag{502}$$

is constant for each petit ensemble. The grand ensemble, therefore, is in statistical equilibrium with respect to specific phases.

If an ensemble, whether grand or petit, is identical so far as generic phases are concerned with one canonically distributed, we shall say that its distribution is canonical with respect to generic phases. Such an ensemble is evidently in statistical equilibrium with respect to generic phases, although it may not be so with respect to specific phases.

If we write H for the index of probability of a generic phase in a grand ensemble, we have for the case of canonical distribution

$$\mathrm{H}=\frac{\Omega+\mu_1\nu_1\cdots+\mu_h\nu_h-\epsilon}{\Theta}.\tag{503}$$

It will be observed that the H is a linear function of ϵ and $\nu_1,\ldots\nu_h$; also that whenever the index of probability of generic phases in a grand ensemble is a linear function of ϵ, $\nu_1,\ldots\nu_h$, the ensemble is canonically distributed with respect to generic phases.

The differences therefore, in the case considered, between the quantities which may be represented by the notations[*]

$$\overline{\mathrm{H}_{\mathrm{gen}}}\big|_{\mathrm{grand}},\quad\overline{\eta^{\mathrm{gen}}}\big|_{\mathrm{grand}},\quad\overline{\eta_{\mathrm{gen}}}\big|_{\mathrm{petit}}$$

are not sensible to human faculties. The difference

$$\overline{\eta_{\mathrm{gen}}}\big|_{\mathrm{petit}}-\overline{\eta_{\mathrm{spec}}}\big|_{\mathrm{petit}}=\lfloor\nu_1\cdots\lfloor\nu_h,$$

and is therefore constant, so long as the numbers $\nu_1,\ldots\nu_h$ are constant. For constant values of these numbers, therefore, it is immaterial whether we use the average of η_{gen} or of η for entropy, since this only affects the arbitrary constant of integration which is added to entropy. But when the numbers $\nu_1,\ldots\nu_h$ are varied, it is no longer possible to use the index for specific phases. For the principle that the entropy of any body has an arbitrary additive constant is subject to limitation, when different quantities of the same substance are concerned. In this case, the constant being determined for one quantity of a substance, is thereby determined for all quantities of the same substance.

* In this paragraph for greater distinctness $\overline{\mathrm{H}_{\mathrm{gen}}}\big|_{\mathrm{grand}}$ and $\overline{\eta_{\mathrm{spec}}}\big|_{\mathrm{petit}}$ have been written for the quantities which elsewhere are denoted by $\overline{\mathrm{H}}$ and $\overline{\eta}$.

To fix our ideas, let us suppose that we have two identical fluid masses in contiguous chambers. The entropy of the whole is equal to the sum of the entropies of the parts, and double that of one part. Suppose a valve is now opened, making a communication between the chambers. We do not regard this as making any change in the entropy, although the masses of gas or liquid diffuse into one another, and although the same process of diffusion would increase the entropy, if the masses of fluid were different. It is evident, therefore, that it is equilibrium with respect to generic phases, and not with respect to specific, with which we have to do in the evaluation of entropy, and therefore, that we must use the average of H or of η_{gen}, and not that of η, as the equivalent of entropy, except in the thermodynamics of bodies in which the number of molecules of the various kinds is constant.

(e) POSTSCRIPT

In discussing "The Present Crisis of Mathematical Physics" in his *La Valeur de la Science* (1906), the French mathematician Jules Henri Poincaré (1854–1912) commented with respect to irreversible physical phenomena, "All this Maxwell and Boltzmann have explained, but the one who has seen it most clearly in a book too little read because it is a little difficult to read, is Gibbs, in his *Elementary Principles in Statistical Mechanics*."

Gibbs' book appeared in a period when statistical methods were being utilized more and more: there was considerable interest in (1) the kinetic theory of gases and its extension to the newly discovered "free" electrons in a metal, (2) the mechanical wave field of standing acoustical waves, (3) the new investigations of fluctuations phenomena (*cf.* the German theoretical physicist Albert Einstein (1879–1955) and the (Polish) Austrian physicist Marian Smoluchowski (1872–1917)) such as colloidal solutions (Brownian movements) and the instability of the critical state of a fluid.

Owing to Gibbs' prestige at the time of its publication his *Statistical Mechanics* received considerable critical review, particularly with respect to the foundations of statistical mechanics, which are based upon the assumption that the time average for a closed system can be replaced by a statistical space average. From Liouville's theorem one can show that two elements lying in the line of motion of an ensemble are statistically equivalent. But what about the relative *a priori* probabilities of other elements? The so-called *ergodic hypothesis* of J. C. Maxwell (1866) and L. Boltzmann (1871) stated that the phase curve of certain closed systems passes through every point of the ergodic surface $\epsilon(g_1, \ldots, k_n)$ $= \epsilon$. A critique of this principle was given by the Austrian theoretical physicist Paul Ehrenfest (1880–1933) and his wife the Russian Tatyana Alexeyevnar Ehrenfest (1876–1964) in their 1911 review article for *Encyklopädie der mathematischen Wissenschaften*. Their concern, viz. the possible self-contradiction of the ergodic hypothesis in the light of the modern theory of aggregates, was later (1913) verified by M. Plancherel and by A. Rosenthal. An earlier objection had been raised in 1896 by the German mathematician Ernst Zermelo (1871–1956), who used the so-called 1890 recurrence theorem of J. H. Poincaré, namely, that every mechanical system must return to its initial domain after a finite time. In 1930 the American mathematician George David Birkhoff (1884–1944) and the Hungarian mathematical physicist John von Neumann (1903–57) proved independently that the great majority of non-integrable dynamical systems satisfy the Ehrenfest *quasi-ergodic hypothesis*, namely, the curve of such closed systems (many degrees of freedom) in phase space passes infinitely close to every point of the ergodic surface. (The great majority of non-integrable dynamical systems satisfy the quasi-ergodic hypothesis.)

In an address given in April 1900 at the Royal Institution in London W. Thomson (Kelvin) spoke of two "Nineteenth Century Clouds over the Dynamical Theory and Light". It was the silver lining of one of these clouds, the one concerned with thermal radiation, that ultimately illuminated Gibbs' work. In December of that very year M. K. E. L. Planck postulated the existence of a quantum of action h which made possible a new principle of partition of energy to replace the classical equipartition of energy.

Five years later A. Einstein conceived of light as consisting of particles, i.e. light quanta (photons). The new quantum statistics was quite successful in explaining thermal radiation and the variation of specific heats at low temperatures. The cellular structure of phase space became significant in that the cells became individualized and therefore susceptible to statistical treatment. The Bengalese theoretical physicist Satyendra Nath Bose (1894–1974) considered in 1924 the statistical distribution of phase cells for photons; in that very year A. Einstein made the same application to ideal gases—hence the so-called Bose–Einstein quantum statistics. In 1926 the Italian physicist Enrico Fermi

(1901–58) applied the restricting atomic principle of the Austrian theoretical physicist Wolfgang Pauli (1900–58) to phase cells; he limited their occupancy (representing a definite quantum state) to a single particle—or to none at all. The same suggestion had been made by the English theoretical physicist Paul Adrien Maurice Dirac (1902–), hence the designation Fermi–Dirac statistics. At very low temperatures ideal gases exhibit phenomena of so-called degeneracy. The German theoretical physicist Arnold Sommerfeld (1868–1951) showed in 1928 that the "free" electrons in a metal behave like such a degenerate gas. The increasing importance of the statistical conception of physical phenomena became evident with the 1927 announcement of the uncertainty principle by the German theoretical physicist Werner Carl Heisenberg (1901–); it is fundamental nowadays for the interpretation of phenomena. A phase cell for a single degree of freedom has the size h, Planck's quantum of action, but the indeterminacy of mechanical action is of the same order of magnitude. Hence individual determinacy based upon some universal causality is apparently beyond man's micro-techniques; he must be satisfied with an ensemble of atoms in lieu of a single definite atom. Gibbs' statistical mechanics is not only practicable for classical statistics (Boltzmann), but necessary and applicable for quantum statistics. His nineteenth-century foundation, the statistical conception of physical phenomena, was so broad and rigid as to support our twentieth-century superstructure.

Name Index

Subject Index

Academic Institutions
  Berlin 7
  Bowdoin 8
  Cambridge 9
  Collège de France 7
  Erlangen 20, 23
  Heidelberg 7
  Johns Hopkins 8
  Oslow 20, 24
  Paris 7
  Princeton 3, 4, 20, 23
  Williams 20, 23

Life
  American Hall of Fame 20
  birth and death 3, 21
  Copley Medal 20, 24
  engineering 5, 7, 20, 23, 39
  Gibbs' governor 6
  Gibbs' medal 20
  Hopkins Grammar School 4, 15
  Gibbs' Lecture 20
  Gibbs' Professorship 20, 24
  Gibbs' Research Laboratory 10, 21,
    24, 41
  Gibbs' Tablet 21, 24
  Gibbs' railway car brake 6
  home 4, 21
  Mathematical Club 15, 18
  mathematical physics 7, 9, 21, 39
  National Conference of Electricians
    16
  New Haven 3, 8, 21, 23
  Physical Club 18, 21
  religion 16
  Rumford Medal 14, 20, 23, 190

Sloane Physical Laboratory 15, 30,
    43
  Yale College 4, 6, 8, 23; Sheffield
    Scientific School 5, 8
  vacations 7, 15

Mathematics 18, 20, 190
  American Journal of Mathematics
    186
  Fourier Series 237, 238
    Gibbs phenomenon 68, 238
  quaternions 13, 229, 234
  multiple algebra 13, 190, 191, 216
  vector analysis 14, 24, 216, 218, 229,
    234
Physical chemistry 11, 18, 96
Physical optics 9
  American Journal of Science 9, 78,
    174
  crystal propagation 173
  ether 173, 174
  speed of light 174

Mechanics
  dynamics 186
  metric system 6
  units 6

Societies
  American Academy of Arts and
    Sciences 20, 23, 32
  American Association for the Ad-
    vancement of Science 13, 15,
    23, 190, 191, 241

ISE